The Evolution *of*

LIFE

Worth Living

~ Why we choose to live ~

C. A. Soper, Ph.D.

With foreword by **Todd K. Shackelford**, Ph.D.

Book design by: SWATT Books Ltd

Printed in the United Kingdom
First Printing, 2021
Second Printing, 2022

ISBN: 978-1-8383439-0-3 (Paperback)
ISBN: 978-1-8383439-1-0 (eBook)

C. A. Soper
soper@cantab.net

CONTENTS

FOREWORD
by Todd K. Shackelford, Ph.D.

Several years ago I received an email from a graduate student studying evolutionary psychology in the United Kingdom. Cas Soper introduced himself as a practicing psychotherapist who had decided to go back to school to earn his Ph.D. in evolutionary psychology. Partly inspired by his career as a psychotherapist, Cas was developing an intriguing theory that human psychology included adaptations designed by natural selection to thwart self-killing. Cas was asking not why people kill themselves, but why more people *don't* kill themselves. His dissertation proposed an answer that I found both theoretically exhilarating and existentially haunting: We have evolved anti-suicide adaptations. These included common mental disorders, intended by design to disrupt the cognitive and motivational machinery of the mind to make suicide more difficult. I was familiar with the existing evolutionary psychological work on suicide, and his ideas offered a unique reframing of the topic of suicide, one that might inspire progress in an area of work that had become stagnant and stale.

Cas asked whether I would consider serving as an external member of his dissertation committee. I was thrilled to accept, if only to learn more about this fresh perspective on suicide. He promised to send me a draft of his dissertation in the coming months. The draft arrived as promised. Hardly a draft, it was beautifully written and comprehensively argued. It majestically reinterpreted a century of empirical and theoretical work on suicide according to Cas's devastatingly unique and compelling theory that humans evolved psychological adaptations designed to thwart a would-be self-killing. I could offer very little in the way of improvement, and his dissertation committee was unanimous that this was one of the single best dissertations any of us had ever read.

As an established academic evolutionary psychologist, one of my great joys is doing what I can to support aspiring members of the field.

Deeply impressed with Cas's new evolutionary theory of suicide, and convinced that this theory should be widely known and discussed among evolutionary psychologists and suicidologists, I invited him to submit his dissertation for publication in the 'Springer Series in Evolutionary Psychology,' published by Springer Nature and for which I serve as series co-editor. *The Evolution of Suicide* was published in 2018. To support the launch of this book, and eager for my colleagues to be alerted to his new theory, I invited Cas to submit a précis of his book for publication in *Evolutionary Psychological Science*, an academic journal I founded. 'Adaptation to the Suicide Niche' appeared in 2019 and immediately generated a vibrant intellectual buzz for his recently published book, followed shortly by several popular science articles showcasing Cas's work. Soon after I began encouraging Cas to produce a book for the intelligent, curious layperson, one that might complement the academic volume he published in 2018. Cas's rethinking of suicide is important and deserves to be widely known outside of academia.

This brings us to the book you are about to read. *The Evolution of Life Worth Living: Why We Choose to Live* is stunningly crafted and succeeds in communicating an ingenious theory in eloquent prose that is deeply engaging but never sacrifices scientific accuracy. This book will challenge what you think you know about suicide, why it occurs, and why it (usually) does not.

Todd K. Shackelford
Distinguished Professor and Chair
Oakland University
Rochester, Michigan
November 2020

1

THE EVOLUTION OF LIFE WORTH LIVING

You and I want to enjoy our time in this world. Most of us, most of the time, do seem to like being here. This book asks why: how is it that we like living? Put another way, what if we don't?

These questions touch on what it means to be human, an experience that connects us all. It sounds soft and abstract, a topic perhaps best left to poets and philosophers; but we are going to tackle it from a hard, biological, point of view. I will argue that our love of life sprang from a pivotal event in our evolutionary past, one that cleanly divides our species from the rest of life on earth. Indeed, this book sets out a new scientific theory of how *Homo sapiens* evolved.

We wouldn't normally expect living things to enjoy being alive. Other animals are programmed just to get on with the business of surviving and reproducing. They obey their instinctive drives, and there is no particular need for that to be fun. For sure, they seem to have a good time doing certain things — playing, having sex, grooming each other, and so on.[1] But that's not the same as enjoying *life*. Their lives overall don't look to be much fun, at least in the wild, to judge by the daily grind that is their usual lot; an endless struggle for food, territory, mates, and the rest. Anyway, who knows or cares if squirrels, snakes, or sardines are happy? Their opinion is not sought, if indeed they have an opinion. Nature isn't bothered one way or the other. It doesn't matter if animals like living, because they'll carry on doing what they do, whether they like it or not.

Not us. It matters very much if we like living, because in our case someone important does know and surely cares — ourselves. Our own opinion is continuously sought as to whether we enjoy being here. It bothers us if we cannot answer to our own satisfaction, and rightly so, because unlike other animals, we have a choice. We have a dark, barely speakable alternative; to shun life, to opt out, to end it. This book argues that humans evolved a love of life precisely because we, and we alone, evolved the capacity to choose not to live.

So, behind the question of loving life is a subject that many of us would rather not look at: suicide, the act of intentionally, deliberately, killing oneself.[2] For our enquiry, unfortunately, there's no skirting around it. It's like a biological shadow, following us everywhere. I will argue that this dark possibility has been with us since the dawn of our species. To find our answers, just for a while, we'll need to turn and face the shadow squarely.

I am going to explain, step by step, how I think we humans adapted to survive with the capacity to take our own lives. Much of what follows is a plain-English summary of my previous book, a technical text called *The Evolution of Suicide*.[3] I'm calling this *The Evolution of Life Worth Living* instead, partly because people tend to baulk at opening something with 'suicide' on the cover. More importantly, the title better explains how the story ends. This book carries an upbeat message. Yes, suicide is an ugly topic, but by equal measure, its evolutionary flipside is breathtakingly beautiful. The astonishing payoff of suicide is that *Homo sapiens* acquired a zest for life.

We are made for happiness. Granted, we're not always happy, and we can't expect always to be so. But I will argue that happiness is our normal position, our default stance, and with it comes a bouquet of related blessings — such as love, hope, charity, forgiveness, and faith. The potential for these delightful states is part of human nature. It resides within us as an ancient, innate resource, ready and waiting to be tapped. We have a tendency towards happiness that can, and usually does, overcome any adversity. Protracted misery isn't a fixture or pre-ordained state; it is a deviation from our designated path, a temporary aberration. We are designed to recover from sadness because we are built like a centrally heated home with a thermostat; when the door opens to a chilly draft from the world outside, we are pre-set to restore ourselves to feeling warm.

To some jaded readers, this may sound naively cheery. But I will offer an argument that is based on facts, logic, and probability. That we are designed to be happy can be deduced, I suggest, from first principles of modern evolutionary theory and from real-world evidence. There are differences of opinion in every field of course, but I aim to offer a chain of logic that few informed scientists will easily dismiss. It has withstood academic scrutiny for a few years — long enough to suggest it is ready to go before the public. This is not to say that everyone will like it: the conclusions challenge several long-held assumptions, especially in the field of mental health. In this matter, I ask readers just to keep an open mind for a few chapters. If you still disagree after that, then perhaps you are right — I could be wrong. Nonetheless, a fresh perspective could channel debate and research into useful directions. We could avert misery and save lives.

I aim to offer a theory that not only stands up scientifically, but is one that readers won't object to on moral or religious grounds either. I take it that virtually everyone, religious or not, has a moral code and a notion of their place in the universe. I am not planning to talk anyone into or out of any faith. Those with faith, strange as it may sound, may find the evolutionary message of this book affirming. The conclusions are, to my mind, as supportive of theists, creationists included, as they are for atheists. But again, it may be necessary to park doctrines and doubts for a while to reach that point of agreement. The religiously minded might treat my evolutionary theorizing as a playful puzzle, like a word game that turns out to spell a surprisingly God-friendly message. Indeed, in due course we will talk about God, with a capital 'G'. The word may snag the sensibilities of some readers, but I hope it won't block their path. I use the term as shorthand for what might also be called a higher power, love, karma, goodness — or any other superordinate force or moral order with which the human mind tries to make sense of its own existence. I will argue that the evolution of life worth living points to the origins of spiritual and religious belief.

I will put to you three basic proposals. First, I will argue that the possibility of suicide is part of what makes us human — it's a distinguishing feature of our species. Several chapters are devoted to this point, because it is important and not obvious. I will explain how we humans are united in having to live with the option *not* to. With the signal exception of young children and the severely intellectually disabled, virtually all of us have the cognitive wherewithal to take our own lives.

It is not that the human mind is badly built. It is just that there is a lot that can go wrong. It is rather like the way almost any of us, any time, could succumb to a massive brain haemorrhage or heart attack. The cardiovascular system is prone to the odd catastrophic failure not because of poor engineering, but because of the extraordinary challenge of the job it has to do. Every day, the human heart contracts and expands about 100,000 times, forcing thousands of litres of blood through a network of pipes longer than the water mains of a large city. The marvel is that the system usually works so well. I will argue that, likewise, the human psychological system cannot help but be vulnerable because of the similarly extreme nature of its special task.

The human mind must house two elements that, when mixed together, ought to produce suicide. One is the unpleasantness of pain. Pain is meant to hurt. It's a vital biological motivator that is precisely designed to drive a suffering animal to do something to end or escape it. The other ingredient is the extraordinary intelligence of *Homo sapiens*, an animal so smart that it knows it can stop itself hurting by making itself disappear. These two conditions, pain and brain, are not just necessary for suicide, they are sufficient. Pain, especially emotional pain, is the motivation; and human braininess is the means. Wherever these two combine, we should expect wilful self-destruction to be the outcome. And they *do* combine — in all normal post-pubescent human beings. From adolescence onwards, almost any of us could, and many do, find ourselves with both an urge and a thought to end it all. The curiosity is not that so many of us sometimes think about taking their own lives — that much is understandable. The wonder is that so very few of us go on to act on those thoughts.

So, I will argue that the risk of suicide comes with the territory of being human. It has probably always been so. We can deduce, as a second basic point, that suicide is a biohazard that has been on the scene throughout the evolution of our species. It appeared when a population of our ancestors became smart enough to grasp their own mortality. They either adapted to the new threat or died out. They clearly did not die out, because here we are. We are the offspring of those who survived. We have inherited ways to live with the capacity for choosing death. In the parlance of evolutionary science, suicide is an adaptive problem. It is so severe a problem that I think it drove a wholesale reshaping of the human psyche. The question is often asked: What makes us distinct from other primates? Bipedalism? Hairlessness? Language, consciousness, tool making? These are important attributes, no doubt. But none of them will make much of a difference if the primate that has them is dead. Making the choice to live was, and remains, every adult human's primary biological challenge.

My third basic proposal is that anti-suicide adaptations guide what we think, feel, and do in our daily lives. They explain much of what is unique and mysterious about human psychology. We are not rational for the simple reason that it is possible to be too rational for our own good. The rational solution to pain is self-killing; any animal that knew it could escape pain by switching itself off would reasonably do just that. Evolution's answer to this biological problem is to make us tactically irrational, especially when we are in emotional pain. When full contact with the real world could threaten the human mind's survival, it protects itself by editing its perception of reality. I suggest this is why people in drawn-out distress find themselves emotionally numbed and mentally befogged by symptoms of depression, addiction, and other conditions that we take to be forms of psychiatric illness. I will argue that most mental disorders are not disorders at all but strategies by which the human psyche keeps itself safe from self-destruction. Almost all of the time, they work.

We are designed to live not entirely in the real world, but in a mentally constructed enhanced reality, a heaven on earth, where the tenets of unconditional love, not Darwinism, hold sway. We are spiritual beings. The outermost shield against self-destruction is our yearning for a life worth living.

But let's not jump ahead. First, we need to get to grips with one of humankind's most common, urgent, and baffling questions: Why do people kill themselves?

CHAPTER 1: *This book argues that the brightest aspects of human experience arise from the darkest of possibilities. Uniquely among animals, our species evolved a zest for life. It's a survival necessity, because humans have to live with the possibility of wilfull self-killing. So, to understand the evolution of life worth living, we need to explore the origins of suicide.*

CHAPTER 2: *A major cause of human death, suicide is a global calamity that science has not begun to understand. Despite decades of research, we cannot explain why some people kill themselves rather than take some other course of action. We cannot predict suicide, or accurately assess an individual's risk. Why not?*

2

WHY DO PEOPLE KILL THEMSELVES?

Here are two facts that may come as a jolt — if they don't, they should do. First, year in year out, close to a million people around the world take their own lives.[1] The scale of the ongoing disaster is almost beyond imagining. For perspective: 1.5% of human deaths happen this way, suicide killing more people than all other forms of violence put together, more than homicide and war combined. The death toll due to the Covid-19 pandemic is even higher than suicide at the time of writing, but we might nonetheless reflect on the world's forthright response to one of these public health calamities, its seeming deafness to the other.

The other startling fact is that science does not know why people kill themselves. More precisely, it remains unknown why some people take their own lives while, under apparently similar circumstances, most people don't. There is no sign that we are close to finding out. It is a gap in our species' knowledge of itself — an ignorance that endures despite more than a century of scientific enquiry. A special '-ology' grew up in the post-war decades; suicidology, a multi-disciplinary field focussed on trying to understand suicidal behaviour. Generations of researchers have produced thousands of scientific papers — more than 40,000 in the last three decades.[2] Yet, despite this mighty effort, as to the central question of why people kill themselves, we are none the wiser.[3]

Granted, we have learned a lot about suicide's risk and protective factors — conditions that raise or lower the odds.[4] For example, we know that people are slightly more in danger if they have a background of suicide in the family, a mental illness, a feeling of hopelessness, a gun in the home, a history of self-harming behaviour, a recent divorce, and so on.

Gender has an effect — men are more likely to suicide* than women. But then, women are more likely than men to try: women's protection, such as it is, comes from a tendency to use less immediately lethal methods, such as poisoning instead of hanging. Age has an effect: young children virtually never suicide, an important point we will come back to. The elderly are more likely to die by their own hands than younger adults — again, partly because their actions are more deadly, older people being medically more fragile and, often living alone, they're less likely to be discovered.[5]

Some risk factors seem obvious. One of suicidology's founders, Edwin S. Shneidman, pointed out that suicide is virtually always linked to emotional pain: people do not kill themselves out of joy, another important point that we will unpack later.[6] Other factors are less obvious: according to some reports, living at a high altitude, having tattoos, warm weather... There are thousands of variables that measurably nudge the risks up or down.

But measurable is not the same as *useful*. The nudges are so weak that no factor, or mix of factors, has been found that comes close to forecasting who will take their own life, or when. Depression, for example, is widely assumed to be both a danger sign and a causal driver. But the vast majority of people with depression do not take their own lives, and most suicides happen among people who did not seem to be particularly depressed.[7] If depression does not predict or explain the behaviour, neither does anything else. In clinical settings, psychiatrists are professionally obliged to assess their patients' risk. But the best assessment methods are so inaccurate, so reliably wrong, that they may as well take a view by rolling dice.[8]

That tells us that science has not begun to understand the problem. A recent review, examining hundreds of studies since the 1960s, found that we are no more able to predict suicide now than we were then. Science has not even discovered a clue, a signpost that might point the way.[9] By

---

*   Grammatically it may grate, but I sometimes use the word 'suicide' as a verb (as in 'to suicide') as a way to bypass the 'c-word' — *commit* (as in 'to commit suicide'). As I will explain later in the book, 'commit' has judgemental connotations, being a hangover from the time when suicide was a criminal offence. It is one of the ways we unthinkingly pass on society's negative attitude towards the behaviour; we do not say people 'commit cancer' or 'commit sex'.

this measure, across half a century of concerted scientific enquiry, there has been no progress whatsoever.

Where have we gone wrong?

One reason for this ongoing failure, the claim goes, is that suicide is too rare in the course of an individual's lifespan to be easily studied. It is indeed rare in that sense — it is literally a once-in-a-lifetime event. The chance of any one of us dying by our own hands on any given day is in the order of a thousandth of one percent. But not all rare events defy scientific understanding. Aviation disasters are rare, but investigators usually expect to get to the bottom of why they happen. Full solar eclipses are rare, seen at any particular spot on earth only once in hundreds of years, but astronomers can still predict them to the day. The problem with suicide is that, unlike aviation and eclipses, science has no working model of the underlying processes, no framework to make sense of what is going on. Progress has stalled, not because of the rarity of suicide, but because of a vacuum in suicide theory.[10]

Many theorists have tried to make sense of suicide. There are dozens of rival theories on offer, but they tend to follow much the same format, and, I suggest for this reason, they are uniformly unhelpful. The standard-pattern suicide theory proffers a selection of input conditions, curated according to the author's field of interest — psychological, psychiatric, genetic, neurological, economic, sociological, or what you will. These inputs are sometimes proposed individually but more usually in combinations (e.g., 'biopsychosocial' theories) and/or in sequences over time. They are typically presented with the aid of a flow diagram, with arrows joining the inputs to an output — a final box marked 'suicide'. The problem is that these arrows are not explanations. They are substitutes for theory, proxies for causal processes that are implied but not spelt out. To my knowledge, no theory has explained why any given set of conditions should produce suicide, as opposed to some other outcome.[11]

It has been this way since the earliest scientific work in the field. The 19th-century sociologist Émile Durkheim blamed suicide on a feeling of not belonging, or what he called *anomy*, among other societal troubles.[12] But he nowhere explained *why* anomy would lead people to kill themselves, rather than do something else. As it happens, there are any number of deviant behaviours aside from suicide — petty crime, addiction, homicide, and so on — that could equally lay claim to anomy as a causal factor.

We can fast-forward through more than a hundred years of this style of non-explaining. The most prominent example at the moment is the Interpersonal-Psychological Theory of Suicide. Whereas Durkheim proposed a single input, this one has three: a sense of not belonging (essentially, Durkheim's anomy); a feeling that one is a burden to one's family; and a supposed learned ability to override an instinct for self-preservation — a fearlessness acquired from, say, a previous suicide attempt.[13] As with Durkheim's offer, there is silence as to why these states would cause someone to kill themselves, rather than pursue an alternative course of action. On the face of it, the same conditions could easily produce any number of *non*-suicidal outcomes. A sense of not belonging could be answered by, say, joining a church, a political group, or a book club. If we feel we're a burden, then we could resolve to be more useful, move away from the people we think we're burdening, or just put up with feeling useless. And a learned capability for suicide, if indeed it exists, is not a death sentence, determining the future. Suicidality can be *un*learned, and often is. Most people who attempt suicide and survive never attempt it again. Many manage to forget they ever tried.[14] In sum, even if people met all the criteria of the theory, there is no particular reason to think they would kill themselves. For the tasks of telling apart likely future suicides from non-suicides in a clinical setting, there is scant evidence that this genre of theorizing is useful. There's no logical reason to think it would be.[15]

Evidently, the current approach to suicide research, whether by surveying or theorizing, doesn't work. In the United States — the birthplace of suicidology and the country where modern prevention techniques are most readily to hand — the suicide rate is about the same now as it was a hundred years ago.[16] The global rate has fallen in recent decades, but it's doubtful how much of this is down to suicidology; it may be more a side-effect of migrations, especially in China, from countryside to cities, where there is less access to the agricultural pesticides that are often used for self-poisoning.[17] Around the world there are wide and persistent variations in rates and trends, and these remain unexplained.[18] Despite a massive growth in research, interventions to prevent suicide are no more effective now than they were decades ago.[19] In sum, the ongoing failure of the research effort is matched by humankind's continued inability to get to grips with suicide as a major cause of global mortality.

What is the problem? The main one, it looks to me, is that the bulk of research in this field is built on a faulty premise. For more than a hundred years, science has held a conviction that the causes or predictors of suicide are out there, waiting to be discovered. Suicide is thus, in principle, foreseeable. I am not aware of any evidence to support this stance. It is an article of faith, although it's rarely voiced as such.[20] The faith, rather, shines through in the way scientists report unrelenting defeat in a tone of hope — like a candle that, when blown out, keeps reigniting itself.

An expert review in the medical journal *The Lancet*, for example, frankly admits that suicide can't be foreseen, but still claims it "might help" if doctors knew more about risk factors.[21] How exactly it might help is anyone's guess. There is no way known to science by which medics, or anyone else, can usefully divine risk, however clued up they are about risk factors. Given the same patient information, different clinicians reach markedly different assessments.[22] It was this subjectivity that spurred a move towards more formal methods decades ago. But even with these tools, some 97% of supposedly 'high risk' patients do not take their own lives, and most suicides happen among people who were not thought to be at high risk.[23]

In a similar vein, a leading authority comes clean in *Scientific American* that neither he nor anyone else knows how to predict suicide, and there is no prospect of that situation changing anytime soon. Even so, the piece is headed "Suicide Prediction Remains Difficult Despite Decades of Research."[24] Not 'beyond reach' or 'futile' — only *difficult*.

Bitter scientific facts are thus sugared with euphemisms. When a risk assessment method is described as "still far from perfect", that is code, as I understand it, for 'useless.'[25] It is not that the causes of suicide are unknown or unknowable: they are 'multifaceted', 'multi-factorial', or 'heterogenous' — pseudo-scientific verbal fig leaves, I suggest, that serve to cover the nakedness of the project.[26]

The 'yeti' position

Faith in suicide's predictability clings on only by what could be called the 'yeti' position, after the abominable snowman said to lurk in the Himalayas. We may never be able to prove by exhaustive survey that somewhere there is not a yeti, hiding in a cave or under the snow perhaps. For sure, science has found no trace of a yeti, dead or alive, which could be taken as strong evidence that they don't exist. But a determined believer can always neutralise this evidence by adding the word 'yet'. It's not that we haven't found a yeti — we just haven't found one *yet*.

Likewise, it's not that we can't predict suicide; we just can't do it *yet*. To find a solution, so it is believed, we just need to look harder. It's just a technical matter, needing more time, resources, and ingenuity invested into essentially the same pursuit. Every generation tries a new technique, each as ineffective as the one before.[27] Hopes are currently pinned on artificial intelligence and machine learning; but there is no reason, beyond wishful thinking, to expect computers to deliver the long-awaited breakthrough either.[28] Despite the scorecard showing zero for more than a hundred years, faith in the root assumption — that suicide's causes are waiting to be found — holds firm. It is so pervasive that it may be hard to detect, as proverbial fish are said to be oblivious to water. The question "Why do people kill themselves?" just takes for granted that there is, in fact, an answer.

Why the *Why?* How come researchers are so determined to believe that suicide boils down to cause and effect? I suggest it is because researchers are people, and people feel that suicides must happen for a reason. There *has* to be a reason. Families bereaved in this way are haunted by the question: *Why* did they do it? They need an explanation.

It is not just about gaining closure, important though that is. We want to arm ourselves, to be better prepared in future. Going back to air disasters: when planes crash, we don't just shrug our shoulders and put it down to one of those things. Crash investigators are sent in. They expect to find out what went wrong, with the intention of stopping it from happening again. This mode of thinking often serves us well. It's thanks in good part to investigators' success that, despite increasing air traffic, flying has become safer. Fatalities follow a downward trend. The same approach ought to work for suicides. It sounds like it should work, but it hasn't. I am suggesting that it probably won't.

The hunt for causation in suicide seems to me to be fundamentally flawed. It is a barking up the wrong tree that can and does happen in science. It shows several parallels, for example, with another famous scientific wild goose chase: 18th-century chemists' search for the mythical element *phlogiston*. Phlogiston is the substance that was supposed to be given off when things burn. The idea felt like common sense at the time. Anyone seeing the flames and smoke billowing out from a fire would intuit that some primal material was being emitted and ask the obvious, but fallacious, question: *So, what is it?* Suicidology, for the most part, rests on the same fallacy: suicide presumably happens for a reason: *So, what is it?* Researchers thus set off in pursuit of 'it' — something that is only intuitively presumed to be there. I have called phlogiston's twin in suicide research *suigiston*, the conditions that lead to suicide. Putting folk psychology aside, there is no scientific or logical reason to believe that suigiston exists. Indeed, the blank drawn from a century-long search points to its non-existence.

Having already spent careers hunting suigiston, despite it likely being an illusory prize, researchers may be stuck with it until a better idea comes along. Phlogiston was never found, of course, despite a search that also dragged on for more than a century. It could have gone on longer. It was only the discovery of oxygen that allowed chemists to call the search off. The oxygen idea changed the mental landscape. Suddenly combustion could be seen in a wholly new way — one that was inconceivable beforehand. It became possible to perceive that something was being captured, not released. That shift of paradigm released a surge of scientific advances and paved the way for much of modern chemistry. As Thomas Kuhn explains in his *Structure of Scientific Revolutions*, no scientist can let go of a theory, however defective, until a perceptibly better one is to hand to take its place.[29]

Suicidology needs a new paradigm, but what will it be? This book offers one. I will argue that the air safety-style causal approach does not work in suicide research because, of course, human beings are not like planes and suicide is not like a plane crash. Humans were designed not by engineers but by natural selection. If we want to understand why human beings sometimes kill themselves, and what we can do about it, then we first need to get our minds around the biological origins of suicidal behaviour. We need to understand how natural selection has produced an animal with this self-destructive tendency. We may then be able to perceive suicide as not a machine malfunction, not as an engineering failure, but as a biological feature.

This may call for a 180-degree perceptual turn: psychologically not easy, but the payoffs of such a re-conception may be great. I believe it likely that evolutionary science holds the key to making progress in suicide research, and indeed in mental health generally. Evolution could be to 21st-century psychological sciences what oxygen was to 18th-century chemistry — an opportunity to look at a puzzling phenomenon from an opposite, previously unimaginable point of view. Properly informed, and in large part only then, clinicians and policy makers would be in a position to intervene in a cognizant way, to relieve misery and hopefully save lives.

Strangely few scientists have looked at suicide from an evolutionary stance. At least not closely. Only five books have previously been published on the topic as far as I know.[30] This is odd because, even from a basic understanding of natural selection, suicide sticks out as an anomaly that shouts for investigation. Charles Darwin himself told us, "Natural selection will never produce in a being anything injurious to itself, for natural selection acts solely by and for the good of each."[31] Modern evolutionists would add some ifs and buts, but let that pass. The gist holds true. As a rule, 'survival of the fittest' ought to promote fitness, not self-destruction. As Darwin explained, natural selection follows essentially the same process as the domestication carried out for centuries by plant and animal breeders. Familiar forms of roses, rice and racehorses are as they are because of an artificial fine-tuning of the breeding pool. Weed out the weakest; let the strongest procreate, and the rest die. In the natural version, any inherited trait that helps an organism's offspring to survive and reproduce will spread across the population. In the other direction, any heritable trait that handicaps them will be duly driven out.

This being so, a trait like suicidality, which is heritable to some extent and makes life harder for those left behind, seems almost sure to harm the reproductive prospects of a suicide's offspring — if indeed there are any offspring. The less suicidal ought to breed more vigorously than the more suicidal, thereby pushing the behaviour out of the breeding stock.

But obviously this has not happened. Instead, and seemingly contradicting Darwin, natural selection has saddled humankind with a heritable behaviour that is self-injurious to the extreme. Generation after generation, a fairly steady percentage of us deliberately kill ourselves. Something doesn't fit.

Animal suicide?

There are two special features of suicide that add to the evolutionary enigma. One is that it is almost certainly a uniquely human behaviour. You may intuitively disagree. Many people are quite sure that other animals think and act as we do, and feelings run high on the matter. Animal suicide is an especially emotive topic, not least because it ties into the question of animal sentience — and, for some people, that touches on animal rights. There is a sense that if other animals did "commit" suicide, then that would be all the more reason to treat them humanely. I can understand the passion in this line of thought. Perhaps, also, we tend to go with the flow of our culture — poetic anecdote, fable, and urban myth — which are all rich in stories of animals dying at will. We want to believe it is true.

But the fact remains that there is no reliable evidence — none that meets a scientific standard — that any non-human has ever deliberately killed itself.[32] Belief in animal suicide has to rely on the 'yeti' position: it's not that science hasn't found non-human suicide; it just hasn't found it *yet*. The blank record can actually be taken as powerful and positive evidence, that other animals do not die in this way. Why so? Because, if they did, it would almost certainly have made headlines in the scientific press by now.

There has been no lack of opportunity: countless naturalists, zoologists, and breeders have studied animal behaviour long enough and closely enough to collect evidence, if it were there to be collected. If cats willingly leapt to their deaths from tall trees and dogs set out to drown themselves, we would know about it. There is no lack of means either. Researchers devised an experiment half a century ago that would demonstrate non-human suicide happening under laboratory conditions.[33] Would, that is, if it ever happened; there are no reports of positive results. And there is no shortage of motivation. A researcher who could stand up and announce "FIRST ANIMAL SUICIDE KNOWN TO SCIENCE" would rightly win professional and public acclaim for so historic a discovery. There would be material rewards too, not least because a well-funded pharmaceutical industry is standing by, keen to know if, despite every sign to the contrary, experiments with animals could potentially shed light on how suicidality may be affected by drugs.

By the way, other scientific happenings are sometimes also called 'suicide' — in astronomy, cellular biology, the study of insects, and perhaps other domains. As a vivid metaphor, it can describe many things: how neutron stars implode, the programmed death of cells, kamikaze-like bees, and so on. But let us be careful not to take a colourful turn of phrase literally, or to assume that, when scientists in different fields use the same word, they are talking about the same thing. We will get muddled if we mix deliberate, intentional self-killing — that is, literal (human) suicide — with what are categorically different events. It doesn't help that there are many definitions of suicide floating about (and a finicky philosopher could probably sink any of them).[34] But suicide for our purposes is essentially deliberate. It entails, however fleetingly, a choice being made between two courses of action: life or death. And it requires the intention specifically to kill oneself; not (as is presumably the case for, say, bees fending off an attacker) the pursuit of some other goal, which unfortunately puts oneself in lethal danger. In legalistic terms, suicide is self-murder, not self-manslaughter. I will come back to supposed insect 'suicide' because it is sometimes confused with the real thing, even among suicidologists.

Also by the way, the story of lemming suicide is a fraud. It stems from faked footage in a prominent 1950s wildlife documentary. What the film actually shows is captive lemmings being thrown off a cliff. Hold that thought a moment. Reputable makers of a mainstream 'real-life' nature film, no less, felt obliged to mistreat animals on camera and pass it off as suicide. The incident says a lot about the commercial pressure on naturalists to deliver an 'animal suicide' story.[35] It also speaks volumes about the public's yearning to believe the lie — we unquestioningly took it to be true. We accepted the myth of suicidal lemmings and passed it down the generations, willing it to be real. Nonetheless, despite the media and popular pressure, the scientific record remains steadfastly blank.

There's more. The evidence that other animals do not suicide is stronger than the lack of signs that they do. It is unlikely even in principle that they could. The idea probably couldn't cross their minds. For an animal to intentionally kill itself, it would first need some idea of what it intends; its own mortality. But the concept of personal mortality is so difficult that not even 9- or 10-year-old humans can wrap their heads around it.[36] If elementary schoolchildren can't meaningfully conceive of their own death, then animals that aren't nearly so smart almost certainly can't either. Adult chimpanzees, among the cleverest known non-humans, are thought to be on an intellectual par with human infants of perhaps 12 to 18 months. One remarkable study reckoned a particularly smart chimp, a zoo inmate called Josie, might possibly be a match for a human 4-year-old.[37] Even at this extreme, chimps are a long way from having the mental wherewithal to imagine their own death. In this light, we can expect non-humans to be generally immune from taking their own lives. Young children are also likely protected for the same reason, as we will discuss in a later chapter. Also later, we'll discover another strong reason to think that other animals cannot suicide.

All this is interesting because a uniquely human trait, as suicide almost surely is, is probably a novelty in the history of life on earth. It emerged at or after the fork in the road where our species' evolutionary path veered away from that of other living primates. The roots of suicide lie in some unique, and fairly recent, aspect of hominid evolution.

The other curiosity about suicide is that, among humans, it is ubiquitous. As far as can be known, no era, region, or sizeable culture is exempt.[38] Where we can't observe it directly, we can see its footprint. The aforementioned Émile Durkheim pointed out this 'social fact': anti-suicide laws and moral codes can be found almost everywhere. That tells us that suicide has been a problem in the past almost everywhere, and it must have been a big enough problem everywhere to warrant moral codes being ranged against it.[39]

This matters, because universal human traits, suicide included, were probably already part of human nature when our common ancestors migrated out of Africa some 50,000 to 70,000 years ago. As humans spread around the planet, human nature came with us.

The fact that suicide has *stayed* universal tells us that, somehow, natural selection has actively kept the trait in place across the millennia since. Traits that offer no reproductive benefit tend to fade away. Such is the fate of the eyes of cavefish, the limbs of snakes, the tails of humans, and many other useless features that have either disappeared or remain only in vestigial form. There is no sign that this kind of degeneration is underway with suicide. That it remains with us is evidence that there's an ongoing biological benefit connected to suicide that makes it positively worth preserving.

The evolutionary puzzle

Suicide links to a biological *benefit*? Intuitively this is hard to grasp, but it is important. We can deduce that the capacity for suicide is not entirely destructive.

Indeed, we can say not only that there's a biological upside, but that upside is immensely valuable. It must be so, to be worth the immense cost. This sounds like a question of economics, and in a sense, it is just that. Costs and benefits in the natural economy are traded in the currency of *fitness* — the ability of an organism's genes to transfer copies of themselves into future generations. To be more precise, we are referring to *inclusive fitness*, which takes into account the way genes run in the extended family. Genes that an organism shares with its kin relations can be passed on indirectly, via those relations' offspring. When I talk of fitness, it's shorthand for inclusive fitness.

For an idea of the scale of the suicide's fitness upsides, we need to get a measure of the fitness downsides. They are extreme — triply extreme, as I will explain.

First, human death by any cause is a genetic disaster. Being dead is very bad for our ability to procreate. It is as bad for our reproductive prospects as, indeed, it is for virtually any other mammal's. We are *iteroparous* organisms — geared, that is, for multiple rounds of reproduction (as opposed to *semelparous*, such as certain salmon — they reproduce only once in a lifetime). We mammals are designed literally to breed like rabbits. Rabbits are an extreme case, but you get the point. A typical man is potentially able to father children at any stage of life, even though his fertility declines with age. A typical woman can carry on conceiving up to menopause.[40] Death costs mammals dearly because it cancels out the benefit of this strategy of repetitive reproduction. It defeats the point of being a mammal. A typical mammal will thus go to extreme lengths to stay alive, killing rival kin where necessary and abandoning even its own offspring to preserve its own reproductive future.

This point explains why (human) suicide is categorically different from the behaviours of so-called *eusocial* insects. In colonies of ants, bees, termites, and the like, all the reproduction is usually done by a single queen. All the other members of the colony are siblings — the queen's closely related offspring, sterile slaves that are kept in service to help with her continued reproduction. In that special family set-up, there is genetically little to lose, and potentially much to gain, from the heroic self-sacrifice of a slave if that action safeguards the queen and colony. Indeed, to talk at all of 'self-destructive' colonial insects misses the point of insect colonies: the relevant 'self' in their case is not the individual insect but the colony, acting as a single super-organism. What's lost when a sterile worker or soldier dies defending the colony is not genes but energy — much like when a tree sheds a leaf in the fall. By contrast, human organisms are heavily invested in staying alive because for us, in the Darwinian struggle to survive and reproduce, death is genetic 'game over'.[41]

So, death by any cause is genetically disastrous for humans. But, second, death by suicide is worse. The stigma adds a special inclusive fitness cost in the form of punishments meted out to a suicide's surviving kin. The tradition probably originated for a hard-nosed reason — for communal self-protection. It keeps suicide seriously unappealing as an option for other members of the community, as I'll explain in later. So perhaps it is by unfortunate necessity that people who lose loved ones in this way face a special ordeal. In the modern West, grieving relations suffer a relatively mild form of social penalty, but it can still be deeply upsetting. They find themselves shunned, pariah-like, as if contaminated by association. Spectacularly harsh treatments are routine in some other cultures. In parts of Africa, families face the burning of their homes, disinheritance, and exile. Similar cruelties would have been common-place in parts of Europe not many generations ago. The bereaved are thus left with special psychological wounds that can be deep and lasting. Kin face a future of poorer mental and physical health, and a heightened risk that they too will take their own lives.[42] In sum, measured by its genetic outcome, suicide is literally a fate worse than death.

For good measure, third, attempting suicide is a genetic disaster even if the attempt is not immediately fatal. Surviving attempters can be left permanently injured and/or disfigured. Especially in the absence of modern health care, these injuries could well lead to premature death. The damage is often mental as well as physical: a third of suicide attempters in one study were found to be seriously traumatised by their own actions, to the extent of qualifying for a diagnosis of PTSD (post-traumatic stress disorder).[43] People who try to kill themselves are at greater risk of trying again. And although (or perhaps *because*) survivors are often judged to have manipulative motives — seeking attention, forgiveness, or the like — they actually win little sympathy and few concessions. Quite the opposite. Much like bereaved relations are punished for a suicide's actions, the actors themselves face stigmatising treatment if they survive.[44] A study among US students (people who I'd take to be relatively open-minded) found that most wouldn't want to date someone who had recently tried to take their own life, let alone start a family with them. The power of this prejudice outranks even racial discrimination. People would rather marry someone dying of cancer — this is as a *life* partner, mind you — ahead of someone who had survived a recent suicide attempt.[45] Their access to mates thus cut away, survivors can expect to suffer a severe and direct reproductive forfeit.

Let us review the costings, the biological tab to be paid for taking one's own life. There is the genetic catastrophe of death, by whatever cause. If that were not bad enough, death by suicide incurs an extra inclusive fitness penalty, in the form of special punishments for the bereaved family. And even to live is to lose: dire fitness outcomes follow a suicide attempt, even if it isn't fatal at the time.

We might feel like diners at a restaurant, baffled by a shockingly expensive item on the menu. What possible dish could justify such an exorbitant price? Why would any diner choose it? And why would the restaurant even bother to offer it? There is, in other words, an evolutionary puzzle underlying the question that began this chapter. What overriding fitness advantage could possibly be worth so genetically harmful a tendency?

CHAPTER 2: *Suicide research is hobbled by a faulty paradigm of causation. Evolution offers an alternative framework. Unique to and universal among humans, and very costly in fitness terms, suicide poses an evolutionary puzzle. Selection ought to have driven the trait out of the species, but clearly hasn't. Why not?*

CHAPTER 3: *In search of a fitness benefit that makes the potential for suicide biologically sustainable, we start by looking at adaptationist explanations. These theories claim that sometimes the human organism can improve its genetic prospects if it deliberately kills itself, or tries to do so. It's a tough case to argue.*

3

'JUST SO': HOW THE HUMAN GOT HIS SUICIDALITY

The previous chapter set us a challenge: to find a biological upside linked to suicide that is rich enough to make the costly downside worthwhile. There's good news and bad news. The bad news is that the challenge is formidable, because the fitness downside of suicide is clearly extreme — forfeited reproduction, and harsh penalties for kin. There are serious fitness costs even if an attempt is not immediately lethal. It will be a tall order to come up with adequate compensation. The good news is that, the order being so tall, it shouldn't be too difficult to spot. It is as if we are searching a house for a missing key: it shouldn't be hard to find, because we know this key is gigantic.

One preliminary thought is that perhaps the downside of suicide is not so huge after all. The idea was one of many put forward in the 1980s by pioneering psychologist Denys deCatanzaro. DeCatanzaro was the first scientist to explore the evolution of suicide in depth. Going where others feared to tread, his name rightly crops up a lot in this field.[1]

He considered, among other things, the idea of reproductive potential, something we discussed in the last chapter. You'll recall that, at one extreme, some species of salmon get just one opportunity to breed in their lifetimes. Once their reproductive work is done, genetically there is no point in staying alive, and so they die. By contrast, mammals are designed to carry on repeatedly reproducing. Rabbits, breeding like rabbits, have an ongoing genetic reason to stay alive. But, argues deCatanzaro, even a rabbit may have no reproductive future to look forward to if it is completely isolated, and/or disabled by age, sickness, or injury. In such desperate circumstances, perhaps like a spawned salmon, it may as well die. DeCatanzaro stretched this idea to a possible explanation for human suicide: people who are too old, sick, or solitary to have any more children, he argued, might kill themselves for want of any genetic reason to stay alive. For that reason, perhaps it is understandable that high rates of suicide would be found among the elderly, seriously ill, and lonely.

Interesting though this theory is, I don't find it helpful. I see at least three problems. First, it clashes with the facts. For example, most of the world's suicides happen among younger rather than older adults — people who, on the face of it, might have looked forward to raising families. At the same time, certain groups with surely zero prospects for having children — post-menopausal women, and castrated men, say — are not known for being particularly suicidal. Second, however unpromising the situation, a living human being almost always remains a genetic going concern. Being alone, sick, or (except for post-menopausal women) old doesn't rule out the possibility of conceiving more offspring. Even if someone is sterile, they may still be able to spread copies of their genes by proxy, by helping genetic relations with their parenting. So, following the principle of inclusive fitness, as we touched on in the last chapter, they still have a biological reason to stay alive. And, third, even if people did lack reproductive prospects by any route, that's still not a genetic reason to kill themselves. There are any number of other ways to respond to the situation. They may as well just keep plodding on, as animals generally do. Denied opportunities to mate, a mammal's best strategy is to hang in there in case of a change for the better. Even spawned salmon do not commit suicide, by the way. They carry on doing what salmon do — feeding, and trying to evade predators, for example. They die of exhaustion in the end.

In all, it is illogical to link suicide to low reproductive potential. It is like saying that my car may be running low on fuel — therefore, I'll just have to drive it off a cliff. It is virtually always genetically worthwhile for mammals to stay alive because, biologically, where there's life there's hope. We are still looking for a fitness payoff for suicide, and one big enough to compensate for the extreme genetic handicap of being dead.

The 'burdensomeness hypothesis'

Regarding that payoff, deCatanzaro offers another interesting idea, one which some researchers find persuasive. Again, I don't, as I will explain. He suggests that suicide might make sense on inclusive fitness grounds if an individual becomes such a drain on his close relations that they'd be better off without him. A troublesome individual's death could be good in that situation, not only for his family's reproductive prospects, but indirectly for his too. His genetic gain comes indirectly via the genes he shares with relations — relations who, without him, would be better able to raise offspring of their own. In such a scenario, self-destruction could paradoxically serve genetic self-interest.

This 'burdensomeness hypothesis' is certainly an intriguing thought. Intuitively, it strikes a chord: suicidal people do sometimes feel that their families would be better off without them. The sad truth is that exhausted family members, pushed to the limit after years of caring for a chronically distressed loved one, might even agree. The hypothesis finds echoes in stories from some nomadic tribes, in which an elder too frail or sick to survive the next journey may volunteer for assisted suicide, although within a strict code of ritual.[2] It finds a match in certain statistical links between measures of burdensomeness and measures of suicidality. It has inspired other theorists to put forward various ideas on a similar theme, and it has sparked an interesting academic debate.[3]

But there are two snags. One is that the hypothesis swims against another tide of facts. No measure of burdensomeness — feeling, or actually being, a burden to one's family — usefully predicts suicide. Sure, statistical correlations can be found; but as we saw in Chapter 2, that's not saying much. There are thousands of such risk factors. None are powerful enough to predict suicide much better than chance, burdensomeness included. The vast majority of people who feel they're a liability to their families don't kill themselves. At the same time, there is marked suicidality among many groups who are far from useless: high earners; gifted and talented people; police, firemen, doctors, vets, and certain other professionals; active young adults; and so on. Suicide is also relatively common among people who have become isolated — that is, they have no family around to be a burden to. And there is the bottom line that suicide rarely comes as a blessing for those left behind. People bereaved in this way generally find life a lot tougher, not easier. Whatever burden might be lifted, if any, it is heavily outweighed by new burdens loaded in its place.[4]

The other problem is a hole in the theory's logic. Even if an individual were such a trouble that they needed to be removed, that would not require the individual to be killed, whether by their own hand or anyone else's. There are non-lethal solutions, such as exile (voluntary or forced), abandonment, or quarantine. Importantly, these alternatives have the genetic upside of preserving, however briefly, the individual's reproductive potential, however slight. Even if a killing were required for the sake of others' reproductive success, that would still not call for suicide. The killing would, rather, be done by those others. They have better information on whether the load is in fact too heavy to carry — it's their burden, after all — and they have genetically more to gain. Probably for this reason, the grim reality in the animal kingdom is that infanticide or fratricide, not suicide, is how nature deals with burdensome individuals. The pattern holds for humans too. Infants, however sickly or unsupportable, do not spontaneously die just to relieve the burden of their existence from their families. Quite the opposite; they will cry, cling, and generally do all they can to induce kin to carry on looking after them. Infanticide, on the other hand, is common practice across many cultures, it being the way mothers remove the burden of a baby when that unburdening would help their overall reproduction, current and future. This kind of biological response is particularly well documented among birds. In starvation conditions, which is just about the only scenario where suicide might be worthwhile on grounds of inclusive fitness, a nestling will let its entire brood starve rather than kill itself. If there are too many mouths to feed, the weakest nestling won't push itself out of the nest to save its family the trouble, or meekly shut its beak and wait to die. Eventually, it will be killed by a parent or sibling.[5]

Adaptation versus 'just-so' stories

What to conclude? None of this says that troublesome people don't sometimes take their own lives, perhaps even in an effort to improve the lot of their families. It does say that, from a genetic viewpoint, suicide is not an outstandingly good solution to the problem of being a burden to one's kin. Other solutions make better sense. In other words, it doesn't appear that suicide was custom-made for the purpose of unburdening families. It fails, on that score, the acid test of *adaptation*.

Adaptation is the way an organism's form and behaviour can be shaped by selection to solve a recurring survival or reproduction problem that its ancestors faced in the evolutionary past. It is one thing to propose, as the burdensomeness idea does, that the trait of suicide came about as an adaptation. But without good evidence of evolutionary shaping to support it, the hypothesis is open to being attacked as a 'just-so' story — that is, no more scientific than one of Rudyard Kipling's whimsies, of the "How the Elephant Got His Trunk"-variety. Palaeontologist and pop science writer Stephen Jay Gould made this dig at some evolutionary theorizing in the 1970s.

The jibe was unjust, as others have pointed out. All scientific hypotheses are 'just-so' stories inasmuch as they put forward ideas about how things come about. It is also unreasonable to complain, as some do, that evolutionary hypotheses about the human psyche are frivolous because they can't be disproved. Many solid theories in the biological sciences cannot be absolutely proved one way or the other — even Darwin's, which remains 'just a theory' to many people despite overwhelming evidence in its favour. The best we can do is weigh the facts and reach a judgement on a balance of probability, as juries often do. Such verdicts can be valid.

To be fair, behind Gould's and others' nit-picking is a serious concern. The underlying worry is that evolutionary ideas in human psychology may be misused, exploited to give false legitimacy to ideologies of racial purity and eugenics. There is a slippery slope to hell here.

Take the burdensomeness hypothesis of suicide, for example. Suppose we decide it is true — that suicide is nature's way of getting rid of deadweights. Instead of us trying to prevent people from committing suicide, wouldn't it be better for society if we just let them get on with it? Before you dismiss that as unthinkable, be aware that the author of the burdensome hypothesis suggested exactly this as a reasonable policy implication.[6]

Anyway, why stop there? Even better, we could *help* genetic undesirables to kill themselves. Better still, let's exterminate them. Such supposedly evolution-based logic led, step by step, to the atrocities of 1940s Germany. Some warn that it could happen again, arguing that the political conditions that drove us into the Holocaust remain in place around the world today.[7] It is right, therefore, to be wary. But this fair caution shouldn't block scientists from the positive task of trying to understand how evolution impacts on human affairs. Mocking evolutionists as storytellers isn't the way; it doesn't help.[8]

But another prominent biologist, George C. Williams, argued (and years before Gould chipped in) that the criticism is sometimes deserved — some evolutionary theories are indeed mere stories. It is easy to point to an interesting biological trait, propose a plausible reason as to why it emerged, and leave it at that. Williams also pointed out a common pitfall, which is to decide too easily that a biological feature is an adaptation. Any claim that a feature is evolutionarily adaptive needs to be backed up by specific evidence, because not everything in biology came about in this way.

There are two other possible, and simpler, evolutionary explanations. One is that, under certain conditions, certain trivial features can appear and persist simply by happenstance, as a kind of background genetic *noise*. The other is that, because every adaptation brings trails of secondary effects in its wake, many features are *by-products* of adaptations. And, by the way, such side-effects may show little obvious connection with the primary adaptation that caused them. These alternative explanations are important: many features in biology did not evolve to serve any particular purpose, but more likely arose by one of these other routes.[9]

To help us move beyond story-telling, and before we jump to the conclusion that something is an adaptation, Williams counsels us to look for evidence of special design. Does a trait's form tally precisely with the function that's being ascribed to it? Could it have come about for one of those simpler reasons?

The heart is a good example. We can be sure the heart is an adaptation — in this case, a device shaped by natural selection for the purpose of pumping blood. The reason we can be sure is that it appears precisely engineered to serve that function. There is no other credible way to explain the arrangement of blood vessels, valves, and ventricles; the sequence of its muscular actions; its neural wiring; and so on. Importantly, we reach this conclusion by intuitive hunch, not proof: there may be no way to prove the point by inductive logic, as if it were a puzzle in mathematics. We use common sense to decide, for example, which aspects of the heart are relevant: it's the plumbing that strikes us as noteworthy and not, say, its colour or smell. Nonetheless, intuitive though our thinking is, we can make a reasonable judgement based on the evidence of special design — which is that, on a balance of probability, the heart is an adaptation.

The thumping sound the heart makes, on other hand, probably isn't an adaptation. Heartbeat is more likely a by-product: it doesn't serve any particular purpose, but arises as a side-effect of the heart's pumping action. But how can we be sure? After all, medics and lovers have long read meanings into a patient's health or partner's passion from clues given by their pulse. Plausibly, heartbeat could be an adaptation — an honest signal, broadcasting details of the organism's physical and emotional state. Let's call this the 'communication hypothesis' of heartbeat. How would we take this from a mere story to the status of a coherent theory? Following Williams's advice, we should look for evidence of special design. Does heartbeat tally precisely with the design we would expect of a device that evolved for communicating?

Well, no, it doesn't. Once we start looking, we can't help but be struck by anomalies. The sound is oddly muffled: detectable only at close quarters, and then only with difficulty. And where are the acoustic features for amplifying and directing the sound? There is a suspicious lack of the kind of components we find in audio apparatuses elsewhere in nature. Moreover, the beat keeps thumping away, 24/7, supposedly transmitting its message even when there is obviously no-one around to receive it, which is an unaccountable waste of energy. And of course, there is a simpler alternative explanation — a 'by-product' hypothesis, which says that heartbeat is the sound that the heart would be expected to make just going about its business of pumping blood. All in all, even though heartbeat may have some social utility as a source of information, there is little reason to believe that it was selected for that purpose. We would reasonably conclude that the communication hypothesis is probably wrong.[10]

This method of deciding whether traits are adaptations, looking for signs of special design, is not failsafe, for several reasons. Here are two. First, selection produces features that are good, but not ideal, because it can't build anything from scratch. It has to work with what it is given, co-opting and tweaking pre-existing biological raw material. So, even the best solution is an improvised workaround. Kipling's yarn says the elephant's trunk came about when a nosy animal had its snout pulled. That may not be far from the truth, but evolution's version is much more interesting — selection lengthening the snout in tiny increments, by genetic mutation and selective pressure, across countless generations of elephants' ancestors. Selection has created, in effect, a fully functioning extra limb. It's good, but we can imagine how it could be better. Perhaps the elephant's trunk would be even more useful if it had a spotlight on the end, or a machine gun for taking down predators. But spotlights and machine guns, potentially advantageous though they might be, were not evolvable from the kind of mutations that are likely to originate from a snout.[11] Evolution runs like the old joke: Question — Excuse me Sir, what's the best way to Dublin? Answer — Well now, you don't want to be starting from here. The danger is that it is often possible to look at an adaptation and spot imperfections in what is nonetheless a purposeful, fitness-serving design.

Second, biological features often don't get the luxury of being designed for a single purpose. Back to the elephant's trunk, it is hard to say what it is specially designed to do, because it has taken on so many tasks — breathing, touching, gripping, making sounds, bathing, drinking, olfaction, perhaps others. Which came first? Perhaps we can't be certain about the origins of heartbeat either. But, without claiming to be 100% sure, we can still reasonably conclude that there is no compelling evidence of special design to support a communication hypothesis for heartbeat.

The 'communication hypothesis'

Have we strayed off track? A communication hypothesis for the evolution of heartbeat seems a long way from the task of this book. But as an analogy, it takes us close to home. There is, in fact, a communication hypothesis for the evolution of suicide; or, rather, two hypotheses, put forward by sharp-minded evolutionists, Kristen Syme and colleagues.

The adaption, they argue, is not so much suicide but *attempted* suicide — they suggest there could be a direct fitness upside to be won in trying, or threatening, to kill oneself. Interestingly, this theory starts from the opposite premise to that of the burdensomeness hypothesis. That, as you'll recall, presumed (against the facts) that suicide brings a fitness upside to close kin. Syme and colleagues' 'bargaining hypothesis' presumes, more realistically, a downside. Death carries a fitness cost not only directly for the one who dies, but also, though inclusive fitness, for the deceased's relations. So, one may be able to blackmail family members by threatening or trying to kill oneself. If the blackmailer survives and succeeds in extracting fitness concessions, then the gambit pays off. If a suicide attempt is fatal, everyone loses. Suicide in this light is a Machiavellian gamble. The stakes are high because there needs to be some prospect of actual death for the blackmailer's threat to be credible. So, the theory goes, the act or threat of attempting suicide may be an adaptation, a fitness-enhancing means of communicating a coercive message. The researchers also propose a variation on the theme, suggesting that suicide evolved as a drastic way to express remorse — when saying sorry isn't enough.[12]

Now, let's apply the test of special design. Can we judge suicide, or rather attempted suicide, to be custom-built for communication? Does the pattern of suicide attempts precisely match a communicative purpose, like the detailed construction of the heart tells us that it was designed to pump blood?

It seems to me probably not. There are several anomalies. Suicide attempts, whether lethal or survived, show patterns that not only wouldn't help with communication but would actively get in the way.

People who are bent on killing themselves would not logically be expected to tell close family about their plans, at least not in enough detail to invite interference. Nor in practice do they tell them. Characteristically, suicides are marked not by communication but precisely the opposite — secrecy. There are some rare exceptions. But for the most part, suicide hits families like a bolt from the blue. The standard reaction of close relations is shock, confusion, and disbelief — that is to say, they had no fair warning.[13] For sure, with hindsight, they might be able to pick out some incident from the past and re-read it as a hint — possibly, maybe, a sign of suicidal intent.[14] A passing comment, an angry outburst, a dark joke. But being supposedly wise after the event is not the same as being adequately informed before it. Many people admit to thinking about taking their own life — one in four young Americans in a single month, according to that survey I mentioned earlier.[15] But such confessions very rarely go any further: they're of no value as a presage of action. Even with the benefit of hindsight, families usually struggle to make sense of what happened. They're left bewildered by the act's apparent senselessness. As we noted in the last chapter, they're left asking 'Why?' — they yearn for closure. In short, suicide is rarely heralded by a specific communicated threat.

The same pattern of secrecy holds where a suicide attempt is survived — except, in these cases, relations usually don't get to hear about it at all, either before the event or after.[16] Survivors typically do their best to keep their actions under wraps, and for a very good reason: they know the damning stigma that awaits if they get found out. They know they'll likely be presumed to be up to some ploy — trying to manipulate loved ones, get attention, win sympathy or whatever. They're (mis)judged like this even by health professionals charged with looking after them.[17] In other words, the communication hypothesis isn't a brainchild of psychologists. It forms part of the prejudice that is already out there, doing the rounds in society, as it has done for generations. It is part and parcel of our generally jaundiced attitude towards suicide and the people who do it. Judgement is one of the ways society penalises suicide attempters for their deviance. We'll come back to why there are such penalties in a later chapter. But we can note for now that the social stigma against suicide is a powerful motivation for survivors to keep quiet about their actions. Contributing to the stigma as it does, the folk version of the communication hypothesis can't help but be self-defeating. It has precisely the opposite effect to the one it alleges — it *blocks* communication.

And then we should consider all the other available ways of communicating that don't entail trying or threatening to kill oneself. There are any number of drastic threats that people could use to blackmail their families, if that was indeed the goal — actions that wouldn't necessarily involve a suicide attempt. Moreover, other threats offer better fitness logic, because they would cause more damage to the victim's fitness than to the blackmailer's. A threat of homicide would make more genetic sense than suicide. We can also note the gamut of other ways — evolutionarily more ancient and more informative ways — by which humans communicate with each other, which would lead us to wonder why suicide would evolve as an apparently redundant extra.

But most awkwardly for the communication hypothesis, people who survive suicide attempts are evidently not rewarded with a biological upside, at least not one that comes close to compensating for the extreme risks they take. As we've discussed already, the predictable outcome of an attempt is grim, even if it is survived: mental trauma, physical injury, disfigurement, and social stigma. The stigma alone looks sure to impair reproductive fitness. We noted that people baulk at the idea of dating someone who has recently tried to take their own life, let alone marrying them.[18] Then of course, a suicide attempt comes with the risk of death — genetic extinction. In a calculation of biological pros and cons, it is hard to imagine any reward or ransom, even in theory, that could make it genetically worthwhile to try to kill oneself. As there is no obvious fitness logic in going through with a suicide threat, there would be no obvious fitness reason to accept such a threat as being credible: as a biological adaptation, it wouldn't work.

All in all, then, suicide — whether done, tried, or threatened — doesn't look like it was purpose-built by natural selection to solve an adaptive problem of communication. It does not, to my mind, pass the test of special design that the communication hypothesis requires. I think we can reasonably reject the hypothesis on this basis. We can reject it even though many people believe, allegedly wise after the event, that they can read meanings into suicidal acts. We can reject it even if, as with the true emotion betrayed by a pounding heart, there may in fact sometimes be useful information to be had.

As I suggested, the communication hypothesis is quite right in one important respect: suicide attempters, when they survive, are often presumed to have a manipulative agenda — trying to win attention, sympathy, or the like from people around them. In a similar vein, they are also said to be selfish, pathetic, feckless, irresponsible, cowardly, weak, incompetent, dishonourable, immoral, and so on.[19] Survivors themselves will often agree, internalising the stigma. In their distress and demoralisation, they will often accept whatever judgements others put on them.[20]

But to judge suicides in this way says more about the observer than the actor. Around the world, depending on local tradition, observers post-rationalise suicides in different ways. They are rarely approving.[21] Some cultures select manipulation-type stories. Others see evil spirits or bad luck at work. Yet others regard suicides as sick, or stupid. In the West a few generations ago, many would have viewed them as either morally defective or criminal — we are still in the habit of using the legalistic term 'commit' as in 'to commit suicide' — a word I'm trying not to overuse in this book. These days we prefer a certain psycho-social genre of suicide theorizing, along the lines of Durkheim's and the Interpersonal-Psychological Theory of Suicide that we talked about in Chapter 2. For those brought up with it, this stance feels like common sense — self-evidently correct. But it is as much folk theory as any other interpretation, and it has no more substance. Its spin-offs in suicidology are only popular notions repackaged as 'science'.[22]

It looks to me that the same can be said of the communication hypothesis.

A giant missing key

Although I don't think they stack up, I hope I have not come across as dismissive of deCatanzaro's bargaining hypothesis, or of the ideas of Syme and colleagues. There are other competent theorists in this field also doing valuable work, and I don't want to minimise their contributions either. These other proposals, also rightly published in serious scientific journals, envisage suicide as an adaptation shaped for other purposes. They suppose that the behaviour may have evolved to control the spread of disease, to prevent conflict within a group, or to encourage heroic deeds in battle situations.[23] Others suggest that suicide might be a fossil adaptation — a hangover from when it was fitness promoting in our Stone Age past, even if it isn't now.[24] I don't find these proposals convincing either, and for the same reason, to my mind, they fail the test of special design — the hallmark of adaptation. They don't take us beyond the telling of adaptationist stories.

But I do think they are important, and useful, if for what may sound like a cock-eyed reason. If, over several decades, the best efforts of some of the world's smartest evolutionists haven't found a robust adaptation-type explanation for suicide, then that tells me that what has been looked for probably isn't there. If it exists, it should not be that hard to spot. We can avoid the 'yeti' position — clinging to a myth on the grounds that we haven't found evidence of it 'yet'. In science, finding nothing useful can be a useful finding. It is one of the frustrations of a reporting bias in the scientific press: researchers are more likely to submit a paper for publication, and to have it published, if it claims to find what they were looking for, although a null result can be a major step forward too.

Let us wrap up. Recall that it's as if we are searching a house for a giant missing key. We now know that there are three, and only three, known ways by which any biological feature can evolve. That makes the search easier, because it means our house has only three rooms to search in.

We looked in Room One, where suicide may have come about as an adaptation because it solved a particular fitness problem in our evolutionary past. But we drew a blank. The behaviour does not look well designed for the supposed adaptive tasks put forward to explain it, and there is no obvious fitness payoff from the behaviour that would compensate for its catastrophic fitness cost. We have found no plausible fitness problem for which the genetically logical solution is to kill oneself, or even to try.

Room Two holds that sometimes a heritable trait can spread through a population by happenstance, as background genetic noise. I only touched on this option, but we can set it aside fairly straightforwardly, because traits have to be trivial in their fitness impact to spread in this way. Suicidality surely doesn't fit that criterion. It is hard to think of many traits that do, for that matter.

We are left with Room Three, in which a trait may not serve any adaptive purpose but is, rather, a by-product of an adaption. Into this category of explanation falls the sound of heartbeat, as we discussed. If this is the best explanation of suicide, then the compensatory fitness payoff we are looking for would come not from suicide itself but from the upsides of an adaptation, as yet unknown, which gives off the behaviour as an unfortunate side-effect.

So, by elimination, we should expect to find our gigantic missing key in this third room, where suicide is an evolutionary by-product. Let's take a look.

CHAPTER 3: *We wondered if suicide might be an adaptation — a behaviour favoured by natural selection because it solved a recurring fitness problem faced by our ancestors. But we found no compelling evidence of special design to support that idea. Most likely, then, suicide is a costly side-effect of some other evolved trait that is adaptive. But what could that adaptation be?*

CHAPTER 4: *We go looking for an evolved adaptation so powerful that it was worth bearing a downside as biologically costly as suicidality for its sake. Following the trail, we find one: pain. The universal stimulus for suicide, the need to escape unbearable emotional pain, has ancient adaptive origins.*

4

PAIN: THE MOTIVATION

The story so far: We are trying to understand why human beings kill themselves. To that end, we want to understand the evolutionary origins of the behaviour — how is it that natural selection has landed the human species with so self-destructive a behaviour?

The key, we think, is to identify a biological payoff, a reproductive upside big enough to outweigh the reproductive downside. We looked for this advantage in some kind of an adaptation, thinking that suicide might have been favoured by selection because it solved a recurring fitness problem in our ancestral past. But we found no obvious problem for which suicide, or attempted suicide, offers an especially neat solution. We concluded that the fitness payoff probably does not come from the act itself.

By elimination, suicide's missing upside is more likely to be found in some other trait, of which suicide is an unfortunate by-product. We're expecting humans to be equipped with an adaptation so valuable for survival and reproduction that it is worth paying the price even of suicide for its sake. Such an adaptation will be so powerful that it holds suicidality as a fixture in the human species, despite the enormous selective pressure that would otherwise drive it out. So, what could that overpowering adaptation be?

Darwin meets Freud

Few scientists seem to have put much thought into this question, at least until recent years. Darwin himself dodged it, a remarkable omission for such an otherwise bold thinker — especially as the existence of suicide could be seen to pose a threat to his entire theory of natural selection.[1] What little he does say is interesting. At least it nods towards the problem. Darwin viewed suicide as a race-preserving mechanism, a tool that weeds mental defectives out of the human breeding population, according to this comment in his book, *The Descent of Man*:

> In regard to the moral qualities, some elimination of the worst disposi-
> tions is always in progress even in the most civilised nations. Malefactors
> are executed, or imprisoned for long periods, so that they cannot freely
> transmit their bad qualities. Melancholic and insane persons are confined,
> or commit suicide.[2]

We can take what is useful from this musing and leave the rest. Some ideas that were fashionable in Darwin's time — that moral fibre can be bred, and deviants make poor breeding stock — have been discredited and duly dumped.[3] We need to make sure they stay dumped, as we noted in Chapter 3. And we know today that there's no simple causal link between suicidality and 'melancholic and insane' (which I take to mean depression and other mental disorders, in modern parlance), although that particular myth still circulates.

The useful point for our purposes is that Darwin expects suicide to have a selective effect. It is obvious why: whatever 'bad qualities' suppos-edly cause people to kill themselves ought to disappear along with their dead bodies. But that leaves us with the problem of explaining why such a culling device hasn't eliminated itself by now. Why, once the 'melan-cholic and insane' have been swept from the breeding pool, hasn't suicide made itself redundant? It is as if we brought in cats to rid the farm of mice, only to wind up infested with both mice and cats. Suicide's stability tells us that some evolutionary force, as yet mysterious, is holding both it and its casual drivers in place, in defiance of the selection that should have pushed them both out. It is a force that perhaps even Darwin found too grim to face.

It took four decades and an even more fearless thinker, Sigmund Freud, to look this dark tendency in the eye — named and framed in his 1920 essay, 'Beyond the Pleasure Principle'.[4] Freud's idea is that all life-forms, humans included, come with a built-in death drive, or *Todestrieb*. It operates like a primordial bungee; attached at birth, stretching in life, and tending to pull the organism back to the inorganic state (that is, dead) from whence it came. With a century of hindsight it is easy for us to pick holes in the idea. One problem is tautology: zero equals zero. If the answer to 'Why do people kill themselves?' is merely 'Because they are driven to', then all Freud gives us is a placeholder, awaiting an explanation as to where the supposed drive came from and how it works. On this matter, he was clutching at straws. There's no known biological means by which a death drive, at least of the primordial bungee variety, would come about. Indeed, psychoanalysis generally seems so left behind by modern evolutionary theory that Freud's relevance to our debate may be hard to see.

But as a pioneering evolutionist of his day, making the best of what was known at the time, Freud offers several ideas that should interest us. He tried to make sense of suicide and other destructive behaviours within a grand theory that combined the elegance of both physics and Darwinism. Physics inspired his notion of mental equilibrium; a psychic system of weights and counterweights, checking and balancing each other. In his scheme, a death drive was needed to oppose and temper a sexually energising life force. And therein lies the connection with Darwin: Freud took the point that winning the battle of natural selection depends on sexual success.[5] So, dated though they are, for many people (some evolutionists included), Freud's ideas hold at least a few grains of truth.

Let me pick out three grains that I think may help us. First, we have to accept that some kind of suicidogenic force, a death drive of sorts, exists — Freud having put the idea on the table, at least he gives us something to work with. Second, Freud reminds us that, while there is single-mindedness in what we do, we can be in many minds before we do it. Imagine the battle as a death drive versus a life force if you like, but it is important to be attuned to the intrapsychic conflict that goes on before the choice of suicide is made, before the point when the urge to live is overwhelmed by the urge to die. Third, balances have to be struck, because too much of a good thing, even of a life force, can be pathological. We will look at these points again at the end of the chapter.

Escape from psychache

Some of the loose ends left by Darwin and Freud were tied up in a remarkable couple of lines by psychanalyst Henry A. Murray and anthropologist Clyde Kluckhohn, in a 1948 essay on personality:

Suicide does not have *adaptive* (survival) value but it does have *adjustive* value for the organism. Suicide is *functional* because it abolishes painful tension.[6]

In other words, the behaviour makes biological sense if we keep in mind that pain is one of nature's great motivators. It is a need state, like hunger or thirst, precisely designed to induce an animal to act to end it — that is, to relieve what Murray and Kluckhohn call 'painful tension'. The human animal can satisfy this need to end pain by ending itself. So, suicide is not an adaptation: it is not designed to solve a fitness problem, as we deduced in the last chapter. But it is functional inasmuch as it answers the organism's need to do something about pain. It has been well said: nothing hurts less than being dead.[7]

Murray and Kluckhohn's message has travelled a long way in suicide research, although not in the biological direction you might expect. The quote was often cited by Murray's protégé and fellow clinician, Edwin Shneidman, who cemented it into suicidology's very foundations. Shneidman held a father-like influence over the field until his death in 2009; and indeed beyond — many of his proposals live on, as, for example, tenets of the Interpersonal-Psychological Theory of Suicide that we mentioned in Chapter 2.[8] Suicidology's main professional body, its leading journal, and its standing as a distinct field of research were all Shneidman's creations, so it should come as no surprise that suicidology's research priorities have tended to reflect his.

Evolution was not one of them. Apart from accepting Murray's position, that suicide was not an adaptation, Shneidman showed little interest in evolutionary matters. What caught his attention was, rather, the psychological functionality that Murray highlights — suicide's implied cause-effect, stimulus-response mechanics. Insufferable pain is the input; suicide is the output. To explain the link, Shneidman argued that the point of suicide is to end consciousness. At times of intolerable suffering, the appeal of death is that it puts an end to the ability to feel bad. No one kills themselves out of joy. For Shneidman, it was self-evident that 'the common stimulus in suicide is unendurable psychological pain'.[9]

Such was Shneidman's leadership in the field of suicidology that he gave it new vocabulary — including its name, 'suicidology'. Another of his invented words captures the emotional distress that can lead people to take their own lives: *psychache*.

Psychache refers to the hurt, anguish, soreness, aching, psychological *pain* in the psyche, the mind. It is intrinsically psychological — the pain of excessively felt shame, or guilt, or humiliation, or loneliness, or fear, or angst, or dread of growing old or of dying badly, or whatever.[10]

That final 'whatever' sweeps into Shneidman's framework just about every theory of suicide that came before or after. Rival theories have piled up by the score since Durkheim's more than a century ago. Durkheim, as you may recall, claimed he traced the cause of suicide to (among other social ills) a feeling of not belonging; anomy — or, to put it in Shneidman's terminology, psychache. Other theorists have drawn attention to the suicidogenic power of other stressful states, such as hopelessness (that is, psychache), defeat (psychache), failure (psychache), feeling one is a burden to one's family (psychache), and any number of other varieties of misery, all of them describing psychache. A catalogue of suicide theories looks like a tester pad for pens that all write in black. Even set against each other to highlight the contrasts, what is striking is not their differences but their similarity — indeed, I suggest, their unity.[11]

To understand why this is true, and why it matters, we need to take a short detour into the biology of pain.

One malady, many names

Pain has two components. It is like a messenger who delivers a message in two parts, one in each hand. One hand holds all the qualitative details — where we hurt and why. We need these particulars. If a pain signal is to tell you that, say, there's a thorn in the sole of your foot, then you need to know which foot, and where, so you can decide how to respond: pull out the thorn. We can assume this information is important because pain is a biological need state, as Murry and Kluckhohn described. It is an evolved, protective mechanism. Pain exists to alert the organism to some condition that mattered to its ancestors' reproductive prospects. Back of every individual's pain is the bitter experience of countless forebears, stored in the individual's genes. In our example, it is that people who pulled the thorns out of their feet tended to survive and reproduce more successfully than those who kept walking and eventually lamed themselves. So, part of pain's message, on the one hand, is potentially life-saving information.[12]

What is the message in pain's other hand? The other hand *is* the message: it comes as a clenched fist, and it packs a punch. The punch is meant to make us stop, pay attention, and take action. It also gives us something to remember, so that we will take care not to, say, step on a thorn again.

Now, qualitatively, the punch is always the same: a punch is a punch. It varies only quantitatively; how hard it strikes. The painfulness of pain can vary in only one dimension, how much it hurts, because the mind has to locate every pain (and, indeed, every pleasure) on a single scale of nastiness-niceness. This is a fact of animal life, because decisions need to be made. We, like other animals, are generally not good multi-taskers. Animals usually do only one thing at a time — sleep, eat, fight, flee, have sex, and so on — because they cannot do more than one thing at a time very well. You cannot stop to remove a thorn and at the same time keep walking: you have to make a choice. So, conflicting motivations have to be prioritised, traded off against each other with the use of a standardised measuring system.[13] What hurts more; the thorn in your foot or your rising panic that your gang is disappearing over the hilltop and might leave you behind? There is neurological truth in the ancient Greek quip, "All pain is one malady with many names."[14] There are many names to describe the informational details of pain. The one malady of all pain is that it hurts.

We need both parts of pain's signal — information and motivation — to make use of it. The information part is pointless on its own. There is no value in an animal just knowing there's a thorn in its foot. It has value only if the animal knows it needs to do something about it. So, to be of use, pain has to motivate, with an imperative 'STOP! END THE PAIN! NOW!' Likewise, motivational force on its own is useless. We can do nothing with an order to stop the pain unless we know *how*. For the human organism, it may be worse than useless: meaningless pain can feel all the more unbearable precisely because of its meaninglessness — there is no way to make sense of it, and nothing that can be done to end it. Except, there is something that can be done. Humans nearly always have one final resort for ending pain.

In the light of that explanation of pain, let's go back to Shneidman's 'whatever'. I mentioned earlier that there are dozens of scientific theories of suicide. The reason there are so many is that they tend to focus on the 'many names' side of pain: they look at the details of human suffering in search of reasons why people take their own lives. It is not that they are wrong. It is just that they miss the point, that the act is an effective solution to pain's one malady — its painfulness. Suicide answers a unitary need, to abolish painful tension. So, as Shneidman observed, it is the degree, not the type, of pain that makes it suicidogenic. You could potentially come up with any number of suicide theories, one for every hue of distress you care to describe. But one theory would do, because they are all varieties of black. Suicide is an all-purpose response to pain's universal command: 'END THE PAIN! NOW!' The type of pain matters only inasmuch as some types may hurt more than others.

Indeed, they do. A thorn in the foot is usually more painful than, say, a pimple on the neck. The degree of pain we feel generally reflects the importance of the triggering injury — that is, the degree of fitness danger that was linked with that injury in the evolutionary past, and the importance of doing something about it. Walking with a thorn in the sole of the foot damaged our ancestors' reproductive prospects more than walking with a pimple. So, a thorn in the foot needs more urgent attention, and consequently, it hurts more.

Why rejection hurts

What type of pain can get so bad as to induce people to kill themselves? Not generally physical, bodily, pain — although that can certainly drive sufferers to extreme measures.[15]

The kind of pain that most strongly demands an escape is psychological or emotional. That's the thread running through those examples given by Shneidman in his definition of psychache: shame, guilt, humiliation, loneliness, fear, angst, and so on. These and other psychological miseries form a unifying feature of suicide theories, as we have discussed.

Psychological pain (or emotional pain, or mental pain — I take these to mean the same thing) is especially powerful not because there is much special about its neurological wiring. Far from it — bodily pain and emotional pain, while not identical, use similar circuitry in the brain.[16] And common experience, likewise, is that it is possible to feel very bad without hurting anywhere in particular. The pain of hurt feelings probably evolved in mammals by re-purposing the more ancient neural circuits of physical pain. We intuitively sense an overlap: we talk of feeling hurt, of being stung by cutting remarks, and of being homesick. Indeed, to talk of 'feelings' at all is to use the language of physical sensation. The physical/mental cross-over can also be felt in the way we can sometimes experience emotional distress as a bodily thing — fear can be a sinking feeling in the stomach, separation an aching heart, and so on. And all pain, physical or psychological, necessarily has an emotive element — it is meant to motivate. In that sense, all pain is emotional. So mental and bodily pain are closely related. But nonetheless, mental pain is especially unbearable.

Why is mental pain so dire? Before answering that, let us sharpen the point a little further: the mental pain that induces suicide is usually specifically social. *Social pain* is the special aversive feeling that strikes because of an injury, or threatened injury, to our interpersonal capital — family supports, reputation, status, allegiances, and other social assets.[17] Recall, in this light, the kind of mental states that head up Shneidman's examples of psychache: shame, guilt, humiliation, and loneliness. These are social emotions — they speak of damage to personal relationships. Durkheim, a sociologist, attuned to social effects, picked up on this point a century ago: it was a sense of not belonging, anomy, that caught his attention. Other suicide theories follow a similar theme.

Like any other pain, social pain is a product of our evolutionary past; it records the kind of fitness threats that were faced by our ancestors. That history pre-dates humans, going deep into our roots as social animals. Every mammal's survival depends on guarding at least one social tie — as a suckling, with its mother. And every mother's reproductive success depends on keeping safe her attachments with her young, at least until weaning. For social mammals, the need to dominate and/or depend on other members of a group creates a web of potentially threatened relationships, all kept in place by the individual's feelings of, and responses to, social pain.

We humans, the most social mammal of all, seem set up to feel social pain to a unique degree.[18] A network of supportive relationships is a lifelong survival necessity for us. It was presumably ever so, because we are surely not designed to go it alone. We are physically unimpressive (not especially thick-skinned, fast, strong), and we lack the kind of personal protection equipment (fur, fangs, claws) that is standard kit for other mammals, even social ones. Our protection lies in teamwork. Not all psychological pain is directly social. Humans can suffer a devastating loss of meaning — the despairing 'What's the point of carrying on?' that can come from a collapse of faith or a crack in the certainties with which we make sense of the world and our place in it. Even so, this kind of distress often has a social side. What could be called existential pain is often sparked by the loss of the kind of love relationships that make life feel worthwhile. We'll come back to this in later chapters.

The shocking feature of social pain is its sheer painfulness when it hits. At its worst, it can be experienced as more excruciating, more intolerable, than any physical pain.[19] The agony can override all other concerns. One command takes over: the pain has to stop.

So, the sharper question is this: why is social pain so painful? I have already made the point that, as with pain generally, social pain alerts us to a fitness threat in our evolutionary past — broken relationships, in this case. But I don't believe that is the whole story, or even the main story. I suggest the special intensity of social pain is there to compensate for our relationships' special fragility. Let me explain with a bodily parallel. If you asked a man where in his anatomy he would least want to be kicked, testicles would be high on the list. This isn't particularly because a man needs his testicles in order to reproduce — he does, of course, but they're not the only body part he needs for that task. Reproduction also requires a working set of internal organs (heart, lungs, kidney, etc.), and he isn't so worried about them getting in harm's way. Testicles are of special concern because they are especially sensitive; and the reason they are so sensitive is because they are highly prone to damage. Sperm production is best done in conditions cooler than normal body temperature — hence the need for the testicles to hang outside of the body's protective envelope — which unfortunately means they are physically vulnerable. Pain systems step in to compensate for the lack of other defences: the testicles' extreme sensitivity to pain motivates their owner to take special care in that department.[20] The same is likely the case for eyes: they are important, but not uniquely so. The practical difficulty of safeguarding eyes is that there is only so much physical protection that can be set up without interfering with their primary function — vision. Because eyes are necessarily open to the elements, pain systems gear up to make us prioritise their safekeeping.

I suggest the same principle applies to social relationships. Secure attachments are vital for survival and reproduction. But even more than testicles and eyeballs, our vital relationships are out there, exposed to the world, and all but defenceless. The painfulness of social pain makes us pay special attention to their wellbeing and act promptly to make any necessary repairs. There is no other safeguard available.

Pain's lethal by-product

Putting all this together, it looks to me that suicide is an unfortunate side-effect of pain. There's no getting around it — being alive is going to hurt. Every motile organism from bacteria upwards needs some kind of aversive stimulus, some internal cattle prod, to steer itself around fitness hazards in its environment. For mammals, and especially social mammals, those hazards are often about relationships — hence the necessity for social pain. Separation stings. For humans, the most social mammal, our pain sensors are probably uniquely sensitive in this area. We are especially attuned to the potential for damage to our family and other interpersonal ties precisely because they are so otherwise vulnerable. And whatever we have to say about the matter, damage to these ties is probably inevitable, because our friends, relations and other associates have lives of their own. People grow up, move on, shift their allegiances, and, sooner or later, die. The human experience, then, involves being repeatedly kicked where it hurts — in the attachments. We are left with, at times, unbearable psychache, and its command, 'STOP! END THE PAIN! NOW!' A famous leprosy surgeon well described pain as a gift nobody wants.[21] We are not meant to like it. We are meant *not* to like it, but we can't live without it. Unfortunately, as human animals, with self-extinction as a way to respond to pain's imperative to act, sometimes we can't live with it either. Suicide offers an all-purpose way to stop hurting.

In the light of all this, let's take a fresh look at those three Freudian grains of truth I picked out earlier in this chapter. First, we can understand why humankind finds itself lumbered with a death drive. Pain comes with the territory of being an animal, and pain is meant to be intolerable: it is designed to force the animal to act. We humans have self-killing as a universal, default way to obey that demand. We will explore the matter of human uniqueness in the next chapter. For now, it is useful to see why suicide endures as a fixture in our species, despite what ought to be a selective pressure against it. Suicide's chief motivator, social pain, is part and parcel of being a social animal.

Second, we have a new way to make sense of the inner conflict involved in a decision to take one's own life. We can think of suicide as an unfortunate result of the human psyche having split biological interests. A Freudian psychoanalyst might think of the inner conflict as the *ego* trying to manage the conflicting demands of an instinctive *id* and higher, moralising *super-ego*. I suggest, rather, that the human organism is caught in the middle of an argument between its phenotype and its genotype. The *phenotype* is the organism we see — the physical being, its behaviours, life history, and reproductive career. The *genotype* is the organism's genetic code, the blueprint for the phenotype's physical construction and behavioural programmes. The genotype's genes are a store of information about how the organism's ancestors successfully dealt with fitness opportunities and threats in the evolutionary past. Those genes have just one goal — to replicate themselves.

Let's dramatize the dispute by calling these characters by name: Organism, Phenotype, and Genotype. Phenotype and Genotype need each other. Genotype's genes cannot replicate without Phenotype's physical reproduction equipment and services; and Phenotype wouldn't exist and couldn't survive without Genotype's assembly plan and operating instructions. But sometimes their interests clash because, not least, only Phenotype feels pain. For Phenotype, suicide appeals because it is a good way to stop hurting. For Genotype, suicide is a disaster because it annuls any future prospects for replication. If there is no other way to end unbearable suffering, Organism must choose one or the other — it can't satisfy both. Either it obeys Phenotype, ending the pain along with itself; or it obeys Genotype, by disregarding the pain and staying alive. So, who wins? Phenotype's interests are probably bound to win sometimes, because its pain is designed precisely not to be disregarded. Indeed, Genotype programmed it that way. Suicide is Phenotype doing what it is meant to do — relieving painful tension. This is my attempt at allegory, of course, but I hope it illustrates how the human organism has to pick one of two mutually exclusive biological demands in deciding whether or not to live.

As for the third Freudian grain of truth, we can understand why the need for a psychodynamic balance has to be struck. Natural selection tends towards fitness-maximising trade-offs. It is not in the business of ideal solutions, as discussed in the last chapter, because it never starts with the luxury of a blank page, and the solution to every fitness problem has to be a workaround. Rather, selection seeks out the best available, or least bad. Let's imagine if a Freudian 'life force' ran rampant, avoiding suicide at all costs. It would let us ignore pain, enough to take away the motivation to escape it. But such a sop would contain its own poison. Without the motivation to escape pain, the organism would be defenceless against lethal fitness threats in its environment. We can't live without pain, so we have to put up with a compromise. Paradoxically, human thriving, indeed our very survival, probably carries a 'death drive' along with it — an above-zero risk of self-destruction.

This chapter set out to find an adaptation so powerful that it was worth paying the huge fitness cost of suicide for its sake. Provisionally, the painfulness of pain seems to fit the bill. Without pain, there is no need for suicide. But also, without pain, animal life would be impossible. All animals need an aversive stimulus that alerts them to fitness dangers and makes them take evasive action. The human animal can evade pain effectively, but maladaptively, by opting out of life. Suicide is a price we pay for pain.

So far so good, but this cannot be the whole story. If pain motivates action to escape it, and all animals feel pain, then why don't other animals use suicide to escape it as we do?

CHAPTER 4: *We've found an adaptation that creates suicide as a by-product. Pain is an ancient motivational signal that is precisely designed to induce an animal to act to end or escape it. Social pain, to which humans are susceptible, is especially unbearable. Unfortunately, human animals have the option to escape pain by self-extinction. But that raises the question as to why other animals don't use the same exit route.*

CHAPTER 5: *We need to explain not only why non-human animals don't die by suicide, but why young children and people with severe intellectual disabilities are also protected. Their commonality suggests that, alongside pain, intellectual competence is a second necessary criterion. Suicide comes with being smart.*

5

BRAIN: THE MEANS

In our quest to understand the evolutionary origins of life worth living, we have put our finger on an important reason why sometimes people find life *not* worth living: it hurts.

Pain is an evolved, self-protective signal. It is meant to hurt because it is meant to motivate. It demands that the organism do something to end or escape it. Every animal needs pain so it can manoeuvre itself around fitness hazards in its environment — the kind of threats that damaged reproductive prospects for the animals' ancestors. But what if there is nothing that can be done to end pain? The human animal has an all-purpose answer: it can switch itself off. Death brings with it the cessation of consciousness and thereby relief. Contrary to that song from the movie *M*A*S*H*, suicide may not be painless — but it does offer painlessness. We homed in on psychological pain, or psychache, as the most powerful driver of suicide, simply because psychache seems to be especially intolerable. More specifically, the psychache that drives people to take their own lives usually stems from social troubles, to which we are especially sensitive.

This explanation is clearly incomplete. It doesn't explain why, if an escape into oblivion is such a good way to relieve pain, other animals don't do it too. Indeed, it doesn't explain why most humans don't do it either. If to be punched and kicked by pain is our lot in life, why don't we all kill ourselves and be done with it?

This chapter will start to plug these gaps. We are going to look at who or what doesn't suicide. There are three populations that are exempt: non-human animals, young children, and the intellectually incapacitated. What gives these three groups their immunity? What do they have in common? We will look at each in turn.

Animals' immunity

First, animals. We talked about animal suicide in Chapter 2. In short, there is no reliable scientific evidence that any non-human animal (from now on, just 'animal') wilfully kills itself. That "no reliable scientific evidence" is a stronger point than it first appears, because if evidence of animal suicide were there to be found, we can expect it to have reached the scientific press by now. The search for evidence has been thorough enough, and has gone on long enough, to suggest that what researchers have been looking for probably isn't there. In the 19th century, for example, experimenters tried to verify a then popular belief that scorpions sting themselves to death rather than face death by fire. No one knows how many scorpions were burned alive in the enquiry, but they all died for nothing since, as we now know, scorpions are resistant to their own venom. The myth of self-stinging scorpions still does the rounds, even in the odd 21st-century scientific paper.[1] Clearly, the idea of animal suicide has emotional staying power.

I suggest the myth persists not just because of its emotional appeal, but by partial logic. On the face of it, suicide is such a neat way to end pain that you'd think any animal that could do it would seize the opportunity. It's not as if it would be physically difficult. A chimp could put itself out of its misery almost any time by diving from the nearest tall tree. Dolphins, unlike us, don't breathe automatically; so, a dolphin could extinguish itself at will by staying underwater, or it could simply decide not to breathe. A crow, if it were so minded, could crash-land. Many non-humans indeed ought to find suicide easier than we do, ground-dwellers as we are. So, if it were possible at all, animal suicide ought not to be so rare as to elude scientific observation. Rather, it ought to be a commonplace, regular outcome of animal suffering. We should be surrounded by it. There's surely no scarcity of suffering, both natural and human-made, that would be worth escaping from.

Nonetheless, however desperate their situation, animals don't do the obvious thing. That blank tells us that the obvious thing is probably not an available option. The interesting question is not *whether* animals do or don't commit suicide. The scientific silence says they don't; for people who still want to believe otherwise, I doubt there could ever be enough evidence to persuade them. The interesting question is *why* animals don't.

Childhood immunity

Young children are also immune from suicide, or virtually so. It's a pattern of exemption that isn't as clear-cut as with animals, because the boundary between those that do and those that don't is not as clean. There is, rather, an intermediate age band, roughly corresponding to children's passage through early adolescence. It is a fuzzy border, rather like the treeline in the arctic that separates boreal forest from treeless tundra. The treeline is not literally a line but a transitional zone — the forest thinning as one goes north, until trees disappear altogether. But, fuzzy though it is, the treeline exists, as is clear from the contrasting landscapes some distance on either side.

To illustrate, the stretched 'S' shape in the graph below shows the age pattern of suicide across the first three decades of human lives. This is for the United States, but you'll find much the same picture elsewhere in the world.[2] The graph flatlines from birth to about age 11–12 years, when it slowly lifts off the ground. Suicides then rise sharply through the teenage years, and level out again in the late teens. The top of the graph, age 20 and beyond, is not quite flat — it varies for older age groups, sometimes sloping downwards — but it never goes back to zero.

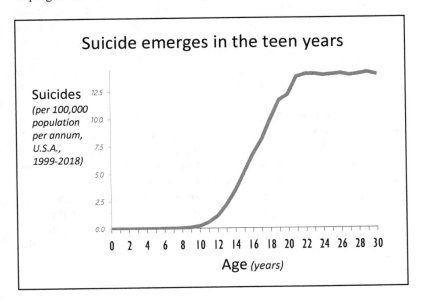

Like trees in the forest, suicidality among mid-to-late teenagers is part of the scenery — it's a normal feature of adolescent life.[3] In the United States, about one in six 18-year-olds admits to having seriously considered killing themselves, and one in twenty say they have actually tried.[4] In a single month at the height of the Covid-19 crisis, more than a quarter of American 18- to 25-year-olds admitted to having seriously contemplated suicide.[5] Even higher rates have been recorded elsewhere. A survey of young adults in Quebec found that, by age 20, one in three had seriously considered suicide, and one in ten had made at least one attempt.[6]

On the other side of the transitional zone, in the tundra, suicidal thoughts, plans, and attempts are virtually non-existent among children under 10 years.[7] The 'virtually' is needed because there are occasional claims of suicide threats, and arguable attempts, among the very young. Even deaths, so it is said. A 6-year-old boy in Limpopo, South Africa, and a 6-year-old girl in Oregon, United States, are said to have deliberately killed themselves, both in 2017, both by hanging.[8] Two suicides of 5-year-olds have been registered in Italy since the 1970s — a boy and a girl.[9] There are other such reports around the world, and it is difficult to know what to make of them. But I suggest they matter for our purposes precisely because they strike us as so strange. If accurate, they are clearly exceptions to a rule. Much has been written in the clinical and popular press about child suicide, stretching back to Freud's theorizing.[10] I am not diminishing this work. But researchers tend to be more interested in the rare cases rather than their striking absence. The first priority, I suggest, is to understand the rule. What it is about young children that protects them — or at least protects them enough for suicide to be such an anomaly?

There aren't many plausible ways to explain young children's immunity. It won't be because of under-reporting: even if all 'undetermined' childhood deaths, plus an arguable percentage of 'accidents', were added to the official statistics, the resulting adjusted rates would still be extremely low.[11] And it won't be because children don't suffer psychache. Many grow up in clearly upsetting conditions of neglect and abuse. Even among the rest, being dependent on nurturing relationships as they are, children would be expected to suffer social pain at least as much as adults do, assuming our analysis of social pain in Chapter 4 was on the right track.

Immunity of the intellectually disabled

The third protected population is what I would describe as the intellectually incapacitated. Completed suicides are very rare, or virtually unknown, among people with moderate to severe or profound intellectual disability (I.D.). I.D. is the kind of mental impairment that can usually be traced to structural problems with the development or functioning of the brain. There is not a lot of data on this population — a rarity of recorded suicides that, I suggest, could itself be taken as useful evidence. What research there is tends to show a similar pattern to the one we saw with suicides among children. There isn't a neat line in the sand — suicides on one side, none on the other. Rather, there's a transitional zone, analogous to children's passage through puberty. And, blurred though the border is, we can similarly tell it exists by looking at the black and white on either side, away from the grey area in between.

The border in this case seems to be a diagnosis of mild to moderate I.D. — that is, a general intelligence markedly lower than so-called normals. People with mild I.D. may be about as prone to suicidality as normals — more so, perhaps, and understandably given the social stresses of their condition. By contrast, across the border, there are no reported cases of completed suicide among people with severe or profound I.D.[12] Again, I ought to add 'virtually' in case an exceptional report surfaces somewhere in the world.

As with child suicide, the literature here tends to focus on the rare exceptions rather than the rule — occasional threats of self-harm, even some arguable suicide attempts, which, contrary to expectations, are sometimes said to happen.[13] Skipped over is the question of why we take such behaviours to be extraordinary. We need to understand why people with severe I.D. *don't* deliberately kill themselves.

Could it be because they tend to live in care homes or are otherwise supervised? Probably not: that protection, such as it is, won't be failsafe. In prison settings, even a dedicated anti-suicide regime — customised cells with 24/7 'eyeball' observation — is no guarantee that people won't find a way to take their own lives. Maybe it is because people in this population are safely happy? Again, probably not: no one would claim that people with I.D. are never distressed.

The common factor

Now, we have these three populations, seemingly unrelated, which are free from suicide: non-human animals, young children, and the intellectually incapacitated. Is there a shared factor that could protect them? What do they have in common?

It is possible to come up with multiple, ad hoc, theories — one for this, another for that. Physical difficulty might be one: perhaps young children and people with I.D. can't gain access to rope or other equipment needed to attempt suicide. But that wouldn't explain the immunity of animals that live in environments replete with opportunities to kill themselves — chimps that could jump from trees and so on. Lack of motivation could be another: perhaps the severely intellectually disabled are too cheerful and well looked after to need a suicidal escape from pain. But then, that wouldn't explain the non-suicidality of abused children and animals.

One of science's guiding principles is parsimony, or 'Occam's razor': don't choose a complicated explanation when a simpler one will do, because the simple solution is usually the right one. The simple solution in this case is intellectual incompetence. Psychologist Jean Baechler drew this important conclusion half a century ago.[14] There is something about suicide that evidently calls for a certain minimum level of cognitive functioning, which animals, young children, and the intellectually incapacitated don't have. Suicide is an intellectual challenge.

It is partly a matter of organisation and planning. The human body is robust in an engineering sense of the word. Like, say, a heavy-duty vending machine, it's built to keep going even when subjected to misuse or damage. As I will argue later in this book, selection has probably equipped humans with many devices that are specially designed to prevent self-destruction. We are resilient to accidental damage too, at least to the kind of avoidable mishaps that might have been regular hazards in our ancestral environment. If not accident-proof, we are pretty well fool-proof. Typical humans cannot forget to breathe: long before we do ourselves permanent damage, the nervous system switches to automatic and makes us breathe whether we meant to or not. We can't strangle ourselves with our bare hands — if we tried, we would pass out, relax our grip, and involuntarily breathe again. Such safety devices can be found throughout the natural world, of course. Unlike us, dolphins can't choke on their food; unusually for mammals, dolphins cannot usually breathe through their mouths, presumably to stop them accidentally inhaling water while swallowing. Likewise with scorpions, it shouldn't surprise us that even if they could sting themselves, the venom won't do them much harm. A gene that let scorpions sting themselves to death, if it ever existed, would presumably have removed itself from the breeding population long ago, along with the self-stung scorpions.

So, like any animal, we are designed not to find self-destruction easy. But the main intellectual challenge involved in suicide doesn't seem to be about its logistical difficulty. People often don't find it hard to come up with a workable plan once they are set on the idea. In one study, about half of suicide attempters, hospitalised because of their attempts, said it had taken them no more than 10 minutes to go from first thought to final action.[15] Of course, these are the reports of survivors: perhaps they survived only for lack of thorough planning. But there is no evidence that the pattern is different for those who don't survive. Suicide doesn't usually need much in the way of complex technical know-how: if the idea is thinkable, then it is probably doable. In this territory, where there's a will, there's a way.

The main intellectual hurdle seems to be, rather, the concept — the realisation that one could, in principle, kill oneself. By definition, suicide would not be suicide without this prior knowledge. Intentional self-killing presupposes knowledge of what is intended; to kill the self. Now to adults in an adult world, the theoretical possibility of suicide may feel obvious. We know the option is there, even if it is not something we want to look at. But for members of those protected populations we have been discussing, suicide is probably beyond their imagination.

Growing to grasp death

The critical step, then, is making the leap from inconceivable to conceivable. We need to find out where the idea comes from and how it comes about. First thing to note: it's complicated. Suicide is not one idea but an assembly of many ideas, and the ideas have to be put together in a logical sequence, each connecting to the one before. We can think of it as of a voyage made up of three legs: The first leg of the journey, by far the longest, is to understand the general idea of death. The next is to understand that death applies to the self — an awareness of personal mortality. The third is just a short hop, to understand that personal mortality can be induced by the self. Let's look at these sections in turn.

The first leg is a long-haul journey to reach an adult comprehension of death. Children under the age of about 4 years have no meaningful concept of death; it doesn't feature in their worlds. Older children often have some idea, but it takes years to piece together the whole picture. The death idea is an abstraction built from abstractions — component ideas which have to be collected and combined to make sense.

Researchers in this field highlight several distinct ingredients, although these can be broken down further.[16] One is death's *irreversibility*: once dead, forever dead. There's no going back. So, understanding death needs a grasp of finality and permanence, and a cognitive skill that has been called mental time travel — the ability to project forward and back in time. Another element is death's *causality*: it happens for a reason — a failure of bodily functions. This calls for an understanding of cause and effect, as well as a grasp of some basic principles of biology and physics. Another is *non-functionality*: all an organism's processes and activities shut down, physical and mental, observable or not. A carcass may be alive with maggots, but that activity is not the organism's own operation. One might imagine a spiritual entity living on. But a child has to understand that, among other things, death is not sleep, even though (e.g., 'rest in peace') we may talk of death in such terms. Yet another is *universality*: death happens to every living thing that was, is, and will be. This idea requires what is called *class operations*: you have to construct a class of things with a feature in common — living organisms, in this case — and then deduce outcomes that will hold generally for everything in that class, whether you have yet encountered them or not.

These building blocks — irreversibility, causality, non-functionality, and universality — not only have to be in place, but joined up. Arranged in a certain way, they form a new overarching concept: 'death'.

By any measure, the death idea is an astonishing intellectual feat, a virtuoso performance of analytical and creative thinking. It is all the more remarkable because children manage to sculpt a mental model of death using general-purpose tools. They make sense of it with the same free-floating thinking skills with which they grapple with the rest of their world — deductive inference, probability, cause-and-effect logic, and other generalised techniques. And children arrive at the death idea spon-taneously, under their own intellectual steam. It isn't taught or learned; at least, not in the same way that children learn about, say, tool making or language, absorbed wholesale from the culture they grow up in. Indeed, some Western communities seem to go out of their way to try to stop children learning about death — by not inviting them to funerals, for example — but the death idea comes about anyway. (By the way, this Western-style squeamishness about death is far from a universal phenomenon; it contrasts with some Eastern and African traditions that see death as something to accept, contemplate, even celebrate.) It is true that, in their journey to understanding death, children make use of their personal experiences, including, importantly, their exposure to the demise of wildlife, pets, livestock, elders, and even peers. But children use these inputs in their own way. They work out for themselves the implications of what they see. There is much variability: different children pick up different bits of the idea at different ages and in different sequences. It's not a linear process either: sometimes there is step backwards before a move forward.

In other words, if death is a jigsaw puzzle, children don't need to be told in what order the pieces have to be assembled and when. It doesn't much matter, because, by however it is done, the end picture turns out the same. Rarely before 9 years, but usually by their teens, most children become able to think meaningfully about death. The idea arrives on the scene, unplanned and uninvited, as a result of children's increasingly sophisticated powers of abstract thinking.

Only humans acquire a death idea, as far as can be known. There is no evidence that any other animal has a generalised notion of what it means to be dead, and there are positive reasons to think they don't, and won't, have it.

Farm animals, for example, show no sign of being upset when witnessing death at close quarters, even while being slaughtered in full view of each other.[17] Monkeys show a remarkable disregard for dead animals, even though carcases might flag up what could otherwise be valuable information, perhaps that there is a dangerous predator at large.[18] Animals can certainly register the fact of death in certain narrow situations. Some seem to grieve the loss of kin.[19] Prey animals can distinguish living predators from dead ones (one is a threat; the other isn't). And predators can tell living prey from carrion (they usually prefer fresh meat). But these are local, context-specific perceptions — they don't stretch out into a universal conception of death.

There is no particular reason to expect animals to have such a concept, because nature operates on a need-to-know basis. There is no fitness advantage in burdening an organism with information beyond what it needs to do its job. Quite the opposite, because information is not free. There's a fitness cost to collecting and processing it. Pointless information is not information at all — it's a distraction and a waste of brain-space. Animals don't need a generalised concept of death in order to avoid dying; they do well enough with an array of simpler situational cues. For example, they can usually avoid suffocation without having to conceptualise death: the central nervous system simply monitors the level of internal carbon dioxide, and motivates breathing when the level gets too high. In sum, a generalised death idea brings no obvious fitness upside, at least not one that would compensate for the extraordinary outlay in mental computing power that it probably requires.

It is not clear, for that matter, whether a concept of death serves an evolved function even for humans. Opening the door to suicide as it does, knowledge of death probably creates a worse problem than any it solves. Some cultural rituals presuppose an understanding of death — funerals, most obviously. But my guess is that we take part in such rites as a form of damage limitation: they help us find comfort and hope. That is to say, they are not primary adaptations that call for the death idea as raw material. Let's recall the test of adaptation: evidence of special design. It's hard to see what a generalised notion of death would be specially designed for — what adaptive problem it could be meant to tackle. Without evidence of special design, we can assume it isn't *for* anything. The journey we have described, children acquiring an understanding of death, probably doesn't have 'Death Idea' as its targeted destination. More likely, it is just something we come across, a blot on the landscape that we can't help noticing while we are on the road to somewhere else.

Anyway, back to the journey. Having completed the first leg, we now have a concept of death. Intellectually advanced though that is, it may not be advanced enough to permit wilful self-killing. The next stage builds on the idea, when adolescents fill an egocentric hole in the middle of their view of the world. Teenagers often understand death, but they don't see it as something personally relevant to them. Probably unlike the death idea, this sense of immunity could plausibly serve an evolved function: it might be designed to encourage young people to test their wings and explore the world. Potentially life-threatening risk-taking behaviour may be a regular, if disconcerting, phase of adolescent development. It may show not that they want to die, but that it hadn't seriously crossed their minds that they could.

It is only a phase. What has been described as a cloak of immortality becomes increasingly tattered as it snags against reality and unravels from its own faulty logic.[20] Eventually it falls away. Then the death idea suddenly gets up front and personal: everyone is going to die — including, sooner or later, ourselves.

Let us not skip over the genius of this realisation. Getting there seems to involve, at a higher level, use of the same general-purpose thinking tools as before. Only now there is an added ingredient: self-consciousness. Two classes of beings have to be held in the mind: 'Everyone' and 'I'. Having mastered the death idea, the 'I' has already worked out that 'Everyone' is mortal. Now the 'I' identifies itself as belonging to that class, 'Everyone'. Therefore, I am mortal. I am going to die too.[21] Some readers may recall a definite point in their lives when the penny dropped, usually in the teen years. It can come as an appalling shock. Life is never the same.

This grasp of personal mortality is not the end of the road to suicide, but it's close. It is only a short hop from there to realising that one's mortality can be brought about ahead of its natural time. This third and final leg of the journey takes us to the possibility of intentional self-killing. The dangerous idea is now in place. As we saw earlier, almost as soon as suicide becomes thinkable, it becomes doable. And, for a few people, almost as soon it is doable, they are ready to do it. Adolescence is marked by the arrival of suicidality in all its stages: from the idea, to a plan, to an attempt, and occasionally to death. First onsets of thought, plan, and action follow each other in quick succession.[22]

In this light, clocking the possibility of self-killing may be a regular phase of growing up. Now we can understand why that graph we saw earlier — the age pattern of child suicides — forms a flattened 'S'. I suggest the curve probably tracks a normal variation in children's cognitive maturation. The earliest stage, from birth to about puberty, is a suicide-free zone: infants live in a world where death, especially their own death, is literally unthinkable. The line lifts off the ground when the brightest kids become smart enough to be able to conceive of their own mortality, and a few of them act on that knowledge. From that point on, the curve reflects the different ages at which different children reach the same milestone of intellectual progress. Some grow up faster than others. A few are early, a few late, but most are towards the middle. Hence the graph climbs steeply in adolescence, and then flattens out again. By age 20, virtually everyone has the intellectual wherewithal to take their own lives. Thereafter, a small but fairly steady percentage of humankind does just that.

Crossing the threshold

So, I suggest that acquiring the potential for suicide is normal part of adolescence. There is an intellectual threshold that virtually all humans, and only humans, cross. But what exactly is this threshold? What measuring stick can we use to mark the minimum brain-power needed to imagine bringing about one's own death? I'm loath to reach for IQ, the intelligence quotient. IQ is a Western-centred invention, and it has little biological meaning. More useful for our purposes, I think, is cognitive capacity as measured by degrees of intentionality.

Intentionality here refers to the 'about'-ness of mental states.[23] When we think, we don't think nothing; we think *about* something — trees, a party, a thorn in the foot, or what have you. And when we hold a belief, we believe something. Likewise, to know, feel, hope, want, plan, and so on, is to hold mental states that refer to some kind of contents. Intentionality can become layered: perhaps, say, I am thinking about whether you know about the party. In this case, I have two degrees of intentionality: the content of my mind (1st) concerns the content of your mind (2nd). The layers can pile up. For example, I could be thinking about (1st) whether you know (2nd) if Mary has asked (3rd) Peter not to tell (4th) James about the party (5th). With each higher rank, the possible combinations of what 'I think you think…' multiply. There's an explosion of potential alternatives. So, to deal with the extra complexity, each degree of intentionality requires a brain with a higher order of processing capacity.

We can use this sliding scale, levels of intentionality, as a way to measure cognitive ability. Unlike IQ, it's good for comparing individuals from different cultures, different stages of childhood, and even different species. Insects rank zero: their minds presumably don't have contents, if indeed they have minds. New-born babies and most non-human animals are thought to have 1st-order intentionality: that's at the basic level of feeling, say, hungry, cold, or scared. It takes humans until about age 4 or 5 years to reach 2nd-order, the stage of having thoughts about what others are thinking. This opens up the possibility of basic *theory of mind*: the ability to mindread. It is a powerful social skill, possessed not only by human pre-schoolers, but — so it is thought — adults of a few other species; probably chimps, arguably orangutans, and possibly more. As far as can be known, only humans go on to develop 3rd-order intentionality, as in, 'I think she knows what he meant' — a capability that opens up the human possibility for teaching. Children get increasingly adept at higher orders of intentionality as they grow through their teens, thereby becoming cleverer social operators. 4th- or 5th-order is probably as far as most of us go, maxing out in our late teens or early 20s.[24]

By the same principle, intentionality can rubberneck backwards into an awareness of the contents of our *own* minds. So, that 3rd-order example could be folded back on itself, into a pretzel-like 'I think I know what I meant.' The internal world of an adolescent is a hall of mirrors under construction: along with a sharpening ability to read the minds of others comes an intensifying self-consciousness.

This introspection is fuel for suicide. It is partly that the mind may not like what it sees in the mirror. But I suggest, crucially, that self-awareness opens the door to understanding one's own mortality: everyone is going to die, including ourselves. The toxin in this dawning knowledge is not that there is something about death that's too dreadful or mind-blowing to mentally take on board, as some scholars have argued.[25] Many people accept the prospect of their own passing squarely and serenely. Some cultures advocate the contemplation of death as a nourishing spiritual practice. We noted earlier that denial of death is rather an oddity of the modern West — elsewhere, death is often accepted, even cele-brated. Even the West, a relaxed death-facing attitude surfaces in, for example, jazz funerals in New Orleans, and in a thriving international movement of 'death cafes', where people gather to "eat cake, drink tea and discuss death."[26] Some people find it positively soothing even to plan how they would take their own lives: it can be comforting to know that this emergency exit is always there, if things ever got really bad. So, the biological problem is not a supposed terror of death. The problem is, rather, that if an organism knows about its own mortality, it is just a short step to knowing it can make its own mortality happen. Suicidality and high-order intentionality go hand in hand.

Let's be more precise. How many levels of intentionality do we need to die by our own hand? I count at least three, probably four. 1st-order would be the simple animal-like stimulus of pain: *I hurt.* 2nd takes us to *I know I hurt* — the pain of feeling pain. According to Edwin Shneidman, whom we met earlier, this is psychache — the motivator for a suicidal escape. If this is correct, then all but a handful of the smartest species are blocked from suicide before even reaching this point. They don't know about their own discomfort. Only humans go further. The next level, 3rd-order, sets up a demand for action: *I need to end my painful self-awareness.* Perhaps this is enough for suicide. A psychologist who has looked closely at the matter, Roy Baumeister, reckons not, on the grounds there are still other ways out.[27] It is possible to exit painful self-awareness through doors that open to the outside world — thinking of something other than the mind's own thoughts. It may only need a distraction, anything beyond the self, to break the circle of introspection. 4th-order self-awareness may be the critical one. It is there that the possible solutions collapse, implode, looping back into self-destruction. Just one course of action remains, for the mind to end its own consciousness — *Therefore, I must kill myself.*[28]

Perhaps there is a 5th order involved sometimes, I don't know. The point is that the intellectual threshold for suicide seems to lie in a certain minimum level of intentionality: 3rd-or 4th-order. If that is true, it rules out all three of the protected populations we have discussed in this chapter. 3rd- or 4th-order intentionality is evidently out of reach for both young children and the smartest known non-human animal, and I imagine it would equally be beyond the grasp of people with a certain level of intellectual disability. The treeline for suicidality may be a fuzzy boundary, but it looks to be here.

Why are humans so clever?

Let's go back to the puzzle we set earlier in this book. We asked how natural selection could produce a behaviour as self-destructive as suicide. We have narrowed the answers down. Now, more specifically, we can ask why selection has given humans such a high level of intentionality, such extreme self-awareness, that we can think of escaping pain by terminating our own consciousness. We wouldn't have the problem if we stayed at the 2nd-order intentionality of, say, a chimp or a human infant — roughly equivalent to each other in their mind-reading intelligence. Selection could have left us there, but it hasn't. Why do we have to be so smart?

There are a few possible answers. I will outline two general ones that I find easiest to believe. The first, an *ecological* answer, says that we evolved intelligence to help us deal with the natural world. The second, a *social* one, says it is to help us deal with each other. There isn't actually so neat a distinction because the ecological and social accounts overlap, and they aren't mutually exclusive.[29] But to keep it simple, let's look at them separately.

According to the first answer, a human being's main opponents are non-humans. It paid us to be clever in the ancestral past because of the advantage it gave us over predators and prey. Braininess allowed us to outmanoeuvre them, and to do so millions of years faster than they could react. Imagine we hunt, say, pigs. The kind of ingenuity that let us use a bow and arrow would have allowed early humans to hunt in a way that was entirely novel for pigs. Pigs are largely helpless against arrow shot because it is not a threat they are designed to deal with. Arrows were not a recurring fitness hazard in pigs' ancestral history. Given millions of years of being repeatedly shot at, and some mutant pigs surviving, perhaps a new species of pig might emerge one day that is adapted to the threat. Maybe it would be armoured, or live underground or in the sea. But, of course, it would be like no pig we know. In the meantime, pigs find their defences suddenly obsolete. Against a natural world that can respond only in an evolutionary timescale, intelligence lets humans mount a surprise attack.[30]

This line of argument helps us understand the usefulness of the kind of general-purpose thinking tools which also happen to lead children to understand death — mental time travel, class operations, cause and effect, and others. Armed with these mental weapons, humans would have had a strong advantage in their struggles with the natural and physical world, improvising solutions to problems never before encountered. Such resourcefulness probably helped our ancestors adjust to the fast-changing climatic conditions of the later Stone Age, and the strange new environments they met as they migrated around the planet. We can understand suicidality, then, as a part of the price we pay for free-floating intelligence — for the kind of mind that can turn its thoughts to any situation or problem it cares to consider. Such thoughts may include, unfortunately, ideas that are self-destructive.

While this all makes sense, the snag is that the enormity and expense of human braininess seems out of kilter with the scale of the supposed payoffs. We are back to the problem of special design. It is hard to imagine a particular ecological problem for which super intelligence would be an outstandingly good solution. True, there may have been a need to cope with varied and varying conditions; but rats, mice, and cockroaches can do that without hauling comparably huge computers around with them. There doesn't seem to be a compelling economic need either. Other primates seem able to feed themselves well enough without minds of our complexity. Indeed, gorillas, chimps, and other apes give the impression of having time on their hands: resting, grooming each other, and generally not behaving as if they are hard-pressed for nutrition. So, to be clever enough to obtain food even faster, and free up even more spare time, would not seem to offer much of a gain. To construct human intelligence for the purpose of better hunting, or for any other obvious ecological challenge, seems to be a case of over-engineering. It is like building an accordion to prop open a door: it works, for sure, but a regular doorstop would have done the job for a fraction of the trouble. It is the extraordinary mind-reading sophistication of human cognition that stands out as an anomaly. A mind that operates at 3rd-, 4th- or 5th-order intentionality probably did not evolve to outsmart the 1st-order brain of a pig, however nutritious.

The other way of explaining the origins of high-order intentionality looks more plausible to me. Sophisticated theory of mind, the kind of intelligence that lets you outwit other humans, gives you a strong advantage within your group. If you can second-guess others' next moves, and exploit that insight, then mates, status, and other winnings are yours for the thinking. There might be several ways this advantage could come about. Self-awareness lets us use our minds as a test bed: we can turn our own feelings to imagining how others would feel, and what we would do if we were in their shoes. The size of the group also matters: the bigger the group, the more complex the social network, and the more powerful the mental computer needed to keep track of the relationships. The human mind seems to be outstandingly well designed for the challenge of living in large groups.

However it is done, if you are winning the game of life by reading the minds of others, then their best defence, perhaps their only defence, is to respond in kind. They need even greater intelligence to outwit you. It is a case of having to fight fire with fire; big guns driving the selection of yet bigger guns in defence. Such an evolutionary arms race would have had a life of its own, independent of whatever utility the arms may have outside of the race — independent, that is, of the intellectual demands of, say, hunting. The workaday hunt won't be so mundane if the hunters have the minds of Machiavellian social engineers. But the invention of better ways to catch pigs (or the like) is probably more a happy side-effect than the main target of extreme intelligence. The hunters' brains evolved for a bigger prize — success within the group. Our intelligence is probably, at root, social.[31]

The intellectual arms race, the chase for intelligence, ran its course over an evolutionary timescale. But it was explosively fast by normal standards, powered as it probably was by a booster rocket: sexual selection.

Sexual selection magnifies a trait's fitness effect, and it accelerates the evolutionary process. If the group's resources tend to flow to the cleverest members, then cleverness itself becomes a sought-after resource. It signals an individual's superior fitness prospects and becomes, of itself, a prime dating criterion — 'Sapiosexual seeks same.' It sets up a positive feed-back loop, the smartest individuals mating with each other, and begetting yet smarter offspring.[32] Within a few thousand generations, a new super-intelligent population may have emerged — possibly a new species.

We may not be the first or only smart hominid, but we are the only one left standing. The great apes, our closest surviving relations — gorillas, orangutans, and chimpanzees — are smart by animal standards, with brains some three times larger than those of other similar-sized mammals. But the human brain is in a class of its own, seven to eight times larger than would be expected for a mammal of our size.[33] It has likely been shaped by runaway sexual selection.

Let's take stock. We set out to discover the biological roots of suicide. We deduced that it likely arose an unfortunate side-effect of an adapta-tion, and we wondered what that adaptation could be. What adaptive trait gives humans so valuable a fitness upside that it is worth the potential cost of suicidality? We found one: pain. Pain is designed to motivate action to escape it, and ending life is an effective way to do just that. But we saw that pain couldn't be the whole story, because some groups do not resort to suicide as an escape, however painful their situations: young children, the intellectually disabled, and non-human animals. We looked at what these protected groups have in common and we found a second adapta-tion that is probably involved: intelligence. More specifically, we can pin the blame on the high-level intentionality of mature humans, an extreme self-awareness. At some point in adolescence, we grow to understand our own mortality. It is dangerous knowledge because, suddenly, bringing about that mortality by our own hand becomes a thinkable option.

Could this adaptation, human intelligence, be important enough to be worth suicidality? Quite possibly. It seems to be primarily *social* intel-ligence, the faculty that lets us to hold our own in large and complex groups. It is the adaptation that makes us the most social of social animals. We're talking about wisdom, *sapience*, the trait that gives us our name — *Homo sapiens*. Intelligence is so important an adaptation that, arguably, it defines our species.

So, I suggest suicide is a by-product of not one adaptation but two. One is a motivator: pain — most of all, social pain, the most intolerable kind.

Pain drives us to do something to escape it, which is just what pain is meant to do. The other is an enabler: a certain level of intelligence comes with the territory of being a mature human and, unfortunately, it lets us escape pain by ending life. Both of these ingredients — the motivation (pain) and the means (brain) — must be present for suicide to happen. I call this the *pain-and-brain* theory of suicide. Both elements touch on the extreme sociality of our species: they connect in that sense. But they come to us from different evolutionary origins, via separate paths.

We can now sketch an answer to the question we asked a few chapters ago: Why do people kill themselves? Pain says they must; brain says they can. But, obviously, this still cannot be the whole story. Even with both conditions met, most of us do not opt out of life. Why not?

CHAPTER 5: *We have arrived at the 'pain-and-brain' theory, which explains suicide as an unfortunate side-effect of two vitally important adaptations. Pain, especially social pain, demands the organism act to escape it. The sophisticated intelligence of the mature human brain opens up the intellectual possibility of making that escape by self-extinction.*

CHAPTER 6: *The 'pain' and 'brain' conditions are not only necessary for suicide, but sufficient. Any animal that knew it could escape suffering by switching itself off would be expected to do just that. We can now view suicide as a universal and severe adaptive problem for our species. How did we evolve to survive in the presence of so lethal a danger?*

6

THE PROBLEM OF
BEING HUMAN

The human tendency to opt out of life looks to be an evolutionary accident. It probably came about as an unfortunate side-effect of two adaptations that combine in our species and ours alone. One of them is pain — an ancient, life-preserving stimulus that demands the animal act to end it. The other, as we discovered in the last chapter, is the sophisticated intelligence of the mature human brain. The human animal, once it reaches a certain stage of maturity, is smart enough to access self-destruction as a way to satisfy pain's demand for action. Thus, we have the *pain-and-brain* explanation for suicide. Both inputs, pain and brain, are needed for suicide to happen: pain provides the motive, and brain provides the means. Motive without means is not a problem, and neither is means without motive. We can imagine pain and brain as two chemicals that are harmless in themselves — indeed, they are necessary for human survival. But mix them together and they react; they make a toxic compound that can kill us.

This evolutionary theory of suicide seems to stack up, and it seems to fit the facts better than any other. As a working model, let's take it to be true. Now we need to think about the implications, because they are many and, I suggest, profound.

We have a problem. Those pain-and-brain conditions are not only necessary for suicide; they are sufficient. If someone has both the motivation and the means to do something, then that is exactly what we would expect them to do. A good crime writer might add a third element to round off the story, alongside a motive and a means — an opportunity. But we are so surrounded by opportunities for lethal self-injury in our daily lives that we can probably take that bit for granted. I am not saying that suicide is easy. I am saying that someone who is determined to kill themselves can nearly always find a way. (Prison guards on a suicide watch will be grimly aware of this fact of life and death. We touched on this in the last chapter.) The problem, it seems to me, is that all typical adult humans carry, in effect, sufficient conditions to take their own lives.

Let's look at the pain condition first. All species-typical humans experience pain. When I say species-typical, I mean the standard-format, properly functioning human organism. There are diseases which impair the ability to feel pain — leprosy, notably. But this is not how human beings are designed. As we saw in Chapter 4, pain is an evolved mechanism, a vital signal that alerts us to fitness threats in our physical environment. In our social environment too; as social animals, we are all fated to feel social pain — unpleasant states that similarly alert us to threats to our supporting relationships. Social pain can be, and often is, experienced as even more intolerable than the bodily variety. We are all going to feel social pain at some stage in our lives because, as mammals, we are put on a path to wean, grow up and move on. As social mammals, we cannot live our lives in isolation, even as we try make our own way in the world. At some stage, we all have to deal with the torment of threatened, damaged, or lost social ties. Such fractures may be experienced as bereavement, rejection, abuse, betrayal, abandonment, divorce, redundancy, estrangement, loneliness, and many other ills. In some form or other, we are all destined to be stung by the mental pain that Edwin Shneidman encapsulated in the word *psychache*. Being alive is going to hurt.

We can't say that some people are safe because they lead relatively pain-free lives, although Shneidman seems to be of this view. He reckoned that people are driven to suicide when their psychache exceeds a certain threshold of acceptability. Below the threshold, we're out of danger.[1] Intuitively that sounds fair, but it logically it doesn't stand up. It's a tautology: to say that pain is intolerable above a level of tolerability doesn't help us. And it skips over the biological fact that all pain is designed to be intolerable at *any* level. The function of pain, whatever its degree of painfulness, is to motivate evasive action. For sure, pain is sometimes unavoidable. Sometimes it is unavoidable because the only alternative would hurt even more. But if there is a course of action available to end pain, it should be taken. This has to be so. Pain that was not meant to be evaded would be biologically pointless. If it were pointless, it would not have evolved, because there would be no selective mechanism to make it come about. If responding or not responding to a stimulus made no difference to fitness, then there would be no fitness advantage in having the stimulus. So, pain at any level should in principle induce action, and the amount of pain that we should be willing to bear, if we knew we didn't have to, is zero. It seems to me that there's biological weight to novelist Cesare Pavesse's observation: "No one ever lacks a good reason for suicide."[2]

Compounding the problem, I suggest it was ever thus. Human life was probably no sweeter in the ancient past that it is now. A 4,000-years old Egyptian papyrus tells of a poet yearning for death to release him from his troubles.[3] Back further, according to the archaeologists, life for our Stone Age ancestors was short and violent — so, presumably, psychache was a regular experience then too.[4] Humans have always lived with pain and, hence, with a motivation to escape from it.

Not only is the motivation for suicide a universal condition, so is the means. It seems to me that virtually all of us have the intellectual potential to kill ourselves, because we are all equipped with a standard-model human brain — that is, with self-awareness above the threshold for suicide. I see three reasons to believe this is so. First, recall that the human mind is a social instrument. It's designed to turn a social network to the individual's fitness advantage. It works like telephones: to operate in a network of other minds, one needs to follow much the same protocol as everyone else. Second, genetically, humans are remarkably alike by normal animal standards.[5] It is easy to spot differences between us (playing 'spot the difference' may be what our minds are attuned to do), and some obvious differences are indeed in the genes — the likes of skin, hair, and eye colour. But human genetic variation, while often conspicuous, is for the most part biologically trivial. Other differences may be caused by environmental factors. Differences in the way we behave, for example, may be learned. We might be inclined towards different patterns of personality depending on how we are brought up, but all these patterns are still typically human. The available range of human personalities rather like selecting items from the menu of a franchised burger chain — it's the same menu everywhere. Most differences between humans probably arise from the way genetic and environmental factors interact, which they do to the extent that it may be extremely hard to split the cause between one and the other. The important point is that none of this variability exempts us from possessing what is a standard-format human mind, as constructed by our species-typical human genome.

That genome is common to us all. Humankind is a puréed soup of genetic evenness. It could hardly be otherwise. Any non-trivial local differences are swamped by the effects of migrations and intermarriage.

Individual differences are mixed and remixed at every generation by sexual recombination: like shuffling and reshuffling decks of cards, a random half from each parent blends into to a new deck at each round of reproduction. There is no reason to think the resulting smooth sameness won't equally apply to the genetic basis of our capability for suicide. It is probably part of standard human construction.[6]

The third reason I expect suicide to be a universal human capability is that the statistics say so. It can happen to any of us. A trace of suicide is to be found in virtually every sizeable community the world over. And within each community, and aside from the two protected groups we discussed in the last chapter (young children and the intellectually incapacitated), suicide is an equal opportunity killer — it strikes indiscriminately, with a randomness that says we all carry some above-zero risk. There is nowhere to hide.

Again, it was ever thus. There never was a place to hide. There is no reason to believe that the standard human mind is not essentially the same now as it was when our ancestors left Africa some 60,000 years ago. Anthropologists call those aboriginal migrants 'behaviourally modern humans' — and for good reason. We identify with their art. Their tools speak for their technical virtuosity. Their monuments show their prowess as social organisers. We can guess that the intellectual challenges they faced were no less demanding than those we meet today. And we were probably as genetically homogenous then as we are now, blended by the same whisks of migration, intermarriage, and sexual recombination. Via our shared genome, the psychic unity of humankind stretches across the millennia as well as the oceans. It is telling that today's remaining hunter-gatherer communities, the closest to ancestral human lifestyles that we will get to see, are about as prone to suicide as anyone else.[7] In sum, in all likelihood, humans have always constituted a well-mixed biological pool, and suicidality has always been part of the mix.

This being so, humankind has lived with suicide as a permanent and predictable biohazard since the dawn of our species. It is a recurring fitness threat, one that virtually every human who has ever survived to puberty has had to live with. It is a blight that we evolved alongside, just as we evolved to live with venomous snakes, parasitic worms, and hungry lions. Like these other standing menaces, suicide risk has to be monitored and managed, and avoided to the point that it usually doesn't kill us or cause us too much damage. But unlike these other threats, suicide is a uniquely human adaptive problem. It looms large in our environment and ours alone because it is a side-effect of a uniquely human adaptation — intelligence, as driven by the relentless, runaway selection that we discussed in the last chapter. In this light, we need to think of suicide in the same way that we think of other adaptive problems that come in the wake of extreme braininess. There are many, and they are extreme. I will outline some to illustrate.

Let's start with the ongoing cost of maintaining a brain that has enlarged to the extraordinary size of ours. It's a millstone around the neck — or, rather, above it. As an organ, the human brain accounts for about 2% of adult body mass. But it saps 15% of the body's oxygen, 20% of its energy budget, and 50% of the body's primary fuel, glucose. Relative to body size, the human brain is said to consume up to ten times more energy than the brains of other land mammals. Our species' diet and life-style seem to be dictated in large part by the demands of keeping our brain fed. To free up metabolic supplies, as the human brain expanded, other organs had to shrink by equal measure, notably the gut. Having a shrunken gut, in turn, necessitates a diet of high-energy food — in particular, meat. The need to support the brain may thus have driven the hunting and eating of meat, and another behaviour as unique to humans as suicide — cooking.[8] The human brain is so complex, by the way, that half of our genome is dedicated to its assembly instructions. For this reason, the brain is thought to be especially prone to construction errors, an added cost that has to be managed.[9]

Then there's the extraordinary investment needed to support children while they grow up — or, more to the point, while their brains grow up. Human young are an economic burden on their parents from before birth until more than a decade after, a long time by primate standards. Young chimps are fully self-sufficient by 4 or 5 years: human offspring in tradi-tional societies can't gather enough food to feed themselves until about 12 years.[10] At least until then, assembling and programming the brain is the human organism's primary task. The physique of human young seems to be purposefully held back, limbs and other body parts staying under-sized until puberty, waiting their turn, probably so that resources can be channelled into brain-building. Children seem to be kept cognitively retarded too: infants are granted only limited access to the kind of high-level mental functions that are needed to plan and execute tasks.[11] Those faculties also have to wait while the brain concentrates on wiring and programming itself. So, maturing the brain takes priority to the extent that young children are deprived even of the possibility of being economically useful, at least until the brain is substantially complete.

This enforced childhood dependency, and the load it foists onto parents and carers, touches almost every aspect of human family life. For example, by some means, fathers need to be motivated to stay in harness, actively supporting mothers in their child-raising. But a scope for conflict then arises, because men and women don't have the same biological interests. A mother's reproductive success depends on her securing the help of a partner. But in so helping, a man risks wasting decades investing in offspring that may not be genetically his, while missing out on opportunities to mate with other women. An adaptive solution to this problem, so it is suggested, is the curious human phenomenon of concealed ovulation. Unlike the red rump of a baboon in heat, a woman's body gives few obvious clues as to when she is in the fertile phase of her cycle. Unsure of when a woman can conceive, a man's best reproductive strategy is to stay close to one partner, repeatedly mating with her throughout the month. In this light, our bent towards co-parenting and forming lasting pair bonds — marriage — looks to be a further secondary effect of human braininess.[12]

Intelligence throws up mechanical problems that also have to be dealt with. For example, the weight of the human brain makes us unusually susceptible to whiplash injuries. Its volume makes us vulnerable to overheating, a hazard that may have led to the evolution of special blood vessels in the head that function as a radiator. The risk of overheating may, according to some theorists, also help to account for our hairlessness and bipedalism — our upright posture minimising the surface area exposed to the sun. And then there is the problem of giving birth to a large-skulled baby through a female pelvis that has other jobs to do. This potentially lethal difficulty may well set the limit on the size of the human braincase — the reason why our skulls are not even bigger than they are.[13]

That last problem is worth a closer look, because it illustrates how the repercussions of human intelligence ripple out into all sorts of secondary effects. It's the obstetric dilemma: how does nature balance the conflicting demands made on the human female pelvis? The pelvis must offer a channel wide enough to give birth to babies with big heads, but still be narrow enough to meet its other design tasks. Rising to the challenge is a cluster of secondary adaptations — multiple design compromises in mother and baby that come together to form a complex solution. I count five elements. (1) There is a fine trade-off in the timing of human birth relative to the brain's development. The safest place for a helpless infant is in the womb, on which basis the longer the pregnancy, the better. But the obstetric risk, worsening over time as the foetus's braincase expands, says that a shorter term is better. A bargain is struck at nine months — not ideal on either score, but a least-bad solution. (2) A woman's pelvis is unusually wide by primate standards. The trade-off here is at least twofold. One is a problem of thermoregulation: the wider the pelvis, the greater the ratio of volume to surface area and the more difficult it is to prevent the body overheating. The other is the need for locomotion: the wider she is at the hip, the harder it becomes for a woman to run. A balance has to be found between safer childbirth and making sure she can make a fast-enough getaway from attackers. (3) Both mother and baby make concessions in the rigidity of their bone structures. A baby's skull can flex to some extent, thanks to its construction from soft and partially overlapping plates — they telescope and streamline themselves for the squeeze through the birth canal. The mother's pelvis has some elasticity too, though not a lot, given that it also has to be rigid enough to act as the lower body's chassis. (4) Perhaps most ingeniously, the pelvis forms a kind of thread, like the spiral groove inside the lid of a screw-top jar. A baby's head is too wide to travel straight through the birth canal in the same way that the shaft of a threaded bolt won't drop straight through a matching nut — but the bolt can pass through if it is twisted. Likewise, the baby turns as it travels to reach the outside. It is a neat solution, but it creates a new problem; having turned, the baby comes out facing the wrong way. That makes it awkward for the mother to draw it out with her hands as a primate otherwise would. Compensating for the mother's helplessness, human births are uniquely characterised by so-called obligate midwifery: (5) in virtually all human cultures, helpers are expected to be involved in childbirth, standing by to pull the baby out.[14]

Despite this package of measures, childbirth is still a challenge, as any mother can testify. There are two points to note, important for later. First, there is still a small risk of death in childbirth, partly because selection could not, and would not, completely eliminate obstetric complications. We could imagine how zero mortality in childbirth might be achieved, but it would only be at the cost of introducing new lethal hazards. For example, as we noted, the problem of birthing large-brained babies might be solved in one sweep by a wider pelvis, but that would bring no fitness benefit if it so hobbled a woman that she fell prey to predators. So, the pelvis is only somewhat widened. Women must put up with a pelvis that isn't ideal for either running or childbirth — but then nothing in nature is ideal. Selection finds compromise solutions. As we will see, zero suicide is probably unachievable for the same reason, there being a similar trade-off of lethal risks to be made.

The other point is that the solution to the obstetric dilemma is made up of a spread of adjustments — a little bit of this, a little bit of that. No feature is so distorted as to stop it from performing its other tasks; but put together, those multiple small tweaks have a big impact. The solution is a compromise built from compromises. All in all, selection has evidently done a good job of managing the risks. Deaths in childbirth are rare even in communities without access to modern medicine, and there is no evidence in the archaeological record that the mortality was much greater in the ancient past than now.[15] All has turned out well. But let us keep in mind the root cause of so complex and far-reaching a problem: human intelligence.

The adaptive problem of suicide

From metabolic load, to the burden of child-raising, to obstetric complications — this isn't meant to be complete list of the biological drawbacks of being smart, but it makes the point. Human intelligence, a primary adaptation, drags incidental fitness problems along with it. They are many, varied, and costly. The need to contain the costs has driven, in turn, tiers of secondary adaptations: kludges and compromises that pervade human physiology, psychology, and society. Hardly any aspect of our lives is untouched. This is interesting for two reasons. First, we can get a measure of the overriding fitness value of intelligence from the breadth and cost of the by-products we bear for its sake, and the tortuous lengths to which the human organism goes to deal with them. Second, if, as seems the case, suicide is another by-product of human intelligence, and an extremely costly one at that, then we shouldn't be surprised to find that similarly far-reaching and complex countermeasures had evolved to keep that cost under control too.

Suicide looks to be at least as troublesome as those other side-effects of braininess — and worse. Unlike, say, a dietary shortfall or weary parenting, suicide spells summary death. It's a fork in the road, between staying in the genetic game and instantly checking out. Granted, victory by the 'survive-and-reproduce' rule of natural selection isn't just about staying alive. The organism needs not only to survive, but also to reproduce. But the verbs come in that order — survive, then reproduce — for good reason. Threats to reproduction affect the number of offspring, but threats to survival affect whether there are any offspring at all. So, staying alive is usually the first call: as long as the human organism lives, there is at least the possibility of reproduction. But dead, no.

There is a wider point here. Scholars have highlighted many important features of *Homo sapiens*, traits that mark us out from other primates and may have helped us to colonise and dominate the planet. We have come across some already: theory of mind, consciousness, bipedalism, hairlessness, tool making and tool using, culture, language, cooking, concealed ovulation, monogamy, and so on. Perhaps all of these are essential human faculties. But as I flagged up in the opening chapter, none of them will have much of an impact on human success if the human being is dead. For them to make a difference, the human organism has to stay alive. Hence, I suggest, the task of voluntarily enduring pain — hanging in there for one more day, perhaps just an hour — ranks first in human priorities. In this light, suicide looks to be the pre-eminent adaptive problem of our species.

It is an exceptionally awkward adaptive problem. In a mathematical sense, suicide is a catastrophe. For modern humans, the threat suddenly appears in adolescence as the threshold of intelligence is crossed. Suicide is impossible before; possible thereafter. But for our earliest ancestors, suicide was not just possible: it would have been the expectable outcome. Let's recall that suicide's pain and brain conditions are enough. No animal would endure pain if knew it didn't have to, and any animal with the brains to realise it can end pain by ending its existence would logically grab the opportunity. That makes the fitness graph of intelligence cliff-shaped. At first, it ramps upwards: intelligence is good, and more is better — but only up to a point. At the intellectual threshold for suicide, more intelligence is not merely useless: it is lethal. At the point of suicidality, the graph drops vertically to zero. We can argue over where exactly the cliff edge is located: perhaps it is the intellect of a modern prepubescent child, or 3rd- to 4th-order intentionality. But it seems likely to me that, there or thereabouts, a fitness precipice exists.

Organisms usually keep well clear of fitness cliff edges. Zebras won't test their luck by grazing just out of the reach of hungry lions, however lush the grass: there are too many unknowns to be sure where the death line is, and it's not worth the risk of getting it wrong. Much of the unknown comes from the usual random variability of biological traits — some zebras run faster than others, just as some humans are smarter than others. This random spread usually forms a normal distribution, a bell-shaped curve: most individuals are towards the middle, being more or less average, and a diminishing minority tail off to the sides, towards the high and low extremes. If there is a fitness precipice ahead of the bell curve, then the whole breeding population tends to position itself well away from the edge. That is to say, the average, the highest part of the bell curve, stays some distance from the danger — even though, paradoxically, that isn't the optimum spot for most individuals. This over-cautious position is to protect the minority in the bell curve's forward-facing tail, the individuals who happen, by chance, to find themselves closest to the cliff edge. They get protected not out of kindness, but because their reproductive success impacts on the whole population. If the extreme individuals survive and reproduce, then their offspring, varying randomly across the normal range, will populate the main body of the bell curve. But if they're on the wrong side of the cliff edge, then their germ line disappears.[16]

The fitness cliff edge of suicide, and the need to keep clear of it, might account for what has been called a 'grey ceiling' in the animal kingdom — 'grey' as in the brain's grey matter.[17] Other animals may get brainy, but only up to a point, and that point is a long way behind us. As we've already noted, the great apes are clever by animal standards, but we humans are in a class of our own; no other primate gets close.[18] That is curious because, on the face of it, other animals, primates especially, ought to gain as we do from the social and ecological payoffs of being smart. So, why don't they too avail themselves of the benefits? We can guess that, for them, the fitness cost of being smarter is not worth paying. Researchers have wondered what that costly limiting factor could be. Perhaps it is the economic expense of keeping a large brain fed with high-energy food, and the meaty diet that implies. Perhaps there is more than one ceiling. But it seems likely to me that the intellectual 'floor' for suicide, which we cross in adolescence, is a big enough problem to be a grey 'ceiling' for any other animal. It presents a serious enough hazard for their average intelligence to be set well back, at a place that safeguards the smartest.

It may be telling that, according to one test I mentioned earlier, an outstandingly clever chimpanzee (Josie, a resident in a British zoo) was found to be a match for, at best, a human 4-year-old.[19] That is to say, if Josie is a guide, then chimp intelligence looks like it stops safely short of the intellectual level of the youngest documented child suicides we noted in Chapter 5. Crashing metaphors, the grey ceiling and the fitness cliff edge of suicide may be connected. They may be facets of the same biological problem.

The puzzle is that at some stage in human evolutionary past, we found a way through the ceiling, beyond the cliff edge. A breeding population of our ancestors must have got so smart that they defied nature's usual rule of caution. It is a chicken-or-egg conundrum. The ceiling must have been demolished in advance, before our ancestors could pass. They couldn't have touched the ceiling, and survived, while the ceiling was there. But at the same time, our ancestors must have come up against it long and close enough for them to have evolved anti-suicide counter-measures, adaptations that downscaled the suicide hazard to a level that was generally survivable.

How we crossed the threshold

Which came first, chicken or egg? Removal of the suicide cliff edge, or the progress of human intelligence up to the edge?

Here's how I think the problem may have been solved. Powerful, runaway selection for intelligence pushed an early human population close to the intellectual threshold for suicide, and held it there for many generations. The smartest members of the population, randomly appearing at the tip of the forward-facing tail, and unprotected from suicide, fell off the cliff: they exceeded the threshold for suicide, and their germ line ended. But across the rest of the population, set back from the brink, there were occasional genetic mutations that had some anti-suicide effect. Such mutations might spread and fix in the population, despite the cost, and even though most individuals who had those mutations would not have been smart enough to benefit from them directly. The fitness benefit was enjoyed indirectly, via those individuals' cleverer kin — intelligentsia who could thereby survive at the cliff edge long enough to reproduce.

By analogy, adaptations against suicide would be like a newly built home that has doorways wide enough for wheelchairs. The home's first owners might not use wheelchairs, and thus have no use themselves for wide doorways. But the feature adds value nonetheless because the extra outlay is small, and there is a major benefit waiting for future wheelchair users — it makes the difference to them between the house being habit-able or not. If the proportion of potential wheelchair users grows, then it becomes worthwhile to build homes with more costly features to accommodate them: perhaps, say, lifts and special bathrooms.

Likewise, although an anti-suicide mechanism directly benefited only those individuals smart enough to need it, for them the benefit would have been great. Genetically armed with superior, and survivable, intelligence, their offspring thrived. Consequently, the population's average intelligence rose, and the next generation's bell curve was squeezed a little closer to the cliff edge, exposing still greater numbers to the suicide hazard, and justifying ever more costly anti-suicide adaptations.

This process would have repeated through thousands of cycles, the population pressed ever tighter against the cusp of suicide, and becoming more and more resistant. Adaptive defences, specifically designed to block suicide, expanded, coalesced, and were fine-tuned, until eventually a tipping point was reached where the entire breeding population was, while not immune, substantially protected. The suicide hazard was not erased, but it was controlled. A viable rate of suicide was reached — low enough not to destabilise the population.

At that point, the cliff edge disappeared; the fitness function of intelligence straightened out into a continuing upward slope, and off we went. Our ancestors sprang to new heights of intelligence, well past the threshold for suicidality. I suggest this population was genetically novel, and is us — behaviourally modern humans. Suicide remains with us as a fitness threat, but our inherited defences allow the threat to be generally survivable.

We can speculate about the period of human evolution when anti-suicide defences were under construction. It would have been late enough for our forebears' intelligence to have approached the cusp of suicide. There would have been no need for such adaptations any earlier. But it would have gone before the cultural revolution of the Later Stone Age — the outpouring of art, and migrations across Eurasia, that got underway some 50,000 to 70,000 years ago. I suspect that cultural spurt was enabled by the dismantling of the fitness cliff edge we have been discussing. It was a pivotal event. Before then, the death idea was something that we had to avoid being smart enough to imagine. After that point, the death idea became something we just had to live with.[20] Evidence of ritual burials, for example, abounds after, but is almost non-existent before.

The most interesting feature of the period before this revolution is that it isn't very interesting. Nothing much happened for a long time, at least according to the archaeological record. There was a protracted spell of some 150,000 years, when the expansion of the human brain seems to have stalled. The physical size of the human braincase was about the same then as it is today. Our ancestors looked anatomically modern. As I mentioned earlier, it is possible that the braincase had by then reached the limit of what could be handled within the obstetric possibilities of birthing large-skulled babies.[21]

What was going on during this 150,000-year hiatus, enough to ignite the cultural explosion that followed? Anthropologist Richard Klein reckons that critical changes were going on in the brain's 'wetware' — its internal organisation.[22] I suggest this pause may have been forced on us by our arrival at the intelligence cliff edge, the threshold for suicide. Our ancestors could go no further. After that point, although it may look like nothing was happening, a frantic building of neural defences was underway. The priority for selection shifted from chasing greater intelligence to making greater intelligence survivable. It took a fair time to form these protections in the timescale of human evolution, reflecting the complexity of the task, but by the normal standard of evolution, it was over in the blink of an eye.

Exploiting the lag

How come it was our forebears that found a way across the intellectual threshold for suicide, rather than some other relatively smart animal? Why not chimps, or some other social animal — dolphins or crows perhaps?

I think there may have been something special about human lifestyle. Not only were we subject to runaway pressure, pushing us towards greater intelligence, but we also occupied a relatively safe physical habitat — the kind of ecological niche where intelligence at the threshold could have been survivable to some degree. Our hominid ancestors were ground dwellers. They lived on open grasslands, at least in part.[23] It was the kind of environment and regime that would have made a suicidal idea relatively difficult to act upon. Ways and means were there, but it would often have needed some time, planning, and effort to organise. Some minimally complex task was involved — to collect a lethal dose of poisonous berries, walk to a deep enough river, find a tree with a knotable vine, or the like.

By contrast, we mused earlier about the summary death that would be available pretty well continuously to animals that live much, or all, of their lives in trees (chimp), underwater (dolphin), or on the wing (crow).

For them a suicidal impulse, if they ever had one, could be put into action on the spot. It could be enacted, indeed, by *in*action — *not* gripping a branch, *not* breathing, *not* flying. Death would happen by default. Thus, any gene that allowed them to think a suicidal thought would be promptly eliminated along with the body of the animal.

So, I hazard that it was a practical hold-up, the benefit of some minimal delay between idea and lethal action, that allowed our ancestors to survive even momentarily where other animals couldn't — close to the intellectual threshold for suicide. Our ancestors stayed there long enough, both in their individual lifespans and over evolutionary time, for special-purpose defences to evolve. The lag gave selection something to work with, like frost finds a crack in a rock and forces it open. A ratchet effect got underway, levering the gap between thought and deed wider, prising it apart with ever more sophisticated adaptations that stopped people who had suicidal notions from acting on them. Eventually, those accumulated defences got so good at blocking the path from idea to action that, today, most of us never go beyond the idea.

Anti-suicide adaptations could not, and evidently have not, evolved to the point of completely eliminating suicide — or, rather, perhaps they could, but we wouldn't be *Homo sapiens* if they had. We're left with an above-zero risk of suicide for the same reason that the obstetric adaptations we talked about earlier leave an above-zero risk of death in childbirth: selection finds a least-bad solution and stops there. Every adaptation has its side-effects, and at a certain level the side-effects cause worse problems than the one the adaptation meant to solve. Defences evolve only to a fitness tipping point, where the added benefit is annulled by the cost of the defences needed to obtain that benefit — where you're damned if you do and damned if you don't. It seems to me that to attain zero suicidality would involve maladaptively undoing one or other of the adaptations, pain and brain, that created the problem in the first place. Human adults can't live without either. Let's briefly remind ourselves why, because it's important.

First, pain. For sure, if we felt no pain, we wouldn't be motivated to escape it. No pain, no suicide, as Edwin Shneidman put it.[24] But no organism can live long without pain. The disease of leprosy can be crippling precisely because it destroys physical pain systems. Lacking aversive signals, sufferers' hands, feet, and other extremities are vulnerable to repeated injuries and infections, and eventually irreparable damage. We can infer that the same principle applies to psychological pain

— psychache — because that pain is equally there for good reason. Without social pain to alert us to threats to vital family relations and other attachments, and to motivate us to protect them, these attachments would be as prone to injuries as are the physical extremities with leprosy. Wiping out the painfulness of psychache would presumably abolish suicide, but only at the expense of inflicting a new hazard; cluelessness in social relations. Emotional numbness might be good as an emergency anti-suicide measure, but it wouldn't work as a permanent solution.

The other way to eliminate suicide altogether would be to disable the brain's ability to imagine death as a way to escape pain. We could live a wholly suicide-free existence if our thinking were held at the level of the protected groups we discussed: of a non-human animal, a young child, or someone with an intellectual disability. But again, regular adult human intelligence is there for good reason: we need to be clever to compete in a world of clever adults. Intelligence is a powerful fitness boon for us, hence the runaway selection that shoved our species to the point of suicidality and beyond. As with numbed emotional pain, a disabled intellect might be a good way to block the path to suicide in an emergency, but wouldn't make a permanent fix.

To live successfully in our social world, we need both our social pain and our social brain, the co-authors of suicide. We can't do without either for long. It seems to me that the best selection could do is a compromise solution, in the form of partial denials of normal emotional ('pain') and intellectual ('brain') faculties, applied at times of danger. These tactical downgrades need to be disabling enough to keep suicide risk tolerably low, but not so disabling as to make us unviable as social operators.

If this assessment is broadly correct, we owe our existence, as a species and as individuals, to evolved defences against suicide. As a species, without them we would not have found a way to approach, let alone pass, the intellectual threshold for suicide. As individuals, we are the descendants of hominids who, despite having suicidal ideas, tended not to act on them. So defended, our ancestors stayed alive long enough at least to reproduce. We have inherited these anti-suicide adaptations. They are vitally important. In the story of human evolution, they are protagonists, not minor characters. They may be so dominating and so all-pervasive that it is hard to see them for what they are. By close analogy, human universals such as extended childhoods, co-parenting, and cooking seem so normal to us that it would scarcely cross our minds to view them as secondary adaptations — measures that evolved to cope with what is, like suicide, the costly fall-out of human intelligence.

What are these anti-suicide adaptations? What evolved defences tamper with our emotional and cognitive systems enough to stop self-destructive thoughts from escalating into actual deaths? I suggest we can think about this in the same way as, earlier in this book, we thought about searching the house for a huge key. Being so big, the key shouldn't be too hard to spot. We just need to think about where to look.

CHAPTER 6: *Evolved defences against suicide needed to be in place before human intelligence could cross the threshold for suicide. We can expect them tactically to moderate our normal emotional ('pain') and intellectual ('brain') faculties, enough usually to stop people who have suicidal thoughts from putting those thoughts into action.*

CHAPTER 7: *We sketch out the likely features of evolved anti-suicide devices, based on what we have deduced about the adaptive problem they evolved to address. They can't rely on a 'survival instinct', which probably won't exist: they will be special-purpose mechanisms, designed specifically to block the path from suicidal idea to self-destructive deed.*

7

WHY *DON'T* PEOPLE
KILL THEMSELVES?

We asked a question a few chapters ago: Why do people kill themselves? The answer is simple, in the light of the discussion so far. People in pain take their own lives for the same reason that people who are hungry eat and people who are thirsty drink. Pain is a biological stimulus that is designed to force an animal to act to end it. Once humans realise that they can end pain along with themselves — that is to say, once their brains mature to a certain stage in adolescence — then that is exactly the behaviour we would expect. It has probably been this way ever since early humans first crossed the intellectual threshold for suicide.

So, an honest, if unhelpful, answer to the question "Why do people kill themselves?" would be along the lines of "Because that is what people do." If such an answer feels wrong, I suggest that is because, in the context it is usually posed, the question is wrong. It's a nonsensical answer to a nonsensical question. The question is grammatically correct, like asking, "Which is heavier, red or yellow?" But it is unanswerable, because it misconceives the nature of what is being asked about: colours have no weight, and suicide has no identifiable proximal causation.

The puzzling question is the reverse: "Why *don't* people kill themselves?" The remarkable feature of our species' suicidality is not that a near-random 1.5% of us die by our own hands. That we can understand. But what about the 98.5% who don't? Most of us, most of the time, fail to obey the biological imperative to escape pain even when we could. We do not do the expected thing. It is a curious inaction. We have narrowed down the likely explanation. Our species' precursors lived at the margins of suicidality long enough to evolve protections, and we have inherited those adaptations. We are equipped with defences that keep us living when we otherwise would have chosen not to. They stop people who think about suicide from acting on that thought.

These defences surely exist: we can deduce that much from the fact that you and I are here. If they did not exist, then the genetic relay of survival and reproduction, a message carried by an unbroken chain of our ancestors, would not have produced us. We are descendants of people who did not deliberately kill themselves, or at least not until after they had successfully reproduced, even though they had the motivation and the means to do so. Assuming the suicide problem is much the same now as ever it was, the solution will also remain with us: those defences operate in us today.

The defences are surely powerful. They are not minor hurdles but castle walls. That much we can infer from the extreme severity of suicide as an adaptive problem. It should make the defences easy to spot — but only if we train our eyes to see them. Living against the walls as we do, we may be oblivious to their existence. They form the unremarkable backdrop to our lives. We may indeed be predisposed *not* to see them: suicide is so awkward and threatening an idea that, for day to day purposes, it may be better not to know. This chapter makes a start; it aims to make our anti-suicide defences visible. Being big, they shouldn't be hard to see, but we need clues as to where to look.

One place we will look at later in this book is the area of cultural learning. Some important protections will be absorbed from the community around us — taboo, stigma, religious mores, legal prohibitions, and other societal restrictions. I will argue that these barriers probably evolved by a form of selection. Suicide is so grave a fitness threat that multiple types of protections probably work together, including cultural ones, on the principle that it is safer to wear a belt, and braces too. But it seems to me that learned, cultural defences are not where we should start looking. They are unlikely to explain how a hominid managed to get close to the intellectual threshold for suicide. Forbiddance presupposes we know what is being forbidden. That knowledge would not have been available as a communal resource when the brightest members of a proto-human population arrived, and died, at the suicide cliff edge described in the last chapter. For most of that pioneering population, death and personal mortality would have been abstractions beyond comprehension. Some prior defence would need to be in place for those ideas to have been survivable. There is also the problem that culturally transmitted messages can fly off in dysfunctional directions, as evidenced by, say, the copy-cat actions that sometimes follow a celebrity suicide. A primordial grapevine does not strike me as robust enough for the task.

More likely, I suggest, our first and foremost defences were transmitted by genetic inheritance, not by cultural learning. Cultural protections may well have come to our aid later, perhaps spreading during the cultural explosion of the Later Stone Age, but I doubt they could have been the earliest or largest defensive weapons on the battlefield. We will return to this matter in Chapter 10.

No 'survival instinct'

For the sake of thoroughness, there is another place we should look — but in this case, it being a red herring, we can eliminate it from our enquiry. There's a folkloric riposte to the question of why people don't kill themselves. It is because, so it is said, we are protected by a 'survival instinct', or 'instinct for self-preservation', or similar turn of phrase. The survival instinct is supposed to be a primordial, universal, natural drive to stay alive, imbued in all life-forms from modern humans to the humblest microbe.[1] The notion may feel intuitively right, but it is almost certainly wrong. There is no evidence that a survival instinct exists, and plenty of evidence that it doesn't, and won't.

The idea falls over for least four reasons.[2] First, to say that we are driven to live because of a drive to live is a tautology; zero equals zero. It doesn't take our understanding forward, any more than Freud does when he tells us that we're driven to die because of a death drive. It is not an explanation; it's a substitute for an explanation.

Second, a primordial, universal, survival instinct contradicts itself. To have an urge to survive presupposes you know what it is you are supposed to avoid; death. But let's recall, again, that the idea of personal mortality is so complicated an abstraction that probably only humans, and only postpubescent humans at that, can wrap their heads around it. Our species has existed for just a blink of an eye in evolutionary time. So, a survival instinct, if it exists, won't be primordial or universal.

Third, it won't be natural either. If it held sway, a survival instinct would defy the basic rule of thumb for natural selection: survive *and* reproduce. Paradoxically, a survival instinct would be an evolutionary dead end, because success in the natural world is not primarily about survival. Survival is only a means to an end; the end is reproduction, and sometimes the needs of reproduction have to take precedence. Some male spiders, for example, having copulated, offer their bodies to their mates as food. We noted earlier how Pacific salmon swim upstream to spawn, and to certain death in doing so. Even for humans, there are trade-offs to make. Adolescent male lives are especially characterised by competitive risk-taking — a struggle for status and mates — which shows that survival is not the be-all and end-all. Risky behaviour may be much of the reason why male life expectancy is years shorter than female. Sex itself brings hazards, particularly for women; in their vulnerability, they potentially risk assault. And as we have discussed, all mothers face mortal danger in the obstetric challenges of childbirth. So, the genetic propagation of a survival instinct would have to battle against all the women who obeyed it — and who duly strove to be chaste and childless.

Finally, the idea of a survival instinct conflicts with the way instincts come about, through selection. An instinct works like a simple computer programme: feed it an input, and it gives you an output. For example, the reason you cannot suffocate yourself by holding your breath is because selection has devised an anti-suffocation programme to deal specifically with that problem. We touched on this before. The input here is your body's carbon dioxide level, as measured by an internal CO_2 detector. CO_2 above a certain concentration is lethal for animals. When CO_2 gets dangerously high, the programme responds with a command, 'BREATHE!' We have this programme because CO_2 poisoning was a recurring fitness hazard in our evolutionary past. We inherit a vast collection of input-output routines of this kind, recorded and transmitted in our genetic code. Each programme was built and fine-tuned by an automatic process of trial and success, the offspring of those who had the latest upgrade reproducing more successfully than those who didn't.

These programmes usually work well for what they're designed to do, but they won't work if they are fed an input that they don't recognise. For example, if that same anti-suffocation programme is given a build-up not of carbon dioxide but carbon monoxide (CO), the programme will be oblivious to the danger. We can pass out and die from CO poisoning without knowing anything was wrong. There is no instinctive programme to deal with CO because there is no mechanism by which such a programme could have come about. CO was not a recurring fitness threat in our evolutionary past, so there was no reason for a device to monitor and control it to evolve. In any event, let's imagine that a programme to avoid CO poisoning did exist. Its output command wouldn't be 'BREATHE!' but almost the opposite, 'DON'T BREATHE — GET OUT!' In other words, there isn't a workable all-purpose response even to poisonous gases, let alone to survival threats generally.

Thus, for an instinct (or any other biological system) to be useful, it has to be a special-purpose device, at least to some degree. It must be alert to specific inputs and be ready to respond with specific outputs. From this knowledge, we can see that a general-purpose, free-floating survival instinct is probably not evolvable. There would be no particular input to which it could respond, and no particular output it could produce. There being no fitness benefit to the organism in having it, there would be no selective pressure in its favour. It is unlikely, therefore, to be included in our collection of programmes. For sure, the brain's special-purpose programmes are so thorough in their coverage of dangers, and the programmes are packed together so tightly, that it may feel as if we're under the protection of an all-singing all-dancing survival instinct. But that felt oneness is an effect of our perception; it's not how instincts work.

The protection that keeps us safe from suicide will probably be like almost any other biological system: it will take the form of a special-purpose device that responds to specific inputs with specific outputs, to do a particular job. That's useful to know, because it suggests that an anti-suicide programme will likely be identifiable as such. It will be a precision tool, custom-made to block the path from suicidal idea to suicidal action. It will display the hallmark of adaptation: evidence of special design.

Our next step is to draw up a sketch of that design, an outline of some of the features of an anti-suicide programme, based on what we know of the task it needs to fulfil. The rest of this chapter is devoted to thinking about the likely shape of such a biological mechanism, one that evolved to stop our ancestors from taking their own lives. Our aim is to draw up a spotter's guide — something like the Photofit portraits that the police sometimes release. It won't be exact, but we'll want it to be accurate and thorough enough to show us what we're looking for. With such a sketch in our hands, we can then see if there is a phenomenon in the real world that resembles it. If we find a match, then we could reasonably propose that that real-world phenomenon is indeed the anti-suicide mechanism that we have outlined. It wouldn't necessarily be so, but unless there is a better way to explain the similarity, it would be an odds-on bet. If we don't find a match, then we will want to ask why not, and it's back to the drawing board, but at least we will have learned something from the effort. This is a regular research method for evolutionary psychologists. Biology teachers sometimes use a similar approach, learning by designing, because it is a good way to get students (like us) thinking about what is evolvable and not evolvable in the natural world.[3]

Keepers

Let's give this anti-suicide programme a working name. I've picked *keeper*. I mean to bring to mind a goalkeeper on a soccer or hockey team — the last line of defence, all that stands between preventing and conceding a goal. The player is in 'stand-by' mode most of the time, closely watching the game, and ready to leap into action when required to intercept an incoming shot. In our game, a conceded goal could be 'game over', so the job needs a safe pair of hands. But even the best players aren't infallible: sometimes, despite their skill and best efforts, the occasional strike gets past them.

An anti-suicide keeper is an adaptation; it's an evolved psychological system. Like the soccer goalkeeper, our keeper is on stand-by much of the time, closely monitoring developments, but always ready to leap into 'Save!' mode to block suicides that would otherwise happen. It is good at its task, stopping suicides most of the time, but it's not failsafe and occasionally suicides happen.

The soccer analogy is helpful so far, but eventually it breaks down. For example, one prediction I will offer is that we can expect more than one keeper to be protecting the goal mouth at the same time: suicide being a severe threat, with multiple opportunities to counter it, we should expect multiple keepers to be in action. For this reason, we're going to talk of keepers in the plural.

So, let's begin. What features should we expect to see in keepers? We can start at a macro level. We can predict that keepers will exist only in our species: obviously so, because only humans have to deal with the adaptive problem of suicide. Keepers would provide no fitness advantage for any other animal, so there would be no pressure of selection to produce them. That said, other animals may have features that resemble bits of keepers because, as with any other biological feature, keepers wouldn't have evolved from scratch. Selection will have formed them by co-opting and re-purposing pre-existing raw material that we may have shared with other animals — especially our closest cousins, other primates. By analogy, only elephants have a trunk, but many mammals have the trunk's distant precursor, a snout.

By the same token, we can say that keepers will be universal among humans, built into our species-typical genome. They emerged at or before the dawn of our species, and they spread around the world with ancestral migrations. We should expect them to have been carried into all human cultures, just like the suicide that they are designed to block.

A 'pain' input

Next let's think about keepers' inputs. What event or condition will cause a keeper to move out of stand-by and into 'Save!' mode? In the same way that the anti-suffocation programme we talked about earlier was triggered by excess CO_2, we are looking for a biological marker for a suicidal idea. It will be some informational cue that predicted suicidal thoughts in our evolutionary past. But what could that cue be?

This takes some thinking about. A good cue, one might imagine, would be the suicidal idea itself — perhaps akin to a CO_2 detector, we might have a 'suicide idea detector'. Unfortunately, ideal though it sounds, such a detector is probably not evolvable, for two reasons. First, the brain communicates with itself not in the storyline content of conscious thoughts, but in the ancient animal language of emotion. Emotions serve a good purpose: they probably evolved as internal signals, which an animal's central nervous system uses to select the best behaviour for the situation — flee, fight, play, and so on.[4] The brain is intensely interested, then, in the emotional states that accompany our thoughts. But it probably won't be following our thoughts' narrative thread. Rather like hearing a song on a foreign radio station, the brain can't understand the lyrics, but there's no mistaking the mood.[5] It's probably just as well that the central nervous system is oblivious to the plot content of our thoughts, because otherwise for us, as a thinking animal, life would get complicated. We would not want a keeper, or any other automatic programme, to leap into action just because a casual thought popped into our heads. If that were the case, you probably would not have got far in reading this book, or I in writing it.

The other problem with suicidal thoughts as a trigger for keepers is that keepers had to evolve before most humans had the brains to think such thoughts. In the last chapter, we discussed how keepers had to be constructed ahead of their time: they had to be in place before an ancestral population could approach and cross the intellectual threshold for suicide. So, keepers are going to have to operate without being able to directly detect a suicidal thought. They will have to use some other cue.

It seems to me that the best available input for predicting the danger of suicide is the emotional state that precedes it — unbearable emotional pain, or psychache. Pain, let's recall, is a biological stimulus that demands the organism act. Without that stimulus, there would be no motivation for suicidal escape. On this basis, pain would have the specificity we are looking for as a potential input. And, unlike thoughts about suicide, pain ought to be easy for the organism to detect. Pain is already there as an internal signal, so it would just be a matter of turning it to anti-suicide use. In the absence of a better idea, and so we can move forward, I am going to assume from now on that pain is, in fact, keepers' input. Three interesting predictions follow.

First, we can predict that keepers won't be interested in *why* we hurt, only *how much* we hurt. Remember that pain is a signal that comes in two parts. One part is qualitative, with details about the source of the pain. The other part is quantitative — a certain dose of hurt. It is only the hurt part that motivates action, and it is only that part that creates the suicide problem. What drives people to kill themselves is the amount of their pain, not the pain's informational small print. As you'll also recall, this point underlies Shneidman's idea of psychache as a universal stimulus for suicide: unbearable psychological pain, whatever the cause, can lead people to take their own lives. Now we can be more specific about the input that will trigger keepers: it will be the hurt part of pain. Keepers will be oblivious to the qualitative details — the type of pain or the story behind it. Most likely the culprit will be social pain, but only because that seems to be the kind of pain that hurts most.

Second, there ought to be some kind of proportionality. The more we hurt, the stronger the motivation for suicide, the more urgent the danger, and the more drastic should be keepers' responses. So, the input won't be a simple either/or switch — yes, you hurt, or no, you don't. The input will work, rather, as a sliding scale of painfulness. The length of time that we hurt ought to be important too: the longer the pain goes on, the more time there is to plan and organise a suicide action, so the greater the peril. Recall that keepers evolved in an environment where killing oneself would not have been practically easy to do. It would have taken time, thought, and effort to put the thought into action. Therefore, keepers should not activate on the basis of only temporary pain, however sharp. In sum, we can expect keepers' input pain detector to combine both intensity and longevity. It is hard to be more specific, because there could be any number of ways to do the combining, but we have already made an interesting prediction nonetheless.

Third, the pain input ought to work in reverse as well. If intense pain activates keepers, removal of that pain should deactivate them. There is no point in keepers staying in 'Save!' mode once the danger has passed, like a goalkeeper who carries on leaping across the goalmouth, blocking a suicide that wasn't going to happen. Keepers should be alert to the easing of pain, so that the mechanism can stand down again.

A 'brain' input

Now, while pain is a necessary input, it won't be the only one. Suicide is a by-product of two adaptations — pain and brain. We need a 'brain' input too. Organisms that cannot imagine their own death will not intentionally kill themselves however painful their lives may be. We decided this is why non-human animals, young children, and the intellectually disabled are exempt. We've already predicted, for this reason, that keepers won't be found in non-human animals. We can say the same for young children: there will be no fitness benefit in anti-suicide devices mobilising before the stage of life when children grow to conceive of their own mortality. Keepers would activate only after that phase of their intellectual maturing. So, we need to think about a second trigger, a developmental 'brain' input, that must be present, alongside pain, for keepers to activate.

Here we hit a similar problem to the one we found with the 'pain' input. Ideally, keepers should react to the mind crossing the intellectual threshold for suicide, but I don't see how the organism could observe that passage directly. The central nervous system probably can't tell directly whether the concept of personal mortality is thinkable or not. This being so, keepers will have to make do with another indirect, proxy measure — in this case, one relating to intellectual maturity.

We can't be very specific about this. There might be several markers that could be put to use. Perhaps keepers count the passing years. Maybe they monitor a hormone that marks the onset of puberty. Or perhaps there is a device that tracks the physical construction of the brain. Perhaps it is a combination of these. But the organism certainly won't be short of potentially useful signals, ways it keeps tabs on the progress of its own maturation. So, we can safely expect that some trigger, as yet unknown, will act as the second cue, the 'brain' input — alerting keepers to the arrival of danger. Its effect will be that keepers won't activate before the earliest stage of life when suicide typically becomes thinkable and doable — that is, in adolescence. Keepers will follow much the same pattern of first onset as suicide: non-existent in early childhood and spurting up in the teen years.

We can make a couple more predictions regarding this 'brain' point. First, unlike the 'pain' input, the 'brain' input won't be on a sliding scale. Being able to grasp the idea of personal mortality is like being pregnant: you either are or you're not. A threshold is crossed. It follows that the brain input will operate as a switch rather than a slider.

Second, once the switch is thrown, it won't switch back. Having acquired the intellectual capability, humans are usually stuck with it for life. So, also unlike the 'pain' input, the 'brain' input won't be reversible: from adolescence onwards, we can expect keepers to trigger in response to chronic psychache at any age.

Keepers' outputs

Now let's think about the outputs. What outer signs can we expect to see that keepers are doing their job? I'm going to suggest several manifestations. They won't include zero suicide, as we concluded in the last chapter. Zero suicide would be an unachievable goal, unless keepers also wiped out the benefit of one or other of the adaptations that created the problem in the first place — pain systems, and mature human intelligence. Without these, we wouldn't be viable human organisms. The best keepers can do is a least-bad compromise: the lowest possible risk of suicide, traded off against the cost of defences needed to achieve that lowered risk.

One output we can expect is a patterned link between keepers and suicidal thoughts. Keepers will activate among people who are in so much distress that they are prone to have ideas of ending it all. It won't be a precise link because, as we have discussed, keepers won't be sparked directly by those thoughts. Keepers will react, rather, to an indirect cue, the emotional driver of those thoughts — prolonged psychache.

Keepers will err on the side of caution. We should expect false alarms. As the link between active keepers and suicidal thoughts won't be precise, not everyone gripped by keepers may actually have had serious thoughts of ending it all. We can say that keepers may often over-react like this, because they are on a life-saving mission. They will play safe rather than risk death.

Keepers will be linked with suicidal acts, as well as suicidal ideas. We have accepted that they won't be failsafe, and the odd suicide will occasionally happen. Perhaps in some impetuous acts, ones that aren't foreshadowed by prolonged psychache, keepers may not have had an opportunity to activate. But otherwise, we can expect suicides usually to be preceded by signs that keepers had properly mobilised, even though in those unfortunate instances the effort was in vain. Following the soccer analogy, we wouldn't expect good goalkeepers to stay completely motionless as a shot goes past — although, if they're caught by surprise, it could happen.

Even when they fail, we should be able to tell that keepers are at least trying block the path from suicidal thought to suicidal deed by the stage along that path when they activate. They will appear right at the outset, alongside the experience of psychache and the suicidal thoughts that psychache can provoke. Keepers won't wait for those thoughts to progress into plans and action before intervening. Switching analogy, lifeguards at the beach are there to save lives, not collect corpses; they won't wait for floundering swimmers to drown before diving in. Keepers, like lifeguards, will mobilise pre-emptively, at the first sign of trouble.

We can expect keepers' interventions to be costly — potentially drastic; proportional, that is, to the extreme fitness cost of the suicide action that they seek to forestall. Virtually any outcome is better than death; so, keepers may be debilitating, and perhaps extremely so.

However, keepers should only rarely cause death; and being reversible, their interventions will usually be temporary and recoverable. They won't generally be permanently disabling or degenerative conditions. They are designed for a fitness-promoting effect.

A final point for this section. Keepers have been fine-tuned by natural selection over an evolutionary timescale, and under intense selective pressure. Through a blind process of trial and success, across countless generations, keepers will have sought out, and made best use of, any and every snippet of information that predicts suicide at the level of the organism. The predictive value of that information would therefore have been fully exploited and exhausted by a biological algorithm. There should be no useful cues left.

We noted in Chapter 2 that researchers have been unable to find a way to predict suicide, at least not with useful accuracy. Now we can understand why this should be so.

It is one of those paradoxical situations where knowing about the future changes the future. For example; passenger jet disasters are unpredictable, or at least they should be, because any information predicting a disaster is put to use, to stop it from happening. If aviation authorities had good reason to expect that tomorrow's flight AZ1234 will crash, then it almost certainly won't. They would take action in the light of the tip-off and, if need be, stop the plane from taking off. Similarly, stock market crashes are unpredictable. If there were credible news that would cause the Dow Jones to collapse next Wednesday, then it almost surely will not do so, because traders won't wait till then; they'll sell now. Today's share prices reflect everything that is known of the future. It is easy to be wise after the event of course — to say, after planes and stock markets crash, that we should have seen it coming. It is not easy to be wise beforehand.

Likewise, with suicide, it is tempting with the benefit of hindsight to say we should have stepped in before it was too late. But keepers will have got there first. For us to predict suicide better than keepers do, we would need to find a recurring marker that countless thousands of generations of selection has somehow missed. It might not be impossible, but it seems to me unlikely. The 'pain' and 'brain' inputs I sketched above will be only crude cartoons of what is actually going on. All available inputs will be absorbed into keepers' calculations, with the result that all the suicides that could be predicted are indeed predicted, by the organism itself — and duly blocked from happening. Consequently, the self-killings that do manage to slip through keepers' defences will be the least foreseeable incidents. In the terminology of mathematics, they are statistical residuals. They are cases where not even the human brain — the most sophisticated computer in the known universe — could second-guess and forestall its own death.[6] It is extremely unlikely, then, that psychiatrists, bereaved loved ones, or anyone else could see it coming either. It would be unfair to expect them to. I doubt that artificial intelligence, or any other currently imaginable synthetic method, is likely to improve on natural selection in this area. Sometimes it is right to be humble about our capacity to improve on nature.

In sum, suicides probably won't be open to prediction even in principle. Not even the activation of keepers will predict the behaviour at the level of the organism: most people who experience keepers will not suicide, but those who do suicide won't be identifiable in advance. There will be no reliable way to distinguish them.

For the same reason, part of the rate of suicide we see at a global level will be a natural, irreducible, minimum. This will be the residue left after keepers have intervened to block all the suicides that could be blocked. Or, more accurately, it's the residue left by the least-bad compromise we talked about earlier — the tipping point where a further reduction in the risk of suicide is cancelled out by the fitness cost of the organism's efforts to achieve it.

We can also say that, as a result of keepers, suicide rates the world over will be somewhere below the level that would be demographically destabilising. They won't threaten the viability of the population — otherwise, the population would have disappeared. As a species, we would still be stuck behind the fitness cliff edge we discussed in the last chapter, our intelligence held below the intellectual threshold. We should expect to see a sustainably low rate of suicide even among people who experience keepers.

So, we now have an idea of keepers' inputs and outputs. What goes on in between? What would keepers do to stop suicidal ideas from turning into actions? As I touched on before, the pain-and-brain framework suggests that keepers have two, and only two, strategies available. They can make suicide unnecessary, or they can make it difficult. In other words, one sort (*pain-type* keepers) would lessen the motivation (pain — the driver of suicidal escape); while the other sort (*brain-type*) denies the means (brain — the intellectual capacity for suicide). Put another way, the reasons why people don't kill themselves are the reverse of the ultimate, evolutionary reasons why they do.

There may be many ways in which keepers can block the path to suicide, as we will see in next few pages. If there are multiple routes available, then we would expect them to be multiply exploited. That is partly to spread risk — the organism not putting all its eggs in one basket. It is also to spread the load: recall with the obstetric dilemma — the challenge of allowing a wide-skulled baby to make its way through a narrow female pelvis — how multiple adaptations come together. They spread the solution across many small design compromises, thereby minimising the disruption to any one component.

Pain-type keepers as placebo effects

Let us look first at how pain-type keepers might work. They need to dull the motivation for suicide. The stimulus of suicide, let's recall, is unbearable emotional pain — psychache. As a temporary fix, as I mentioned earlier, the most obvious way to remove the need for a suicidal escape would be to lessen the pain; no pain, no suicide.

In principle, biologically, this shouldn't be difficult to arrange, because the neurological machinery to downgrade pain already exists. The pain we feel is in large part the brain's own doing. A thorn in one's foot hurts, and while it won't all be in the mind, it's not all in the foot either, even though that is where the pain is experienced. Our brain does not slavishly take whatever the nerve endings transmit and hit us with it. The central nervous system is a complex network of channels and gates, with checkpoints where the intensity of incoming pain messages can be turned up or down, and sometimes blocked altogether, depending on the organism's wider needs at the time. Before it inflicts the sensation of pain on us, the brain decides how important it is compared to all the other possible calls on our attention.[7]

The psyche's astonishing power over pain struck an anaesthetist, Henry Beecher, during his years as a US Army doctor in World War II. Even for the most serious battlefield injuries — and he reviewed hundreds of cases — there was no obvious link between the pain felt by soldiers and the severity of their wounds. Three-quarters of the men arriving at Beecher's hospital with major injuries had gone without morphine for hours, but they were not bothered by pain. They were more likely to complain of being thirsty. They were not in shock. Rather, Beecher deduced, their perception of pain had flexed to take account of the situation.[8] Paradoxically, for most of the wounded, serious injury was good news: it was the answer to their problems, the end of a nightmare, and a ticket home. If the same damage had happened back home in, say, a car accident, it would be a different affair. It would be the start of a nightmare, not the end. In such a way, the organism feels pain according to its needs at the time — specifically, we can imagine from an evolutionary stance, according to the needs of reproductive fitness. Some threats are more urgent than others, and their importance is matched by the pain signal that duly alerts us to them.

We are talking here about a placebo effect — the way situations and other non-therapeutic influences can alter how we perceive our state of health. Placebo works powerfully on our sensing of psychological as well as physical pain. Indeed, a reputable school of thought says that psychotherapy works entirely by placebo: the pain is psychological and so is the relief. We will come back to this in the final chapter. The main point for now is that we shouldn't be surprised to find that the brain edits psychological pain much as it edits physical pain. This seems to be too good an opportunity for keepers to miss. When faced with suicide risk, the answer looks simple: shut off the pain.[9]

It probably won't be quite so simple, because the pain being shut off may be there for good reason. We discussed this before: if pain had no fitness value, then there would be no point in the organism evolving a routine to trigger it. In the case of psychache, it would be especially odd for the brain to go to the trouble of creating and then blocking a pointless signal that the brain itself invented. Pain is generally not pointless — it is designed to tell us something important. Remember that pain is a two-part message. One part carries particulars of the injury as it relates to a fitness threat (there's a thorn in your foot, you risk social detachment, and so on), and the other part hurts. So, there are two problems with shutting off pain. The first is that pain's informational message refers to a threat that needs the organism's attention. In order to catch your attention, the signal needs to have some alarm attached to it. So, some aversive sensation has to stay. Keepers probably won't erase psychological pain completely, although that could be a possibility in extreme emergencies.

The other snag is that our various pains and pleasures need to be kept roughly in the right order of importance. We touched on this before as well. In order for the mind to decide what to do next, it has to weigh up the pain and pleasure to be had from various competing courses of action, and assess where the balance tips. So, to have proper influence on the scales, all pains and pleasures must be compared using a standard system of weights.[10] If one item is taken off the scales, the priorities will shift. If the pain of, say, one's endangered social relationships were suppressed in isolation, that would make everything else relatively more important. You might, for example, no longer care about being abandoned, because some other stimulus — say, the thorn in your foot — has risen to the top of the agenda by default. That kind of distortion would feed into actions that, while not suicidal, may not reflect fitness needs either. In our example, obeying the new priorities, you might stop to pull the thorn out, while, up ahead, your group disappears over the hilltop, never to be seen again. Such altered priorities may be unavoidable to some degree. But we can expect keepers to try to keep us safe from suicide while causing the least possible upset to our fitness-serving choices.

Putting all this together, it seems likely to me that if keepers are going to stop suicides by dulling pain, they will have to do this in a way that dulls pain and pleasure generally, across the board. When keepers are active, we would be saved from feeling intense psychache — but then, we probably won't feel much of any emotion, good or bad. The original misery will still be there, still dominating the agenda, but numbed along with everything else. Psychache won't much matter, because nothing much matters. People dogged by social pain may not feel strongly motivated to kill themselves, but at the extreme, they may not feel motivated to do anything.[11]

I suggest that pain-type keepers will generally work in this kind of way, downgrading the felt painfulness of psychache. We can't be too specific about how, because there could be several means to the same end. There are many roads to Rome: it doesn't much matter which road we take, provided we get there. We have discussed perhaps the most obvious possibility; an automatic, generalised numbing of emotions. But there are others. We can see them in the sundry ways human beings go about easing pain, whether physical or emotional.

There's an obvious opportunity in so-called *pain offset relief* — you can often relieve pain by applying another, unrelated, stimulus. So, if you stub your toe, you may instinctively rub, hop, slap the wall, bite your lip, or the like. On the face of it, these seem odd reactions, because they are not likely to heal the body part that was damaged. They are no mere distractions either (although distraction works too — we will come back to that). Rather, the added stimulation interferes with the original pain signal. Neurologically, it's like slowing down a tram by jamming the junctions ahead with cross traffic. Exactly how and why this happens is unclear, but the outcome is no doubt real. It may point to the origins of acupuncture. The same tactic works for softening emotional pain too. At times of distress, many people find it soothing to induce some controlled physical pain — cutting, burning, or similar.[12] Pain offset relief is easy to do, and we could expect it to form part of keepers' standard repertoire for taking the edge off psychache.

Pain can be suppressed chemically too. Painkillers are not unique to the modern West. The use of analgesics stretches into prehistory, part of a natural pharmacy familiar to tribal societies long before they were converted into industrial drugs. Extracts of willow bark, the basis of aspirin, has been used around the world for thousands of years. The same is true of several plant-based mind-altering substances. Opiates, notably, were known among ancient Asian and European tribes. Tobacco, coca (the basis of cocaine), betel, naturally occurring hallucinogens, and alcohol made from cereals, are still used today by traditional societies. I imagine keepers would have evolved with access to this kind of natural pain control, because self-medication with plants is not a uniquely human behaviour — other primates and many other animals use naturally occurring substances, and in sophisticated ways.[13] With the goal of managing psychache, a keeper could be expected to organise this kind of self-medicating.

Humans also use various psychological tricks for pain relief. Here are three common ploys. First, I mentioned distraction: it is a powerful pain-relieving tactic, familiar to any parent, and to any medic who has had to take a blood sample from a child.[14] Second, pain hurts less if we see a good reason for its existence — it helps to have some way of making sense of it. People with chronic pain conditions often find relief by holding on to a backstory. If none is to hand, they can, and do, make one up. It doesn't matter if the story is unscientific, or even bizarre. Useful myths could include 'It runs in the family', 'The pain makes me strong', 'It's punishment for my sins in a past life' or the like. As long as it stacks up to the sufferer, then it does the job.[15] Third, a related technique is to invent a positive reason for enduring pain — some payoff or goal that makes it worth soldiering on regardless. This effect is commonplace experience, as in when, for example, we exercise beyond the pain threshold, or keep hold of a scalding pan just long enough to put it back on the hob, rather than drop it. At a higher level, having a goal in life can be an important source of strength for people in chronic pain. It is an especially important buttress at times of emotional distress: sometimes we need something or someone to focus on as a reason to keep going. It keeps despair at bay. Again, it doesn't matter if such a goal makes sense to others: if it inspires the sufferer to endure another day, it works.[16]

Going beyond the usual pain-relieving mind-games we play on ourselves, there may be times when we need to take a mental break from the real world altogether. A keeper could act as a safety valve or a trip switch, distorting or blocking our contact with reality when that reality is too painful to face. An alternative reality might be put in its place for a while — an imaginary world that may make no sense to anyone else, but for the sufferer, it at least makes living bearable.[17]

This "may make no sense to anyone else" is a theme that joins up the last few proposals. Several commonplace methods for easing pain feel self-evidently right to the individual concerned. But to an observer, they could well look weird.

Let's think for a moment about how they would appear from the outside. With a generalised emotional numbing, we would see a distressed person losing the motivation to do anything, even things they normally enjoy. With pain offset relief, someone who is in emotional pain will mildly injure themselves — deliberately causing themselves yet more pain. As for psychological tricks for managing pain, people find relief by holding misbeliefs that may be nonsensical to others. Their distractions, explanations of their painful situations, guiding goals in life, and private anodyne worlds, may be obviously delusional.[18]

These pain-control techniques may look irrational, and in an important sense they *are* irrational — their common factor is precisely that they interfere with the organism's perceptual machinery. Necessarily so: they purposefully meddle with what would otherwise be a rational, and rationally painful, affective response. But they are not irrational in their fitness logic: in the face of the possibility of suicide, they make sense as part of the organism's self-protective programming. We will come back to this point in a moment.

To make one last observation about pain-type keepers, some of them will work together better than others. Pain offset relief could easily run alongside those psychological tricks, for example: a private mythical back-story could plausibly explain my pain (say, it's to punish me for my sins in a past life), while also giving me a reason to endure it (I'm preparing for a better life), as well as a reasonable alibi for pain offset relief (I deserve to hurt myself). Others wouldn't combine well: one couldn't very well be emotionally deadened — that is, lacking motivation to do anything — and at the same time be fired up to chase distractions and a grand goal in life. But these keepers could take turns, flipping from one extreme to the other. I draw three inferences from this. First, multiple keepers could, and probably would, activate in the same person. Second, different keepers could deploy in the same individual at different times, especially where they don't work well together simultaneously. And, third, at a population level, we may see keepers clustering in recurring patterns, reflecting how some combinations are more effective than others.

We have touched on several of a human being's everyday self-help methods of pain management: autonomic numbing, pain offset relief, self-medication, distraction, meaning-making, and goal-setting. Maybe there are others. They can and do relieve emotional pain as well as physical pain, and they would be available in some combination to virtually anyone, regardless of culture, personality, or other aspects of individual difference. They suggest to me that keepers have a selection of taps readily available with which to turn psychache down from a dangerously suicidogenic torrent to a survivable flow. We can see in general terms how pain-type keepers could take away the motivation for a suicidal escape.

Brain-type keepers as induced confusion

Now what about brain-type keepers — devices that deny us the intellectual means for suicide? How could they stop people who have suicidal ideas from acting on them?

We can be fairly sure about how they *won't* work. We have already ruled out what would have been a neat solution: blocking suicide plans specifically. Ideally, the brain would eaves-drop on our conscious thoughts. It would hear that we were planning a suicide mission, and then it would step in to thwart that plot — and that plot alone. But this strategy would be a non-starter, for at least two reasons. First, as we've already noted, the brain can't tell what we are thinking, only how we feel when we think it. If keepers cannot spot a suicide plan, then they won't be able to make a surgical strike on such a plan. In a later chapter I will discuss other defences, cultural barriers against suicide, which could do just that — using emotional associations to ward us away specifically from suicidal projects. But we are focussing here on the earliest phase in the evolution of anti-suicide defences, before a population of pre-human hominids became smart enough to spread rules that relied on an understanding of death or personal mortality. So, the second problem is that, when keepers evolved, most people would not have had the mental wherewithal to plan a suicide anyway.

Assuming the central nervous system can't mount a precise attack on suicidal plans, then survival would presumably call for a general lockdown instead. It is rather like municipal efforts to control the spread of Covid-19: if you can't pinpoint the carriers of the virus, the only recourse is to impose restrictions on a blanket basis. It seems to me that the only way keepers can stop us from organising suicide would be by stopping us from organising anything. Keepers would need to deny access to the kind of high-level thinking tools we need for planning and carrying out any complicated project — cognitive faculties such as memory, concentration, logic, decision-making, and the ability to think ahead. Psychologists call these 'executive functions'. We can expect people who are in enough psychache to think about ending it all to find themselves, in important respects, unable to think straight. The cognitive fog won't prevent daily subsistence, but it should be enough to put a lethal suicide attempt beyond reach. The capacity for mental intentionality might be knocked back to a pre-adolescent level, where even the concept of suicide is beyond reach. As with pain-type keepers, this brain-type response will look, and be, irrational by the standards of normal life. Unbearable psychache should make people tactically, temporarily, confused.

If the scenario I am describing is broadly correct, then it would be very strange by normal animal standards. Any other animal facing a life-threatening danger would be expected to bring all its mental faculties to bear on the emergency. If the animal's mind were a sailing ship in a storm, the cry would go up, "All hands on deck!" We expect the same of ourselves to some degree: we are supposed to perform best when we are under pressure. But the design spec of keepers says that if the storm goes on long enough, we humans can expect certain of our mental faculties to be furloughed. The mind will carry on functioning, but at a degraded level. If the human mind were that ship, senior officers would be sent below.

Taking a broader view, actually this is not so strange. Versions of the same defensive strategy are common in the natural world. It's known as autotomy: the sacrifice of a part in order to save the whole. For example, a deciduous tree sheds its leaves in the autumn in order to survive the winter. A lobster has special breaking joints in its limbs, where sections can be detached without the loss of too much blood and from which replacement parts can regrow. Lizards likewise have fracture planes in their tails, so that, in the emergency of being caught by a predator, the tail can be jettisoned and the body of the lizard can escape. Energy is lost, but the genetic individual survives. Keepers are a human mental equivalent: we sacrifice our rationality, if and when required, for the sake of survival.

To switch metaphors, we can think of keepers as part of a clever software package: when it detects a serious security threat, it switches to 'safe mode'. Certain non-essential modules get disabled in the interest of self-protection. They are enabled again when the threat is resolved, but in the meantime, we have to make do with a downgraded version of the software. It may look like a malfunction, but it isn't. Without that protective routine, an attack could destroy the whole system.

The mind has a mind of its own

These software downgrades will be made without our permission being sought, indeed often without us even knowing. Suicide is too serious a threat for us to be given much discretion about how we go about avoiding it.

Lethal fitness threats tend to be met by strongly automatic defences, because there is often not the scope, or need, to choose the best response by conscious decision. If you are clearly drowning, lifeguards won't be too bothered about seeking your permission before they pull you out of the water. The anti-suffocation programme we talked about earlier operates by reflex: you don't get to choose how long you can hold your breath. Selection presumably found long ago that we can't be trusted with such calls. People who had fully conscious control over their own breathing, if they ever existed, are unlikely to be among our ancestors.

For similar reasons, I doubt that the first and foremost defences against suicide were learned. If a threat is lethal, and the first encounter can kill you, then there won't be much opportunity to learn how to avoid it.

Most likely, it seems to me, keepers' interventions will be pre-programmed and strongly compulsory. We may have no say in the how or the when of it. When keepers disable certain aspects of our mental faculties, we probably won't be able consciously to re-enable them. Keepers' emergency measures — some combination of emotional numbing, drug or alcohol use, self-cutting, distractions, self-serving delusions, the tripping of a mental circuit-breaker, and the like — will leave us with little, if any, power to override them.

All this suggests that keepers won't be hard to see in action. The behaviours they induce will look irrational, be inconvenient, and probably conspicuously so. Keepers may show themselves in many possible ways, but they will all be tactical varieties of the same 'pain' and 'brain' strategies — that is, compulsive pain-managing routines, downgrades of intellectual faculties, or more likely, blends of both. Their common outcome is that people in chronic emotional distress may look like they have become mentally deranged. They will certainly appear abnormal by the standards of regular mental functioning.

Worse, if that derangement is seriously antisocial, then keepers bring with them a possibility of adding to the sufferer's problems. If they damage the sufferer's social supports, then a vicious cycle may set in, social pain breeding yet more social pain. There may be an inevitable scatter of such downward spirals in the human population. It would be akin to occasional times when the physiological immune system malfunctions. Auto-immune diseases are where the body's protective machinery becomes self-destructive. Death sometimes results from adaptations that were designed to save life. There may be such occasional back-firings and own goals, but most of the time, keepers' interventions will be temporary and recoverable. I made the point earlier that they won't usually cause fatal or permanent disability.

Being right to be anxious

Let me add two more items to this forecast of keepers' design features. These relate to the way animals generally, not just us, tend to react to severe fitness threats. Animals deal with serious hazards by one or other of two behavioural patterns: fight/flight; or anxiousness. It's a decisional fork in the road, because a different strategy is needed depending on the certainty of the threat — whether or not it can be seen coming. When a threat is certain and locatable, a fight/flight strategy makes sense. So, if a predator is charging at you, or a rival is squaring up, then you could either run away or join the fight. (Some prey animals also have a 'play dead' option if an immediate escape is not possible — that is, freeze and hope the predator is only interested in fresh meat.)

But what about a severe danger that is not certain or locatable? Suppose a gazelle detects the scent of a lion in the air but can't be sure where the lion is hiding? The gazelle's best response is not to run, because it could find itself rushing towards death as easily as away from it. The best strategy is, rather, for the gazelle to put itself on high alert. It will stop whatever else it is doing, focus its senses on trying to gather more information about the danger, and get ready in case it needs to act fast — blood is diverted from gut to muscles, the heart pumps faster, and so on. This cluster of responses is anxiousness.[19]

So, for humans, which kind of threat is imminent suicide? It is certainly severe — it's lethal. But is it certain and locatable; or uncertain and unlocatable? There is no doubt who and where the assailant is, but there is no one to flee from or fight. A deadly attack of unknown form could strike at almost time, and from no particular direction. There is nowhere to run and no place to hide. Suicide seems to me an extreme case of an ambiguous threat. So it looks to me that the expected pattern of response is anxiousness. We should expect the human organism to move to a state of vigilance. It could be analogous to the close supervision of prisoners who are assessed to be at risk of taking their own lives. Nature and humankind sometimes arrive at similar answers to similar problems; birds and aircraft designers reached much the same solution to the challenge of flight, for example — a wing.[20] Nature and prison governors may have found a common response to their common problem: watchfulness.

Like other animals, humans generally respond to severe, uncertain threats with protracted anxiousness. We stop attending to other interests, we focus our senses on trying to learn more about the situation, and our metabolism gears up for action. We are nervous and restless. Our species alone appears to have an extra feature to add to this standard animal package; mental rumination — circular and compulsive thoughts.[21] So it is this syndromic pattern, I suggest, that will ride along with keepers. I am not arguing that anxiousness is a keeper — anxiousness is, rather, a general style of response to lethal, ambiguous fitness threats, of which suicide is an extreme example. Anxiousness could be triggered by many other dangers, not just suicide. Keepers, on the other hand, evolved specifically to stop suicide and for no other reason, which is why we can infer their anti-suicide design in some depth.

Note that the anxiety that accompanies keepers won't be sparked directly by whatever problem it was that caused the sufferer's psychache. The anxiety is a response, rather, to the problem of suicide as an escape from that psychache. To an observer, the sufferer's nervousness and worry may look out of proportion to the original difficulty, and so it might be. But the observer may not be seeing the power of that difficulty, perhaps as the final straw, to motivate suicide. Our capacity for self-extinction, a universal painkiller, can potentially magnify almost any adverse experience into a matter literally of life or death. If this is true, then people who are anxious may be absolutely right to be in that protective state, however trivial their problems may look from the outside.[22]

A final point: when animals no longer sense a severe, uncertain threat, their return to business-as-usual is delayed, slow, and cautious. A gazelle won't go straight back to grazing as soon as the scent of a lion wafts away. It will stay on guard until it is sure the danger has passed, because it is better to be safe than sorry.[23] We should see the same pattern with keepers. Keepers will deactivate after, and only after, the originating psychache is eased — but only after a lag, and then only slowly. Deactivation might be prompt and sudden if there is an unambiguous 'all clear', although I'm not sure what such a signal would look like in the case of suicide risk. We will touch on that question in a later chapter.

Summing up, this chapter set out to explain why people don't do the expected thing to escape psychache. Pain is biologically designed to demand the animal acts to end it. Humans can answer that demand by ending themselves. But they usually don't. The reason they don't, we think, is because of special-purpose anti-suicide adaptions that evolved in a proto-human population. These defences were strong enough to allow a precursor of our species to cross the intellectual threshold for suicide, and they still protect us today. We gave these defences a label — keepers. Their task is to stop suicidal ideas from progressing into suicidal actions.

What and where are these keepers? To give ourselves a guide, we have sketched out some of their likely features, based on what we know of the origins of suicide, and the special mission that keepers evolved to fulfil. We drew on the pain-and-brain theory of suicide's evolutionary origins. We considered keepers' 'pain' and 'brain' inputs, their 'pain' and 'brain' processes, and the outcomes those processes would be expected to produce. We can't be too specific in some areas, and there may be much we will never know. But we have predicted quite a few noteworthy characteristics. They can be summed in a list, as follows:[24]

Predicted design features of keepers:

1)	Species-specific	*Keepers will occur only in humans (although vestiges may be found in other primates).*
2)	Species-universal	*Keepers will occur universally among humans.*
3)	Psychache input	*Keepers will be activated by chronic psychache as 'pain' input, subject to a qualifying 'brain' input (see item 6, below).*

4)	Proportionality	*Keepers will scale responses according to degree of 'pain' input: the worse the psychache, the more drastic and costly keepers' actions.*
5)	Origin-blind	*Keepers will be oblivious to the origin of the psychache that triggered them.*
6)	Adolescent first onset	*Keepers won't activate earlier than the typical first onset of suicide — i.e., not before adolescence. Thereafter, at any age.*
7)	Reversible	*Keepers will deactivate following relief of the psychache that triggered them.*
8)	Pathology prone	*Keepers will occasionally malfunction.*
9)	Cautious stand-down	*Keepers will deactivate slowly and after a delay, unless the lifting of suicide risk is marked by an 'all-clear' signal.*
10)	Link to suicide	*Where suicides occur, keepers will usually show signs of having activated.*
11)	Pre-emptive	*Keepers will trigger alongside suicidal ideas, rather than actions.*
12)	Sensitivity	*Keepers will be prone to false alarms (i.e., keepers activating without suicide ideas).*
13)	Thoroughness	*Keepers will exhaust all useful predictors of suicide at the level of the individual.*
14)	Demographically sustainable	*Keepers will produce low but above-zero suicide rates. Not demographically destabilising.*

15)	Anxiousness	*Keepers will be accompanied by protracted anxiousness.*
16)	Degrade pain	*Keepers will dull the motivation for suicide ('pain-type').*
17)	Degrade brain	*Keepers will deny the intellectual means of organising suicide ('brain-type').*
18)	Diverse	*Keepers will appear in multiple forms within the same individual, either at the same time or at different times. Some combinations will occur together more often than others.*
19)	Obligate	*Keepers will produce strongly involuntary responses.*
20)	Abnormality	*Keepers will produce behaviours that appear irrational. They will be conspicuously abnormal.*

Now, armed with this template, we can turn to see if there is a phenomenon in the real world that matches it. We are looking for signs of evolved defences that are specifically designed to stop humans from acting on suicidal ideas.

Recall that it is like searching for a missing key: we expect this key to be gigantic, so it shouldn't be hard to see — especially now we have a picture of what we think it looks like. Let's take a look...

CHAPTER 7: *We drew up a pro forma design specification for 'keepers' — psychological systems that evolved to stop our ancestors from acting upon suicidal thoughts. Twenty features are predicted, including inputs, outputs and likely processes. Armed with this blueprint, we can now look for a real-world match — evidence of keepers in action in modern humans.*

CHAPTER 8: *The design specification of keepers finds a match in outwardly diverse mental disorders — states that Western psychiatry calls depression, addictions, generalised anxiety, schizophrenia, and other diagnostic labels. Symptoms of these conditions may not in fact be disorders but, rather, protective anti-suicide responses to lasting psychache.*

8

THE DISEASES THAT KEEP US ALIVE

In this chapter, I will try to persuade you that most common mental disorders — depressions, addictions, schizophrenia and others — are not disorders at all. They are probably, rather, how the human organism keeps itself safe from suicide. Their symptoms are really a combination of psychache alongside the workings of ancient adaptations that, in the last chapter, we named 'keepers', activating in response to psychache. Like a goalkeeper on a soccer team, keepers are our last line of defence: they are all that stands between an attacking adversity and genetic 'game over'.

In case you find this proposal counter-intuitive, let me offer three points that could make it easier to take on board. First, the reason we are at this chapter is because of the chain of logic and evidence that went before. Each conclusion led to the next. If we agree with the argument so far, then whether we like it or not, this is where we stand. Second, we need this chapter as a stepping stone to happier places. The rest of the book will make little sense without this crossing. Third, it is hard to read the last chapter without having a feeling that psychiatric disorders have something to do with our evolved defences against suicide. We concluded that keepers will activate among people in prolonged emotional pain, to stop suicidal ideas turning into actions. We predicted that keepers will do this by tampering with the way we think (cognition), feel (emotions), and act (behaviour), in response to intense and chronic psychache, usually connected with social pain. This does sound like something that would interest a psychiatrist. Indeed, psychiatry's definition of mental disorder uses a remarkably similar wording:

> A mental disorder is a syndrome characterized by clinically signifi-
> cant disturbance in an individual's cognition, emotion regulation, or
> behavior that reflects a dysfunction in the psychological, biological, or

developmental processes underlying mental functioning. Mental disorders are usually associated with significant distress or disability in social, occupational, or other important activities.[1]

The difference is that, if the keeper idea is correct, these conditions may not, in fact, be dysfunctions. They could be proper, protective, reactions to chronic emotional pain. They may be diseases (literally, a state of dis-ease), but they may function to keep us alive when we otherwise might have opted for oblivion.

A bucket of disorders

Before we go further, there some basics you should know about psychiatric disorders, if you don't know already. There is an assortment of mental illnesses that, in psychiatry, used to go by the name 'functional'. The word has gone out fashion in recent years, although the meaning remains.[2] In this context, 'functional' says that a malady impairs one's ability to function, but it cannot be traced to an identifiable biological cause — that is to say, it is not known why functional mental disorders occur. So, they exclude so-called 'organic' disorders, such as Alzheimer's disease, Down's syndrome, the effects of brain injuries, and a few other mental conditions that can be attributed to diagnosable bodily origins. Functional disorders are a hotchpotch of states that we call depression, generalised anxiety, substance use disorders (alcoholism and drug addictions), non-suicidal self-injury, PTSD, eating disorders, bipolar disorder, schizophrenia, obsessive/compulsive disorder (OCD), and other sundry ailments.[3] Such conditions make up the bulk of psychiatric diagnoses.

You could visualise these functional disorders as a collection of differently coloured balls in a bucket. If you think about their classic symptoms, you could imagine each syndrome to be a separate thing — an object that you can pick up and look at, distinct from the others. Depression is feeling low and losing interest in things one usually enjoys. Alcoholism is compulsive drinking. Schizophrenia involves delusions, and so on. You can visualise our bucket as containing many such coloured balls. But, in reality, they are not easy to pick out one by one, because there are no natural boundaries between any of them.

This is more than a problem of boundaries being fuzzy. There are no real boundaries at all. Each disorder blends smoothly into all the others. This continuity occurs, I will argue, because most functional disorders are fundamentally the same thing, even though they appear to be different. Switching analogy, they are like a café menu that offers quiches, omelettes, and scrambled eggs — and anything in between. Let me highlight six reasons to believe this to be so. There are plenty of others (I will list more in the final chapter) but this will make the point for now.

First, the symptoms of functional disorders overlap, like roof tiles. For example, hallucinations (hearing things, or seeing things) are often taken to be the hallmark of schizophrenia, but they also often occur with depression and bipolar disorder.[4] These overlaps are so broad that, second, diagnostic criteria also cross over. For example: difficulties with sleeping and concentrating are among the defining features of both depression and generalised anxiety; and emotional flatness could be taken as a sign of depression, bipolar disorder, or schizophrenia.[5] Third, mental disorders are strongly comorbid, meaning that they often appear more than one at a time. Comorbidity is so common that there's a rule of halves: half the people with one mental disorder also meet the criteria for a second. Half of them meet the criteria for a third disorder, and so on. Different disorders also often appear in the same person but at different times of life.[6] Fourth, so vague and fluid are the definitions of many mental disorders that it is possible for two people to have the same diagnosis and no symptoms in common.[7] Fifth, there is no way to distinguish disorders by a blood test, brain scan, genetic screening, or any other biomedical analysis. No biochemical marker gets close to ruling any particular diagnosis in or out.[8] Choosing a patient's diagnostic label is, instead, down to the personal preferences of clinicians. They have to compare the patient's complaints against a list of criteria for each diagnosis and take a view on which list offers the best match. There's a medical aura about this matching business, but it is not as scientific as it looks. Different clinicians can and often do reach different opinions, and there is no definitive way to say who is 'right'.[9]

The final problem to note for now is that the diagnostic criteria of functional mental disorders are creations of politics, not nature. They are like the way an official presumably used a ruler to draw the US-Canada border across Lake Ontario: whatever the state maps say, Lake Ontario is actually a continuous body of water. The boundaries of mental disorders are marked out just as arbitrarily. They are decided by committee. Indeed, they shift from time to time as different negotiators horse-trade over different deals.[10] Non-science is thus built into the diagnosing process, because the purpose of these boundary-setting committees is not scientific; it's administrative. Their goal is to standardise clinical practice and the collection of statistics, whether or not the resulting diagnostic labels exist in the real world as distinct things. There is no evidence that they do so exist. Rather, in the real world, mental disorders form a single unbroken mass, like the surface of Lake Ontario.

In sum, most psychiatric diagnoses were invented, not discovered — they are labels, no more. For sure, labels can be useful. But in mental health, I suggest diagnostic labels get in the way of understanding because they have come to dominate our thinking.

Normally in science, research takes the lead and the labelling follows. In particle physics, for example, theoretical evidence pointing to the existence of the Higgs boson was discovered long before a community of scientists fell into the habit of using the term 'Higgs boson'. In psychiatry, it's the other way round: labels are decided first, and science plays catch-up, trying to post-rationalise the labels. So, for example, special theories are put forward to explain the origins of 'depression'; other ideas to explain 'schizophrenia', and so on — all based on the fallacious assumption that these refer to distinct real-world phenomena.[11] Diagnostic labels, then, have turned the normal process of science upside down. Tail wags dog, and it has done so for more than a century. Perhaps not surprisingly, with the cart put before the horse, neither has made much progress. Despite decades of intense research, there is no consensus of understanding as to why most mental disorders occur, even among the professionals charged with treating them.

Setting labels aside, I suggest it is more accurate and more useful to re-imagine our bucket of disorders as containing liquid rather than lumps. Depression, OCD, schizophrenia, and the rest are not separate, stand-alone conditions, like coloured balls. Each one blends into all the others, like colours in a tub of imperfectly mixed paint. If you are daubed with a brushful, it may not be easy to say which colour you have most of.

Acknowledging this reality, I am going to call the contents of the bucket by a single name for the rest of this discussion: 'common mental disorder', or *CMD*.[12] This chapter will offer you a novel theory to explain the existence of the bucket of paint: why humans experience CMD. Once that is understood, the reasons for CMD's rainbow-like colours, its superficial diversity, will become clear.

The argument of special design

Whether you accept this theory will depend on whether you are persuaded by evidence of special design. Could I convince you that a device is so well suited for doing a certain job that it could not credibly have been made for any other purpose?

Suppose, say, I gave you an accordion: you would notice the keyboard and buttons, the reeds inside that are tuned to musical notes, the bellows that push air across the reeds to make a sound, the hand-sized straps on either side of the bellows, and larger straps that fit over the shoulders. Taking everything into account, your intuition would tell you that the accordion was probably designed for making music. There is no better explanation. Likewise, as a biological example, we earlier discussed the heart. In deciding what the heart was for, you would be struck by its plumbing — the arrangement of blood vessels, chambers, and valves; you would note its pumping movements, the chambers squeezing in turn; and other features. There is no more plausible way to explain this pattern other than that the heart evolved to pump blood.

Now, likewise, we have a list of design features that we would expect to find in devices that evolved to prevent suicide — keepers. You saw the list at the end of the last chapter. If these features matched, point by point, real-life characteristics of CMD, would you accept that as evidence of special design? Would you take it as fair reason to believe that outwardly diverse symptoms of CMD probably evolved for one purpose and one alone — to stop people killing themselves? Let's see what you think.

I wish I could make the next bit easier, but the argument takes a little time, and it involves detail. There is no short cut, because it is precisely in the detail that an argument of special design stacks up. When you decided that an accordion is a musical instrument, it needed more than one feature to persuade you. You noted half a dozen: keys, buttons, reeds, tuning, bellows, and straps, all aligned with the theorized musical intent. In order to persuade you of the special design of CMD, I will likewise need to show you multiple points of alignment. I'll need to bore you into agreement. I will offer you not six features, but twenty. There is nothing magic about twenty; it just strikes me as enough to convince you without sending you to sleep.

So, now walk with me through the next few pages as we compare the twenty expected features of keepers with patterns found in diverse forms of CMD. Let's see how many we can check off as a match.

1. **Species-specific:** *Keepers will occur only in humans (although vestiges may be found in other primates).*

    Only humans have to deal with the problem of suicide, so there would be no fitness advantage for any other animal to be defended against it. Thus, we predicted that keepers won't have evolved in any other species. There may well be isolated features of what may look like keepers in other animals, especially among our primate cousins, but these will be only remnants of ancient biological raw material from which keepers emerged in our species alone.

    Check. CMD is not found in any other animal. Science has yet to discover a non-human that could reasonably be called depressive, schizophrenic, alcoholic, etc. — that is, with clusters of symptoms characteristic of CMD. There are, for sure, certain animal behaviours that could be said to look like isolated features of CMD. For example, it is possible to induce apathy in dogs, a learned helplessness that is reminiscent of the lost motivation commonly found in clinical depression; but that kind of stand-alone phenomenon is a long way from the constellation of features that typifies major depression as a human syndrome.

    As an acid test, no illness has been found in non-human animals that gets close enough to CMD to be of use as an 'animal model' for drug testing.[13] Like the search for evidence of non-human suicide, this failure to find an animal equivalent is not for want of motivation, means, or effort. Pharmaceutical companies are under intense commercial pressure to find animal models, animal testing being part of the normal way drugs are developed and trialled. But animal tests of antidepressants and other psychiatric drugs have been scaled back in recent years, after a succession of clinical failures have cast doubt on whether this form of testing is commercially worthwhile.[14]

2. **Species-universal:** *Keepers will occur universally among humans.*

    Suicide prevails as a biological problem across the entire human species. Keepers, humankind's primary adaptive defence against suicide, will therefore be found in all human cultures, past and present.

Check. The same patterns of CMD are found the world over, as defined and tracked by the World Health Organization.[15] We can't be sure about the prehistoric past, but CMD looks to be much of a much-ness across recorded human history. The archaeological and historical record, from China, Mesopotamia, and elsewhere, is scattered with references to conditions that look much like what we would nowadays call depression, alcoholism, schizophrenia, and the like.[16]

3. **Psychache input:** *Keepers will be activated by chronic psychache as 'pain' input, subject to a qualifying 'brain' input (see item 6, below).*

We reckoned that suicidal ideas probably won't come with a biological marker that keepers could use to activate themselves. Instead, keepers will trigger on the basis of an indirect cue, probably the experience of prolonged psychache — the motivation for suicidal escape. So, we predicted that intense and lasting emotional pain (most likely, social pain) will go before, and ride along with, activated keepers.

Check. CMD is preceded, and accompanied, by emotional pain. Studies that track peoples' mental health over time show that CMD onsets typically occur a few weeks after major bereavements and similar social losses, or in the wake of recurring social troubles.[17] There may also be a long-term 'kindling' effect, adverse life conditions during childhood that may make people more at risk of CMD in later years. The experience of psychological pain is strongly linked with mental disorders; indeed, it's a defining diagnostic criterion for some, such as depression and borderline personality disorder.

4. **Proportionality:** *Keepers will scale their response according to degree of 'pain' input: the worse the psychache, the more drastic and costly keepers' actions.*

We predicted that keepers will respond to lasting psychache as the triggering input. The worse the psychache, the greater the motivation for suicide, and the more strongly keepers will respond to prevent that outcome.

Check (more or less). There is proportionality in the triggering of CMD. The greater the number and severity of the prior adversities, the greater the likelihood of CMD, at least up to a point. That pattern suggests a scaled response of sorts.[18] I am not aware of evidence that the severity of CMD symptoms also scales in this way, but it would be a reasonable implication. By the nature of the clinical process, any diagnosis of CMD is by definition a pointer to the severity of symptoms.

5.   **Origin-blind:** *Keepers will be oblivious to the origin of the psychache that triggered them.*

It is the one-dimensional painfulness of psychache, not its cause or type, that motivates suicide. It will be the same for anti-suicide defences. Keepers won't be interested in *why* you hurt, only *how much* you hurt.

Check. CMD responds to the degree, not type, of social losses. There is scant evidence that different varieties of emotional pain, or different types of painful events, provoke different forms of CMD. Rather, adversity in general leads to CMD in general.[19]

There is one proviso: anxiety and depression seem to respond slightly differently to different types of problems. Generalized anxiety is more likely to follow dangerous situations, whereas depression tends to happen after social losses. But, recall, we are not anyway putting anxiety forward as a custom-designed keeper; anxiety can come about for other reasons than to stop suicide. This detail doesn't contradict the prediction.

6.   **Adolescent first onset:** *Keepers won't activate earlier than the typical first onset of suicide — i.e., not before adolescence. Thereafter, at any age.*

This is the 'brain' input. There would be no fitness benefit in anti-suicide defences activating among children who have not yet crossed the intellectual threshold for suicide, so we should not expect to see keepers activating before that stage of life. Once the switch is thrown, it won't switch back, so we're expecting keepers to activate at any age after adolescence.

Check. CMD is rare before adolescence and happens at any age thereafter: the peak age for the first arrival of any mental disorder is 14 years.[20] In other words, the pattern of CMD onset seems to coincide with the time of life when the mental capability for suicide arrives.

To be clear, this is not to say that younger children are immune from mental illness. Rather, there seems to be a categorical difference in the kind and frequency of mental disorders that occur before children cross the intellectual threshold for suicide, compared to those that happen after. This is true even when the disorders go by the same name — notably 'depression'. Onsets of major depression are not only much rarer before puberty than afterwards, but they follow a different demographic pattern and clinical course, enough to suggest that pre- and post-pubescent forms may be distinct conditions.[21]

7. **Reversible:** *Keepers will deactivate following relief of the psychache that triggered them.*

Keepers mobilise to stop us killing ourselves when we are in enough emotional pain to make suicide an appealing option. There would be no fitness advantage in keepers staying mobilized once the triggering psychache has gone away. So, we should see keepers going back into 'stand by' mode once the originating distress has lessened, a reversal of the process of activation. Keepers won't usually kill us — they were selected because they save lives, not end them — and they won't normally be permanent, disabling conditions.

Check. CMD eases by itself. This may surprise you — it certainly surprised me. Most forms of CMD lift by themselves, with or without medical intervention: it usually just takes time and minimally favourable circumstances.[22] Recovery is the mirror-image of the pattern of onset, helped along by an easing of the psychache or a resolution to the adverse event that provoked the CMD in the first place.[23]

Recovery usually happens over the course of weeks, sometimes months, occasionally years, but eventually even the severest forms of CMD follow a natural course. They are rarely permanent or degenerative states. Here is a story to illustrate: psychiatrist Karl Menninger recounts how the most hopelessly ill 153 patients in a French psychiatric hospital went missing in 1940 in chaotic scenes ahead of the imminent German invasion. These patients had been assessed as incurable, and they were the hospital's most desperate residents — the ones that were left after all those who could be evacuated had been moved to safety. Tracked down by a special commission after France's liberation, more than a third were found to be living normal lives in their communities — and presumably no longer 'incurable'.[24]

8. **Pathology prone:** *Keepers will occasionally malfunction.*

Suicide being a serious danger, it calls for serious countermeasures. We have discussed how keepers may be drastic in their interventions, any outcome short of death being better than self-killing. But drastic measures suggest a risk that things could go wrong — much like the physiological immune system can malfunction, producing auto-immune diseases, which are sometimes fatal.

Check. CMD can be pathological. This looks like stating the obvious. Psychiatry would have us believe that functional mental disorders not only *can* malfunction but *are* malfunctions by definition. But the idea here is more nuanced. CMD symptoms, as keepers, are bound to be costly to the organism because they disable parts of our normal emotional and intellectual workings. So, yes, they are harmful, but that doesn't make them dysfunctions, and they are usually much less harmful than the suicidal death they aim to prevent. In the light of our design spec for keepers, CMD is only dysfunctional when it becomes seriously and permanently debilitating or degenerative — that can happen, but it is rare.

9. **Cautious stand-down:** *Keepers will deactivate slowly and after a delay, unless the lifting of suicide risk is marked by an 'all clear' signal.*

We are expecting keepers to stand down cautiously from a state of high suicide risk – it's better to be safe than sorry. The return to business as usual could be quick if there were a definite sign that the suicide hazard was over — an 'all clear' — but it is not obvious what such a signal would look like.

Check. CMD doesn't usually lift quickly. It is hard to be more specific because we haven't said exactly what would count as quick, but there is little reason to think CMD normally vanishes as soon as one's troubles are over. Depression usually runs its course over three to six months, and the odds of a new onset fall away only gradually, over a period of years, following the bereavement or other loss that provoked the episode.[25] More serious forms of CMD, such as borderline personality disorder and schizophrenia, can take several years to improve.[26] That said, serious addictions sometimes do end literally overnight, in Alcoholics Anonymous and other so-called twelve-step programmes, following the feeling of a fresh start, often described by recovering addicts as a spiritual experience.[27] Perhaps that might be taken as an 'all clear' signal. But, generally, a gradual release from CMD seems to be the rule.

10. **Link to suicide:** *Where suicides occur, keepers will usually show signs of having activated.*

When suicides do happen, there ought to be evidence that keepers had properly activated, even though they did not succeed in stopping suicide in those instances. By analogy with soccer, when a goal is scored, we would usually expect the goalkeeper to have done something — at least some flicker of a reaction — in an effort to block the incoming shot.

Check. Many or most suicides show signs of CMD at the time of death, according to so-called psychological autopsies. Virtually all forms of CMD show this association. Figures vary widely, but the one usually quoted is that diagnosable CMD is on the scene in more than 90% of suicides. It is difficult to be precise partly because CMD symptoms could have been present at the time of death, but not at a level severe enough to warrant a clinical diagnosis.[28]

11. **Pre-emptive:** *Keepers will trigger alongside suicidal ideas, rather than actions.*

Keepers evolved to stop thoughts escalating into deeds, so keepers aren't going to wait for that escalation to play out before they intervene. Triggered by psychache, keepers will activate at the earliest stage — a yearning to escape pain, and the thinking of suicidal thoughts — rather than with actions that may sometimes follow from those thoughts.

Check. CMD associates strongly with suicidal ideas; but it associates only weakly with the progression of those ideas into firm plans and actual attempts. That is to say, as we expected, CMD is almost as common among the few people who act on suicidal ideas as among the many who don't. The pattern isn't as complete we would expect — there may be some extra activation of CMD at the actions stage — but the general pattern seems to hold nonetheless.[29]

12. **Sensitivity:** *Keepers will be prone to false alarms (i.e., keepers activating without suicide ideas).*

Keepers won't know if one is thinking of ending it all. All they have to go on, as an indirect pointer to the likelihood of having such ideas, is the motivator of those ideas — psychache. That being only an indirect pointer, keepers may get it wrong. They may mobilise among people who, although in emotional pain, never seriously entertained thoughts of killing themselves. But getting it wrong in that direction is probably not a mistake. The danger being grave, keepers will err on the side of caution, and there may be many such false alarms.

Check. About a third of people with CMD have not recently thought of taking their own lives.[30] It is hard to be more specific on this point because we haven't stated what counts as 'many' false alarms. The evidence could be taken to suggest that CMD does well to identify those at risk — the rate of suicidal ideation is markedly higher among those with CMD than in the general population. But CMD evidently sweeps many non-suicidal people into its net too, so it could be said to be playing safe.

13. **Thoroughness:** *Keepers will exhaust all useful predictors of suicide at the level of the individual.*

If natural selection has done the expected thing, then keepers should have sought out, put to good use, and thus burned away every available cue that predicts suicide at the level of the organism. Keepers won't be, and evidently aren't, failsafe: despite their efforts, some suicides will get past the defences. But the suicides that do occur will be incidents that offered the least, if anything, in the way of predictive markers. Keepers, then, will correlate with suicidality, but not powerfully enough to predict suicides at the individual level.

Check. CMD does not usefully predict suicide. There is a measurable statistical association, but the vast majority of people with CMD do not kill themselves. As for the few who do, as discussed earlier in this book, no marker has been found that gets close to accurately identifying them in advance. Suicide is not predictable at the level of the organism by any known means; indeed, the keepers hypothesis predicts that suicide is probably not predictable even in principle.[31]

14. **Demographically sustainable:** *Keepers will produce low but above-zero suicide rates. Not demographically destabilising.*

Keepers provided a protective bridgehead by which a population of early humans got close to, and then crossed, the intellectual threshold for suicide. Thanks to the disruptive effects of keepers in stopping our ancestors' suicidal thoughts turning into suicidal deaths, a novel variety of humans emerged with a categorically higher level of general intelligence than was survivable before. We are expecting keepers to be doing the same job now that they did then. Zero suicide is probably not achievable, at least not without also zeroing the 'pain' and 'brain' adaptations that create suicide. But we can expect modern populations to continue operating with rates held at a sustainably low level — low enough at least not to threaten demographic stability.

Check. The suicide rate among people with CMD is only fractionally higher than the general population, and it seems to be within sustainable bounds.

There are startlingly high suicide rates in the general population in some parts of the world. A scattering of smaller nations — such as Guyana and Lesotho — are said to have annual rates at or near to 30 per 100,000, about three times the global average.[32] The rate in Greenland has been put at 58, and in one of Greenland's towns, Tasiilaq, an astonishing 400.[33] Similar surges can be seen in certain other communities around the globe: among the Palawan in the Philippines, the Aguaruna in Peru, on the Micronesian island of Truk, and elsewhere.[34] It seems that in such places a protective taboo against suicide broke down at some stage, the act becoming a normal topic of conversation and an accepted solution in trying times.

There is no bright side to such grim facts and figures. But there is no strong evidence either to suggest that suicidality even in these hotspots is severe enough to threaten a population's future. Even in Tasiilaq, out of every 100,000 people, 99,600 *don't* take their own lives. We don't see situations in which communities collapse under the weight of self-killings.

This is remarkable. Recall a conclusion made in this book's earlier chapters — that any animal, human or not, would be expected to kill itself to escape pain, if it had that escape route intellectually available. But we see nothing close to that default outcome in human populations. I suggest this resilience is no accident; it is, rather, the purposeful effect of evolved defences. The vast majority of humans, even in the most suicidal cultures, find other ways to deal with psychache.

What precise role CMD plays in keeping suicide rates sustainably low is hard to say. But let us note that the great majority of people even with serious forms of CMD do not kill themselves, despite their emotional pain.[35] Lifetime suicide rates among those affected by CMD are higher than the general population, but they are not out of the ballpark — for depression, 2% compared to a normal 1.5%, for example.[36] Other studies and other forms of CMD show higher rates; 4% among schizophrenics, perhaps 7% among alcoholics.[37] Even at the extreme, suicide among people so disabled that they were hospitalised with CMD are 'only' about the same as the general rate in Tasiilaq[38] — that is to say, apparently sustainable at a population level. If Tasiilaq can maintain itself, then presumably so can the share of humankind that is under the influence of CMD.

15. **Anxiousness:** *Keepers will be accompanied by protracted anxiousness.*

I am not arguing that anxiousness evolved specifically to prevent suicide. Anxiousness existed as an animal state long before human suicidality. So, it isn't a keeper, but it probably runs alongside keepers and is one of the strategies by which the human organism keeps suicide at bay.

We discussed prolonged anxiousness in the last chapter as the way animals generally respond to severe but uncertain fitness threats. The best an animal can do when it is in mortal danger, but has nowhere to run and no one to fight, is to put itself on high alert. It will probably then stay in this state for a lengthy period, until it is sure the coast is clear. Once it is sure, it will stand down only slowly. Among humans, this standard pattern of anxiousness is likely to ride along with keepers because of the potentially lethal, but uncertain, nature of suicide as a fitness threat. We can expect to be restless, sleepless, nervous, and distracted. A specifically human add-on to the standard package is rumination — repetitive, compulsive worrying — which we expect also be on the scene when keepers are at work.

Check. Anxiousness is part and parcel of CMD. For example, more than 70% of people with depressive disorders are said to show anxiety symptoms.[39] The label 'generalised anxiety disorder' is a commonplace diagnosis and often co-occurs with other diagnostic labels.[40] I would hazard that some level of anxiety is (even) more widespread among mental disorders than the clinical data suggest: with a few exceptions, people with psychiatric problems are not noted for their relaxed self-confidence.

A defining feature of clinical anxiety is that it is judged to be out of proportion to the scale of the sufferer's problems. To repeat the point, rarely considered in this judgement is the effect of suicide as a possible pain-relieving solution to those problems, an option which could turn almost any trouble into a lethal danger. In this light, people who are anxious may have good reason to be anxious, however mild their troubles look to others.[41]

16. **Degrade pain:** *Keepers will dull the motivation for suicide ('pain-type').*

We deduced that there are only two strategies available by which keepers can block the path from suicidal ideas to suicide actions. They can either sap the motivation — that is, dull psychache enough to make a suicidal escape unnecessary ('pain-type'). Or they can disable the intellectual means — making suicide difficult to plan and carry out ('brain-type'). Most likely, keepers will deploy blends of both.

Check. Diverse CMD symptoms can be pigeon-holed more or less neatly into 'pain-type' or 'brain-type' strategies.

Let's look at 'pain-type' first. Most CMD symptoms look like compulsive versions of the ways humans ordinarily deal with pain. With depression, the mind seems to do to emotional pain what it often does, in battlefield emergencies, to physical pain: it numbs. Depression is not just about feeling sad, as sufferers will vouch. Depression is, rather, a deadening, not feeling anything. The informational content of psychache remains, the misery is still there, but its motivational power is knocked back to a level that doesn't much matter. Nothing much matters. Depression is not, as is often assumed, about being motivated to kill oneself: it is not being motivated to do anything. Someone in the grip of depression may not have the energy to leave home or get out of bed. I'd suggest that at times of psychache, this may be the safest place to be.[42]

Similarly, alcohol and drug addictions look remarkably like an involuntary self-medicating as a strategy to control unbearable psychological pain. This indeed is how addicts themselves often describe their compulsive substance use. For sure, intoxication brings new hazards, but it serves to take the edge off psychache usually enough to survive another day. Disclosures along the lines of "The drugs saved my life" and "I didn't kill myself, I got drunk instead" are often heard by workers in the field.[43]

Likewise, what psychiatry calls 'non-suicidal self-injury' looks very much like regular pain offset relief — the way one pain can be relieved by inducing another. In principle, the response is no different to the way you might dig your fingernails into your palms in the dentist's chair, or bite your lip when you get cramp. People in extreme emotional pain sometimes cut, burn, or otherwise hurt themselves compulsively but nonetheless carefully: it's soothing.[44]

There are also CMD counterparts for the gamut of psychological ploys that humans use to make pain easier to bear. They may look irrational. There need be no factual basis to the distractions, rationalisations, and callings (sometimes, literally, voices) that help us survive with psyche. Psychosis has been described as a flight from an unliveable reality into a liveable fantasy.[45] And these responses may not be fun (although they might be fun in a way, in manic states, for example).[46] The pain remains, but it is kept sublethal. Psychiatry would label these tactics 'behavioural addictions', 'obsessive/compulsive disorders' or 'psychotic delusions', and the rest. But, however imaginary, if they motivate us to stay in the game for another day, they work. For the organism, they are not necessarily irrational.[47]

17. **Degrade brain:** *Keepers will deny the intellectual means of organising suicide ('brain-type').*

Meanwhile, usually alongside their 'pain-type' allies, we are expecting 'brain-type' keepers to interfere with intellectual faculties usually enough to make suicide (and, incidentally, any other complex task) difficult to do.

Check. CMD makes it hard for people to think straight. Specifically, it interferes with the mental machinery we need to organise complicated tasks: memory, reasoning, planning, and decision-making. Neurological studies of depression show how the sufferer is made oddly befuddled: the brain floods parts of itself with irrelevant, useless information, causing processing speeds to slow down. Memory banks get blocked off.[48] This denial of service isn't specific to depression; cognitive deficit is a cross-diagnostic feature, at work in schizophrenia, eating disorders, and elsewhere.[49] Basic mental programmes are left relatively untouched — people with CMD can usually still go about their lives in a minimal capacity, enough to subsist. It is specifically higher functions that are impaired.

I don't know of evidence that CMD causes people to think at a lower order of intentionality, but it wouldn't be surprising if that were the case. The safest state would be equivalent to a pre-pubescent level of self-awareness, where suicide is not even imaginable. It is safe to say at least that people in the grip of CMD are not known for their self-insight.

18. **Diverse:** *Keepers will appear in multiple forms within the same individual, either at the same time or at different times. Some combinations will occur together more often than others.*

We are expecting the human mind to have a repertoire of keepers to choose from, a toolbox of gadgets with which it can block suicides — some pain-type, some brain-type. Pain-type keepers could make emotional pain easier to bear in several different ways, and there might be several intellectual functions that brain-type keepers could disable to make suicide difficult to organise. If keepers can co-operate, then they probably will. They should work together partly for safety — building in system redundancy and resilience, a belt-and-braces-too approach. It is also to spread the burden, because several small design compromises are less likely to desta-bilise the organism than a single large one — much like the collec-tion of adjustments we discussed in Chapter 6, which combine to solve the obstetric dilemma.

Check. Comorbidity — multiple diagnoses playing out in the same person — is one of the most remarkable features of CMD.[50] There are several sides to this. About half the people with one form of CMD also meet the criteria for one or more others.[51] Multiple forms of CMD often occur in the same person at different times of life as well. Addictions, for example, often switch from one substance to another — or, if substances aren't to hand, to behavioural addic-tions such as sex or gambling.[52] Other disorders may be present but at a subclinical level, below the threshold of severity that would warrant a formal diagnosis, so the 'real' incidence of comorbidity may be even greater than diagnostic data suggest.

Even when only one disorder is said to be on the scene, the way diagnostic labels are devised often masks what is actually a multitude of co-occurring conditions. For the most part, diagnostic labels refer to collections of symptoms that a committee has lumped together and decided to call one thing. The lumping is arbitrary — done on the basis of whether symptoms are often seen together, not because of any causal roots known to be joining them up. It is like assuming passengers must be related just because they are often seen riding the same bus.

To illustrate, there are many possible criteria for 'Major depressive disorder'. Let's pick two of them: lack of physical energy, and an inability to make decisions.[53] These get listed together not because of a known functional connection, in the way that, say, there's both a handle and a blade on a can opener. They are assumed to be linked only because they're often (not always) seen in each other's company. We could just as well view them as separate disorders. In other words, depression could just as validly be split into two and relabelled, say, 'Energy deficiency disorder' and 'Indecisiveness disorder'. Thus, depression is not a unitary thing: it could in principle be carved up into any number of frequently 'comorbid' diagnoses. The same is true of many other diagnostic labels.

Some constellations of symptoms are more commonly observed than others. It is precisely because symptoms tend to cluster that we tend to think of mental disorders in terms of classic syndromes, like depression and schizophrenia. The interesting question is *why* they cluster.

Why are certain symptoms of CMD seen together more frequently than others? I suggest it may simply be because keepers work in teams, and some teams work together better than others. To take the above example, lack of energy and indecisiveness make good workmates; they can operate in the same person at the same time. Other blends wouldn't be so easy. Pain-type keepers couldn't, for example, enforce a depressive lockdown, denying you the energy to leave home, and at the same time have you enthusiastically chasing distractions and a grand goal in life. Spreading the load between these would involve flipping from one extreme to the other — inviting another label; 'bipolar'. There could be many such episodic combinations, incompatible keepers taking turns. But regarding the keepers that ride along at the same time, it may be simply because they can.

So, it may be because of mutual compatibility that certain keepers crop up more often, and more often together, than others. But there are likely other reasons. There could be many points of individual differences — age, sex, genetic factors, childhood backgrounds, personality type, and so on — that make some keepers better protectors than others for a particular individual's circumstances. For example, the leader of the hunt would be better served by keepers that enable business to carry on as usual, away from the camp — say, a powerful goal in life, combined with substance use. An expecting or nursing mother might be better served by depressive keepers that keep her at home. Not everyone is equally susceptible to every possible cluster of keepers.[54] I suspect the genius of the human mind can be relied upon to select the best (or, rather, least-bad) solution for each person.

My proposal is that, despite their outer variety, all keepers serve one mission: to block self-killing. Hence CMD, as the expression of keepers, looks like that bucket of imperfectly blended paint we talked about earlier. It comes in many vibrant colours, but it is all the same heavy-duty sealant, put to use for the same protective purpose. Quantity matters more than shade. CMD varies in severity, not kind.[55] Depressions, addictions, psychoses, or whatever: the combination of means is by the by, provided it achieves the same end — to stop suicidal ideas turning into life-threatening actions.

I suggest this is probably why we differ, one person from another, not so much in our vulnerability to particular forms of CMD but in our vulnerability to CMD generally.[56] Each of us sits somewhere on a scale of psychiatric resilience, a so-called a 'p' factor, that grades an individual's risk of any kind of mental ill-health.[57] Many things influence where we are on that scale — some are genetic, others are to do with our upbringing and lifestyle. But I expect there is one unifying variable: our exposure to chronic psychache and, therefore, risk of self-destruction. The worse our adversities and the less our ability to cope, the more suicidogenic our pain and the more prone we will be to anti-suicide reactions, visible as sundry forms of CMD.

19. **Obligate:** *Keepers will produce strongly involuntary responses.*

Suicide being a matter of life or death, we won't get much of a say in how our anti-suicide defences operate. We won't get to choose which keepers will activate or when. Our ancestors were probably not people who could toy with the protections that kept them alive, and the same will be the case for us. At least in some situations, we won't even be aware that keepers are in control. The psychological tricks we use on ourselves to make emotional pain bearable, for example — distractions, explanations, reasons to soldier on — would presumably be less effective if we knew they were merely tricks. Keepers make us feel, think, and act instinctively, and we may be unaware of their hold on us.

Check. CMD is not a voluntary state. Its symptoms are not easily set aside or consciously moderated.[58] Many forms of CMD, while obvious to everyone else, often operate beyond the sufferer's knowledge, let alone control. To them, their thoughts and behaviours feel natural and regular. To an addict, for example, their life of addiction feels like the only normal one — it's everyone else that seems to have a problem.[59] A psychotic's delusions hold firm against all reasoning.[60] It is pointless to expect, on demand, a depressive to buck up, an alcoholic to drink less, an anorexic to eat more, or a schizophrenic to get real. Perhaps they would if they could, but at times, they can't. This is not a council of despair but a facing of facts.

To people under the control of CMD, I am inclined to say this: You are not mad, or mentally deranged. Obviously, your condition is, at best, a damn nuisance, and it is not pleasant. It feels like your enemy. But you can be assured that it isn't: it is on your side. It is holding you, and it is stronger and wiser than you can imagine. It has been bequeathed to you by your parents, and their parents, and their parents, in an unbroken chain that reaches back across all of human history, to the dawn of humankind. You are the child of a vast family of winners. You have thousands of ancestors, and every single one of those men and women made a success of their lives, to the extent that they all sent another generation successfully out into the world. That is why you are here. Every one of them found a way to survive in spite of their pain and heartache. The condition you are experiencing helped them to cope, and they have passed it to you, to help you cope too. So, don't fight it. Make friends with it. It is part of you. Listen to what it is trying to tell you. It knows that you have been suffering, so much so that it reckons you may even be in danger of taking your own life to end the pain. Perhaps it is mistaken, but perhaps not. It may have kept you alive. Just for the time being, it has taken control of your life, like the co-pilot of a plane. It has no interest in keeping control any longer than it needs to, but it is not going to hand back control until it is sure you are ready. So, how are you going to show that you are ready to manage your own life again? It may not be easy, but it is simple. Your task is to make whatever adjustment is necessary — change something, or accept something — to relieve the psychological pain that brought the condition on. Once the pain is eased, in time (be patient), your condition will stand down. But it will always be watching over you, on guard and ready to step in again if needs be, to keep you safe.

I suggest this offers a more humane, and scientifically more coherent, approach to understanding and restoring mental health than the one that currently prevails.

20. **Abnormality:** *Keepers will produce behaviours that appear irrational. They will be conspicuously abnormal.*

Keepers cause mental impairment. They are designed to interfere with normal emotions ('pain-type') and normal thinking ('brain-type'). Both types will interfere with normal behaviour, and necessarily so. Biologically normal behaviour would involve us obeying the call to escape unbearable pain, and that would expectably result in self-inflicted death. Keepers sacrifice rationality to preserve life. There may be no rational connection between the way keepers respond and the painful life events that triggered them. So, sufferers can be expected not only to be distressed, but inconvenienced and puzzled. They are probably going to present themselves to healers and medics in search of explanations and remedies. Keepers, then, should be well known to science and we won't have to look far for them.

Check. CMD is indeed abnormal, highly visible, and apparently irrational. That is what we would expect to find. As we noted at the start of this chapter, a standard definition of mental illness looks much like our design spec for keepers — it is how we would expect the human organism to interrupt normal emotion, thinking, and behaviour at times of chronic stress. Take this version, for example, from the American Psychiatric Association's website:

> Mental illnesses are health conditions involving changes in emotion, thinking or behavior (or a combination of these). Mental illnesses

are associated with distress and/or problems functioning in social, work or family activities.[61]

The CMD/keepers phenomenon is so widespread that dealing with it keeps an army of modern-day healers busy — psychiatrists, therapists, clinical psychologists, and the rest. In short, CMD looks to be a regular way for human beings to experience, and deal with, emotional pain.

Easier to agree than disagree

Let's wrap up. I am not arguing that depression, or any other 'functional' diagnosis, is an anti-suicide adaptation. There is no evidence that psychiatric constructs exist in the real world as natural phenomena of any kind, let alone as adaptations. To repeat, most mental disorders are labels, not natural entities. It seems likely to me that they describe peoples' commonplace experience of psychache alongside various anti-suicide responses to psychache. That is to say, CMD is the combination of distress, plus the organism's diverse ways of surviving with that distress.

I will end this chapter with three reasons why I think we should accept that CMD is probably a manifestation of keepers in action.

First is the argument of special design. In Chapter 7 we drew up a design specification for keepers, the features we should expect to find in a set of emergency anti-suicide defences. Some points are firmer than others. But it seems to me that the match between that spec and what we actually see in CMD holds up across the board. You'll recall that earlier we talked about the purpose of an accordion. We concluded that it was specially designed for making music on the grounds of spotting half a dozen features (keys, reeds, etc) that were consistent with that function. If I pointed out not six but twenty features that tallied with it being a musical instrument, you'd feel even more certain. By the same principle, we are now being presented with another device and shown a score of its features that would arise from the task of stopping people killing themselves. On that basis, and assuming there's no better explanation, we can deduce that preventing suicide is probably indeed what that device is designed to do. Perhaps you are sceptical about some of the twenty; but even if we set those aside, I suggest there is still ample evidence on the table to accept the case on a balance of probability.

The second reason is that it's simpler here to say 'Yes' than 'No'. It is a like a website with an 'Accept terms of use' option that turns out to be not so optional. If you click 'I don't accept', it hits you with so much fine print that you'll want to go back and click 'I accept' after all. The terms and conditions in this case are the design specifications for keepers — that is, the previous chapter. None of Chapter 7 goes away by not accepting Chapter 8. We can't sit with a vacuum. The fact that you, I, and the rest of the species exist is hard evidence that a solution to the evolutionary problem of suicide was found. If we take on board Chapter 7's specification for anti-suicide defences as the likely solution, but reject CMD as the expression of that specification, then we'd have to find an even better match. We'd have to find something else that looks very much like CMD. I don't see a better alternative. There's no easier way out of the corner.

The third reason is the same in reverse. It is hard to see a better way of making sense of CMD. I can put it more strongly than that: the keepers hypothesis is the only show in town. If it isn't keepers, then some other explanation has to be found for CMD's many continuities. How else do we explain the typical course of CMD, triggered by painful events and standing down after the cause of psychache is eased? What about the patterned symptoms of CMD, its targeted obstructions of emotion, thinking, and behaviour? Why the sudden appearance of CMD in the teen years? These aren't empty, rhetorical questions. They need answering, simultaneously, across dozens of CMD's cross-diagnostic features, including those noted in this chapter. Keep in mind that the disorders we are discussing have drained into a sump of ignorance. They are what is left after everything with a known cause has been classified elsewhere. They have ended up, by default, in a bucket called 'functional' precisely because psychiatry cannot explain why they occur, either individually or as a collection. Their existence has perplexed medical science for centuries. I see no option other than to accept that CMD is probably the expression of anti-suicide machinery.

There's another reason. If we changed our perspective towards mental illness, we could save lives and forestall misery. We could stop treating this kind of dis-ease as if it were a malevolent, incomprehensible monster. We could stop stigmatising those of us who are affected. We could stop making them out to be defective, deficient, or disordered.[62] We could start to treat the human mind with the awe, humility, and respect it deserves. We could view depression, addictions, psychoses, and all the rest as aspects of the regular, healthy way by which the mind responds to the formidable challenge of being and staying alive. We could begin to think more clearly about the best way to answer these conditions. By labelling and stigmatising people, we add to their problems. Relieving mental illness entails, to my mind, trying to resolve the painful situations, real or imagined, that brought them on — and being prepared to wait. The human mind evolved to heal itself, and it usually will do given time and opportunity.

I'd understand if you took this chapter's argument with misgivings. To accept it raises more questions. Top of them for me is this: we humans are all probably destined to feel intense emotional pain in our lives. So, why aren't more of us blighted by symptoms of CMD — keepers? What keeps most of us, most of the time, reasonably sane?

CHAPTER 8: *Symptoms of common mental disorder (CMD) match the design specification for keepers so precisely that it is difficult not to accept that CMD is, in fact, the manifestation of anti-suicide systems in action. We appear to have arrived at a long overdue explanation for the cause, course and comorbidity of psychiatric syndromes.*

CHAPTER 9: *Keepers, as symptoms of CMD, are emergency interventions. They are costly to activate. We should find a further line of evolved anti-suicide defences, adaptations that allow keepers to stay dormant much of the time. We can expect these systems to focus on managing our exposure to psychache.*

9

HAPPINESS

How it is that we humans stay alive, even when we might reasonably choose not to? In the last couple of chapters we began to see the picture. Our minds are likely fitted with a set of purpose-built devices, evolved adaptations that stop us self-destructing when we are in danger of doing just that. They are our last line of defence.

I labelled them 'keepers' because their role is rather like the goal-keeper on a soccer or hockey team. Most of the time the keeper is in stand-by mode, watching the game; but when danger looms, they are ready to react. Their job is to prevent disaster. When we are in so much emotional pain that the idea of ending it all starts to appeal, keepers block our path. They take the edge off the pain, and they interfere with our ability to plan or think straight, enough to make self-killing difficult to do. We found that the expected design features of keepers match, point by point, patterns shared by sundry forms of mental disorder: depression, addiction, self-harming behaviour, psychosis, and similar diagnostic labels. So close is the fit that we concluded that so-called functional common mental disorder, or CMD, probably is indeed the expression of active keepers. It is easy to brand keepers as diseases — when they are at work, we literally feel dis-ease. But they are designed to keep us alive. Almost always, they do that job well.

The picture must be bigger than this, however. Recall that keepers are just one aspect of many evolutionary side-effects of human intelligence. Costly by-products of braininess ripple out into all manner of secondary adaptations, tiers of bodily and mental compromises that make our intelligence survivable. Keepers allow the human organism to survive with a mind so sophisticated and free-ranging that it can choose its own death. They were shaped as crisis interventions, emergency measures that aim to keep people alive if only just for another day. But keepers almost certainly send out costly ripples of their own. They set up a biological need for wider secondary adaptations, to avoid, wherever possible, the need for keepers to act. Keepers are probably only the tip of the iceberg of our defences against suicide. Here are four reasons to think this is so.

First, most of us, most of the time, seem to be able to handle stressful situations without keepers sweeping in to take control. It is not as if we live charmed lives. Most of us can expect to experience at least one seriously traumatic event, an adversity bad enough, indeed, to qualify as a trigger for post-traumatic stress disorder (PTSD).[1] But few of us do go on to be troubled by PTSD or any other obvious mental disorder as a result.[2] Presumably, then, we are equipped with tools that allow us to cope with adversity — mechanisms that usually keep the threat of suicide far enough away for us not to need keepers to intervene.

Second, when keepers do activate, they are costly. They more or less disable us, as indeed they are meant to do. I have argued that keepers work by disrupting two important primary adaptations — two boons that evolved because of their fitness-promoting payoffs, but which together, unfortunately, enable wilful self-killing. One is pain, specifically social pain, the protective signal that warns us of threats to important relationships. The other is the intellect of the mature human brain, a vital tool for social success — so vital that it was worth suffering many costly side-effects, including suicidality, for its sake. Anything that handicaps these 'pain' and 'brain' faculties, as keepers do, is going to impair an individual's social performance. That impairment probably works its way through to a reproductive disadvantage. For sure, as emergency measures, keepers usually keep us alive, but at a heavy cost in forfeited procreation. Mental illness can seriously damage sufferers' prospects of having children, perhaps by half — probably because it puts people in a much weaker position to compete for mates.[3] This suggests that activated keepers are themselves a recurring and severe fitness threat: not as extreme a threat as the suicidal death that they try to prevent, but severe nonetheless. It is exactly the kind of threat, then, that would be expected to drive the selection of countermeasures — adaptations designed to avoid keepers having to intervene. Being blocked from killing ourselves is good, but not needing to be blocked would be better. An ounce of prevention is worth a pound of cure.

Third, keepers do not always work. Perhaps they don't have an opportunity to activate in time: some suicides are impulsive acts, not preceded by the kind of drawn-out distress that keepers likely use as an activating cue.[4] Or perhaps keepers activate and people still manage to kill themselves. Keepers do the best that can be done, at least as far we can tell from the thorough way they seem to have used up all useful cues of risk; there are no markers left with which we can accurately predict suicides at the individual level. But even so, the organism's suicide prevention machinery is still something of a lottery; there is still a small percentage risk of suicide happening anyway.[5] Losing the gamble is so costly — genetic annihilation — that we should see adaptations that stop us chancing it.

Fourth, we can expect keepers sometimes to malfunction, as cautioned in the previous chapter. They are drastic measures for a dangerous situation, so there's probably an inevitable risk of things going very wrong, potentially doing more harm than good. In a battle zone, even with the best preparations, there is a danger of death by friendly fire. That is another risk to avoid.

Fenders: Active, front-line defences

Putting these points together, we can be fairly sure that adaptations to manage the cost of suicide probably begin, not end, with keepers.

We can think of keepers defending us from suicide rather in the same way that the immune system protects us from infections. The immune system gets busy when it detects a virus or other pathogen inside the body, such an invasion potentially posing a threat to life. White blood cells attack the invaders, there may be inflammation and a fever, and the whole organism may be immobilised for a while so that its resources can focus on repelling the attack. All well and good, except that this kind of last-ditch fightback, like clearing enemy occupiers from the homeland, can be dangerous and cripplingly expensive. It saps energy, weakens the organism, and makes it easier prey for predators. The inner battle is not, in any event, sure to be won. Even with the immune system working as it should, infections and infestations can kill. Some bugs can pass unrecognised, causing internal damage before the immune system can react. Sometimes the system overreacts and attacks the organism it was meant to protect.

So, the task of combatting pathogens is not just left to the immune system. Ahead of it are other countermeasures, most obviously a defensive barrier — the skin and other membranes — designed to stop undesirables getting inside the body in the first place. There are more defences ahead of these physical walls. The windpipe is lined with beating hairs that try to stop foreign objects from reaching the lungs. Saliva acts as a gatekeeper further up, spiked with antibacterial chemicals to attack microbes that reach the mouth. Then there are psychological defences ahead of that — behavioural programmes that keep us away from potential sources of infection. We feel instinctive disgust at likely contaminants such as faeces, vomit, and putrid food. We don't like to get too close to people who are coughing, sneezing, or otherwise appear ill. Social distancing isn't a novelty of Covid-19 or unique to human beings — other animals, from lobsters to bats, try to avoid infection by the same strategy.[6] So, the immune system is just the last of several layers of safety measures: it is there as a last resort.

By the same principle, we can expect the organism's defences against suicide also to form layers. Ahead of keepers, a battery of front-line protections ought to keep us safely away from self-destructive crises. Humans need to be emotionally thick-skinned to some extent, programmed instinctively to avoid psychache.

Let's give these front-line defences a name. I suggest *fender*. If an anti-suicide keeper is like the goalkeeper on a soccer team, the last line of defence, then anti-suicide fenders are like the team's other defensive players. It's a useful comparison. Defenders keep the pressure off the goalkeeper; they prevent attacks from turning into shots at goal, crises where only the goalkeeper can stave off disaster. Similarly, the job of anti-suicide fenders is to block dangerous strikes both directly and indirectly — directly where possible, and indirectly by stopping stressful situations from becoming so dangerous that keepers have to activate. As with defensive players, if fenders are successful, then keepers can stay in their dormant 'stand-by' mode most of the time — that is to say, the individual can remain in a good state of mental health. Fenders are front-line, anti-suicide, evolved psychological mechanisms.

While we are here, let me squeeze three intuitions out of the soccer analogy. First, the goalkeeper and a team's other defensive players are on the same side: fenders try to avoid keepers activating not because keepers are the opposition, but because keepers are there only for emergencies. As I explained in the last chapter, symptoms of mental disorder are not pleasant, but that does not make them the enemy: they are on our side. The task is to avoid having to call on their services.

Second, players can compensate for each other to some extent: the weaker the defenders, the harder the goalkeeper has to work. In other words, someone whose front-line defences struggle to contain attacks of psychache will be more prone to bouts of mental illness.

Third, the team's success is not down solely to its own players, but also to the strength of the opposition: that is to say, the more challenging the life adversities that fenders have to deal with, the more likely psychache will get past the fenders, and the greater the risk not just of mental illness but possibly even of a suicide attempt.

So, what and where are these fenders? We can go about finding them in the same way that we uncovered the work of keepers — using the principle of special design. Holding in mind the task that fenders have to fulfil, we can sketch out the features of a psychological system that was designed to meet that task. Fenders keep the lid on psychological pain. They try to stop psychache reaching a level at which it will trigger either suicide or anti-suicide symptoms of mental disorders, keepers in action. Fenders are there not only to stop suicide but to keep us in serviceably good mental health. With that task in mind, pain management, I suggest there are several characteristics that we can expect to see.

People don't kill themselves out of joy, and it's the suicidal danger that lurks one-sidedly in psychache that activates keepers. So, fenders will not be even-handed: they will promote pleasure and suppress pain.

That may sound a trivial point — wouldn't any animal do this? No. Pain and pleasure are usually means to an end, not ends in themselves. Recall our earlier discussion about the special-purpose nature of instincts. Pain and pleasure are evolved motivators that came about because the of the fitness payoffs of the actions they spurred. It is in the same way that hunger motivates eating, and thirst motivates drinking. Each stimulus links to a particular response that is designed to serve a specific biological function — hunger addresses the need for nutrition, as thirst does for hydration. A pain that says you have a thorn in your foot is equally a need state, designed to motivate a specific behaviour to resolve it — to pull out the thorn. The curiosity about fenders is that they will generate pleasure and avoid pain for their own sake, independently of the behaviours that these stimuli originally evolved to induce. That is strange by animal standards — as strange as a system that, say, makes an animal feel thirsty just for the sake of feeling thirsty, whether or not the animal actually needs water.

Fenders came about because with us, perhaps for the first time in the history of life on earth, natural selection has an interest in making an animal happy. Not happy to be satisfying a need for food or water, or happy to be striving for any other a particular fitness goal, but happy, full stop. For us, regardless of the original biological reason for the pain or pleasure, and solely because of the suicide problem, too much pain and too little pleasure can kill. There would be forceful selective pressure, then, favouring a system that manages our hedonic state. Millions of people who were not our ancestors opted out of life because they were not offered a sufficient reward to stay in the game. We are the lucky descendants of people who, despite their troubles, survived and reproduced because they found life pleasing enough to be worthwhile.

Fenders will want us to avoid pain, but not completely so. There is another fitness balance to be struck, between too much psychache and too little. We hit this problem before, as you may recall, when drawing up the design spec for keepers. Wiping out pain completely might be a good emergency solution, in a battlefield situation perhaps. But that numbed state won't be survivable as a permanent fix because pain exists for good adaptive reasons; we need pain to steer us away from fitness hazards. This is why leprosy is so harmful: by destroying the capacity to feel pain in the hands, feet, and other extremities, leprosy makes those parts of the body vulnerable to repeated injuries and infections, which can lead to permanent and crippling damage. Social pain similarly exists for good reason — it alerts us to threats to our social relationships and motivates us to keep them in good repair. So, fenders need to steer a course between two evils, maintaining a least-bad compromise; they must suppress emotional pain enough to avoid triggering keepers, but not so much as to make us insensitive to dangers to our vital social relationships. We need a thick skin, but not too thick.

As with keepers, we won't find fenders in other animals, because no other animal would gain a fitness benefit from such a system. No other animal has to deal with the problem that fenders evolved to tackle — suicide, and costly symptoms of mental disorder that mobilise to prevent suicide. In other words, no other animal needs to block itself off from useful but unpleasant information for the sake of maintaining its emotional composure. That said, as with keepers, we may well find that other animals have vestiges of traits that could be precursors of fenders — ancient raw material that was co-opted and reshaped into fenders in our species alone.

Also like keepers, fenders will be strongly instinctual and involuntary in their routines. They will get on with doing whatever they need to do without seeking our permission. The threat they protect us from is too serious for us to be given the option to tinker with them. Better still, if we don't even know that fenders are in control, we won't be tempted to try. There may be flexibility: fenders might make use of cultural cues, personal experience and other learned inputs. But fenders will decide for themselves what outcomes to create from those inputs, and they will probably do this without us even being aware. Like keepers, fenders will influence the way the individual feels, thinks, and acts, and it will all feel normal, even if it makes no sense to anyone else. Not only will we be selectively blind to bad news; we will be blind even to the fact that we are blind.

Therefore, like keepers again, fenders may well look irrational. At times, it may be obvious to other people that an individual is feeling, thinking, or behaving in ways that defy the facts. Perhaps this is bound to be so, since fenders need to deny us full mental access to the real world when that reality becomes too dangerously painful. It may be expedient for fenders to look sensible for the sake of good public relations. Fenders' truth-bending outputs may come packaged in plausible alibis — coherent backstories that minimise the loss of credibility in the eyes of ourselves and our fellows. But given what is at stake, looking rational won't be the overriding consideration. Fenders trying to look rational would be rather like mixing a cat's medication into its food in the hope it won't notice: if it takes the food, that's good — but even if not, by whatever means necessary, the cat is still going to be made to swallow the pill.

Since fenders, like keepers, are a universal feature of the human psyche, none of us can expect to look entirely rational. Virtually all of us are fitted with the standard-model human mind, even though it expresses itself in a rich variety of personalities. It will be easy to see the irrationality of others and overlook our own; but all humans will be superbly equipped to avoid facing painful reality.

A final point here: so many of these predictions are similar to ones we noted earlier for keepers that it may be that fenders and keepers overlap. They could indeed be extensions of each other, or parts of one and the same system. I worry about falling into the same trap that I think has beset psychiatry, that once you invent a label ('bipolar', 'schizophrenia', etc.) the label takes on a life of its own. We can easily assume that the label is a real thing, and once assumed, it is hard to unthink that assumption. In this discussion, 'keeper' and 'fender' are just labels.

But I think keepers and fenders probably do point to distinct things in the real world, because they need to perform at least partly distinct functions; as biological systems, they use different inputs and will produce different outputs. A tenet of evolutionary psychology holds that the mind is a vast assemblage of such modules — self-contained psychological devices.[7] We could recall, as an example, the anti-suffocation programme mentioned earlier in the book, the device that stops us from holding our breath too long. I'm imagining keepers and fenders to be modules of this type, but they might be parts of the same module or a nested collection of several modules. While staying aware of these pitfalls, I suggest we stick with the keeper/fender labels for now, for the practical reason that they may help us understand what would otherwise be a tangle.

The 'fender' label looks useful. I think it could join up and explain several aspects of human psychology that otherwise appear unconnected and puzzling. In the following pages I'm going to put to you four pain-management systems that I think are probably fenders. Fender I tries to keep our emotional state slightly warmer than neutral. Fender II makes us experts at deceiving ourselves, and in a way that is self-servingly optimistic. Fender III has us devoting much of our time and resources to pleasures that don't seem to serve any direct fitness purpose. And, via Fender IV, we hold fast to hopeful, but illusory, ideas about the world and our place in it — often in the form of religious or spiritual beliefs. These likely co-operate as an integrated system, functioning to keep most of us, most of the time, not suicidal and more or less sane.

Emotional thermostat set to 'warm'

Fender I manages our emotions around an above-neutral resting point. If our balance is disturbed by bad news, the mind restores itself to an emotional equilibrium automatically, and usually fast. First we feel bad; then we feel better. We are not conscious of the process — we know we feel better, but we are often not sure why. In the introductory chapter, I said the mind is like a centrally heated home with a thermostat: when the door opens and lets a blast of hot or cold enter from the world outside, we are programmed to bring our inner temperature back to its normal resting point. Now, I am not claiming that this general kind of mechanism is a fender — homeostasis is a universal biological phenomenon, and perhaps all animals are equipped with something similar. I am suggesting that the human emotional thermostat has two special features, and they are unique because of our need to manage psychache. One is the remarkable speed at which we recover specifically from bad news. The other is that the place we restore ourselves to is not neutral: the thermostat in our emotional home is pre-set to 'warm'.[8]

Speed first. I mentioned that we normally restore our emotional balance quickly. It's not always quick: some forms of recovery, such as the changes of perspective with which we come to terms with trauma and bereavement, can take years to work through.[9] But regular day-to-day annoyances are often dealt with in a matter of minutes or even seconds — so fast that we hardly notice.[10] And even the most intense distress is usually settled within hours: a third of acute suicidal crises resolve themselves in less than an hour. It is one of the reasons why installing jump nets under bridges and other so-called means-restriction measures can be effective. If it makes a suicide attempt just a little more complicated, then it may buy enough time for the mind to stand itself down from danger.[11] We will come back to this in the final chapter. The presence of suicide, a potentially lethal fitness threat, points to a strong selective pressure favouring a swift recall from extreme mental pain. The mental machinery that pulls us back from the brink quickly may be part of Fender I — an adaptation that may be designed to block impulsive suicides.

But the main reason I see evidence of special anti-suicide design is that the place we are drawn back to is not emotionally flat: it's happy. After a shock, the mind usually restores us to a position of feeling fairly contented. So, most of us, most of the time, have a sense of wellbeing — life feels pretty good.[12] This is interesting, because for us, as much as any other animal, perceptions are not normally so biased. Normally, after a disturbance, an animal's senses reset to neutral. Neutral is the universal default position, because an animal needs to update itself about changes in its environment as accurately and quickly as possible, and changes are easiest to notice from a neutral base. The brain plays 'spot the difference'. It ignores the average of what has been sensed before in order to make novelties stand out.[13] For example, we usually don't notice the feeling of clothes touching our skin. Nerve endings in the skin detect clothing that is contact, and they carry on sending those signals to the brain. But once we are dressed, it's old news, so the brain ignores the signals: it only wants us to register what's new.

Human emotional regulation breaks this rule. Most of us, most of the time, carry on re-feeling the same old happiness. I suggest our emotions return to a slightly warm resting point because it has survival logic: it helps to keep us clear of the extreme fitness danger that, for us alone, lurks in unhappiness and, ultimately, self-destruction. We can't entirely shut ourselves off to bad news, but we can be prepared to hear it relatively safely, from a position of feeling good. Default happiness acts as a shock absorber, ready to dampen the impact of unpleasant updates. It may be for this reason that, as Edwin Shneidman argued, humans can cope with adverse feelings up to a point: we have leeway to take pain without too much disruption.[14] It's like the suspension system of a Jeep: it has its limits, it won't stop the vehicle disappearing into a sinkhole, but it is well designed to handle the worst of bumpy roads.

So, I suggest Fender I is a purposeful bias towards feeling good. The scales we use to weigh the emotional value of events in our lives are skewed. They are not true, being permanently weighted on the side of positivity. We can presume there is a fitness upside in having our emotions prejudiced in this way — likely an anti-suicide upside — because the distortion carries at least two fitness downsides, which need a matching upside to be worth the cost. First, the bias will cause us to lose what could have been useful information. We are not standing in the best position to notice changes in the world and ourselves. We are set up to miss details that could otherwise have allowed us to make better, more fitness-enhancing, decisions. Second, propping up our emotional state above the normal baseline, as if defying gravity, is going to be hard work. It needs us continuously to overrule an animal system that would reset our perceptions to neutral.

Indeed, it looks to me that the task of keeping ourselves in abnormally good spirits is a full-time human occupation. There are only two ways to maintain the scales in a tilted position. We can up the ups, or we can down the downs. I suspect that, throughout our daily lives, we do both. You may know the old song, '*You've got to accentuate the positive, Eliminate the negative...*'. I am going to assume these two strategies call for separate fenders, because the tasks are different. Hence, I'll call the avoidance of pain Fender II, and the promotion of pleasure Fender III. Their common feature is a measured irrationality — they need us to stay semi-detached from reality. The arrangement would be maladaptive for any other animal, but it is probably a survival necessity for us, as I will explain.

Lying to ourselves

Fender II manages our intake of bad news. Another balance must to be struck: we need to take on board painful information accurately enough to know what's going on, but without being overwhelmed by its emotional fallout. That strikes me as a major engineering challenge. There might be several ways it could be done.

Suppose the sports news is coming up on the radio, announcing whether or not my beloved soccer team has won an all-important match. If it is good news, then I want to hear. If it's bad, I do not want to know. The bind is that I can't tell if the news is good or bad unless I actually listen to it. What can I do? I could switch the radio off and learn nothing, which certainly avoids pain, at least for now. But if my team won, then I would be depriving myself of a moment of joy, and presumably I'll hear the result anyway sooner or later. Or, I could leave the radio on but prepare for the worst; I could get myself into a mental position, a situation under my own control, where hearing defeat wouldn't be so bad. I'll assume we've already lost. That might look like pessimism, but it is really another pain-relieving defence. Another option would be to hear the news and, if the result is not what I want to hear, then I could *un*hear it somehow.

I suggest this kind of predicament keeps Fender II busy throughout our daily lives. It is a very human business. We fool ourselves — of that, there's no doubt. Psychoanalysts since the time of Freud have marvelled at the skill with which the human mind ducks away from unpleasant facts. The self-deception is systematic (it is the *bad* news we distort), automatic, and largely unconscious. We evade painful realities in so many ways that they may be impossible fully to catalogue, although some of Freud's followers have had a go.[15]

Vocabulary from the world of psychoanalysis has become part of everyday speech: we talk of people (*other* people, mind you) being defensive, delusional, passive-aggressive, projecting, acting out, being in denial, and so on. That is to say, these and other mind games we play on ourselves are not the preserve of a therapist's consulting room; they are the stuff of normal life. If I have heard the news that my soccer team lost the match, and I am not ready to pay the full emotional tab that comes with accepting that fact, then what am I to do? I could find people or things to blame: the blind referee, players' injuries, the incompetent manager, a stupid transfer. I can tell myself it's a fluke, just a one-off. I could think to the future, of victories to come. I could diminish the whole thing, putting it in its place by making a joke of it. Or I could distract myself by getting busy on something else. Or I might get angry, self-pitying, drunk, or whatever: anything to fend off the reality that the object my love may actually be just a run-of-the-mill, not particularly good, soccer team. Not trivially, we use much the same techniques to protect ourselves from the unbearable emotional fallout of abuse, trauma, bereavement, shameful personal failings, and other major losses, real or imagined.[16]

Psychological defences follow some interesting patterns. They all involve self-deception, some form of misbelief.[17] And the deception is finely tuned to make ourselves feel better, which usually involves us feeling superior, or at least special. Most of us hold an unrealistically positive view of us and ours; we over-rate ourselves and the things and people close to us. We tend to think that we are especially righteous, important, or able. We believe we have more control over our lives and the world than is objectively the case, and we tend to be unreasonably optimistic about our futures.[18]

Sometimes the self-enhancement comes in thick disguise. If I believe that I am especially important, then I may become frustrated or demoralised by others who seem to think the same about themselves. If I believe I am responsible for everything, it may be easier to punish myself when things go wrong rather than to accept my powerlessness. My inflated view of my own capabilities can lead me to curse myself for not achieving perfection, or I may carefully avoid putting them to the test. In such ways, our misbeliefs create discomforts of their own — they can look more self-defeating than self-serving[19] But these discomforts may be less painful than accepting a starker reality — perhaps that I am just a standard human organism, about as liable to adversity as any other. Few things are as tough as admitting that the king is naked, and that 'king' is ourselves.

Importantly, our distorted view of reality comes about not because we don't know the facts at some level. For sure, we can and often do stay wilfully ignorant, making decisions that minimise our exposure to awkward news. I can avoid hearing the result of that soccer match by turning off the radio, for example. But the distortion is also down to what the mind does with the facts once we know them. The human psyche has the extraordinary ability to quarantine unpleasant information, keeping bad news out of conscious reach.[20] This hiding of facts from ourselves is no accident: it involves careful and complex neural trickery, as if the brain's internal news service were under the control of a genius spin doctor. We can hold two contradictory beliefs at the same time, one true, one false, and be aware of one and not the other. It is the bad news, not the good, that tends to get buried, independently of its truth. When it hears an update, the mind first scans its content and assesses its emotional potential before deciding what to do with it. If the information is pleasing, the mind will release into our awareness. If the information is going to hurt, the mind can edit it, or put it out of sight, even though it may be true. There's a split-second time lag built into the brain's reporting system, around a tenth of a second between recognising an input and making us aware of the news — if, that is, we're made aware at all. The same censorship applies to our memories; difficult truths can be archived beyond recall.[21]

We are highly selective and strategic about the kind of information we twist. For example, we take care not to pick self-enhancing misbeliefs that can easily be disproved.[22] My mind probably won't delude me that I am a millionaire, since if it did, my next bank statement would surely come as a crushing blow. I could, on the other hand, safely convince myself that I am fit enough to run a marathon; since I never plan to try, the fantasy may never be put to the test. So, our delusions keep us comfortably numb from overly painful realities, without risking yet greater pain from experiencing major failures. All this chicanery goes on without our conscious knowledge, with the result that we genuinely believe we are thinking and acting on the basis of the facts.

The evolutionary origins of denial

Protective self-deception looks to have evolutionary origins, partly because it seems to be ubiquitous across the human species: bad news gets denied everywhere, although different cultures vary in the particulars of what counts as bad news.[23] This universality suggests that self-deception has formed part of the typical human mind since ancestral times. It is also apparently unique to our species. Other animals sometimes adjust their expectations to fit the conditions — it may profit to be a little bullish at times of plenty. But there is no evidence that any other animal systematically overrates its own capabilities or the abundance of its world.[24] We wouldn't expect it to. For an animal to keep itself optimally informed, it needs to be given the news straight. There is no good news or bad news in nature, there is just news.

This point is important for understanding the roots of self-deception in humans: delusion is not cheap. It means losing potentially useful insights, and that exposes us to making inaccurate forecasts, poor decisions, and costly mistakes. We humans are not objective predictors.[25] If a squirrel can't reach a bird feeder by jumping, it soon learns from the failure and tries something else — climbing up the feeder's pole, for example. With us, often not so. We tend to keep doing the same old thing. We are prone, for example, to the planning fallacy: projects take longer than we expected, but we don't use the benefit of hindsight to forecast more realistically next time. So, despite a lifetime's experience of overruns, we keep on underestimating how long projects will take.

Our persistent wishful thinking plays out in all sorts of human errors, small and large — from personal gambling mistakes and business failures, to economic booms and busts, and ruinous wars waged by over-confident leaders. If the consequences are costly now, they won't have been cheaper in the ancestral past. For our forebears, in their daily struggle for survival, even the slightest self-delusion could have had seriously harmful outcomes; a day wasted on a futile hunt, an injury from a foolish fight, the hunger of an underprepared journey. There is a fitness price to pay for over-optimism, which tells us that, somehow, there will be a matching compensation.

What, biologically, could human beings gain from deluding ourselves? The payoff probably won't come from the over-optimistic behaviours we do as result. Even if an over-optimistic behaviour (say, trying to catch hares by running after them) was a worthwhile thing to do, selection could have programmed us simply to do the behaviour (chase hares) without going to the lengths of messing with our entire cognitive machinery — what we believe, what we remember, and how we think and feel. More likely, the payoff of over-optimism lies in those mental states; it matters what we believe and how we feel. But why? Why should our inner beliefs and feelings matter so much?

Most theories in this area expect there to be some kind of social reward. Self-deception, so it is said, is an adaptation that helps us to manipulate our fellow human beings. We fool ourselves so we can better fool others; method acting, to make us better liars.[26] But there are several reasons to think this is not so. It is hard to see what social payoff would be worth the cost of being continually self-deluded — the hunger, injury, misallocation of time, and other penalties that flow from over-optimistic planning. Even if there were a social payoff, it wouldn't be stable, because others would become wise to the ruse. Prizes would go to the sceptics — those who see a bluff and call it. The evolution of bluff would simply drive the evolution of anti-bluff. Perhaps it is for that reason that, in practice, we aren't taken in by others' inflated self-images. First impressions count, but not for long. Braggards soon reveal themselves and are punished, not rewarded, for their puffery.[27] In any case, the kinds of traits that we deceive ourselves about are often in plain view. We can believe ourselves to be stronger, wiser, richer, or luckier than we really are, but everyone else can see the reality, even if we can't. In sum, there is no compelling evidence of special design, the stamp of adaptation, that would lead us to think self-delusion evolved as tool for social manipulation.

The payoff of deluding ourselves probably arises, rather, in keeping ourselves feeling positive and hopeful — regardless of whether others are taken in or not. Self-delusion causes us to miscalculate, but it seems to me that this miscalculation is not a mistake: it is an error. There's a difference.

It is not always a mistake to err on the side of caution. Animal perceptions are often more sensitive in one direction than the other, because the fitness penalties of getting it wrong on opposite sides are rarely the same.[28] For example, we perceive the same vertical cliff as being higher when viewed downwards from the top than upwards from the bottom. Presumably this distortion reflects the presence of unequal fitness risks in our evolutionary past; the fall hazard is a concern at the top, not at the bottom, and our minds adjust our perception of height to encourage us to keep clear where it matters.[29] Likewise, our hearing is biased to detect looming sounds: we hear sounds of the same volume as being louder when they are moving towards us than when they are moving away. Presumably across our evolutionary history it proved to be more important to pay attention to sounds that were heading in our direction (an attacker?) than to sounds that were in retreat.[30]

By the same principle, we need to ask what biological cost of hearing bad news is so dire that it is worth systematically erring on the side of not hearing it. What exactly are we defending ourselves against? You'll guess where I'm heading with this question, but so far science has struggled to find an answer. Few scientists have sought one. They tend to skirt around the matter, nodding towards the darkness but not taking too close a look. Leading the way, Freud called the thing to be avoided 'unpleasure'.[31] And, equally leading the way, he did not spell out *why* — what would happen if we suffered unpleasure to excess. In a similar mode, naming without explaining, later researchers have called it disequilibrium, anxiety, uncertainty, hurt, low self-esteem, a sense of inadequacy, cognitive dissonance, terror, excessive gloom, and so on. They all seem to be getting at the same idea. It reminds me of that ancient Greek quip quoted in Chapter 4 — all pain is one malady, but it has many names. Modern-day wits, psychologists Travis Proulx and Michael Inzlicht, sum up the research in this field with their own catchall word to describe the one malady of intolerable emotional pain: 'disanxiousuncertlibrium'.[32]

Joking aside, I suggest we don't need a new word. Edwin Shneidman coined one already: psychache — the common stimulus of suicide. The link is unspoken, and perhaps for many researchers it's unspeakable. It may be an elephant in the room, but it is clearly there. It seems likely to me that self-serving self-deception ultimately serves to keep humans away from the fitness catastrophe of wilful self-killing. More immediately, it is how we keep a lid on the emotional pain that activates keepers, symptoms of mental disorder, the organism's final protection against self-destruction. Yes, we delude ourselves to avoid unpleasure, but not for its own sake. We avoid unpleasure to keep ourselves serviceably sane — and, indeed, alive.

There is, again, a balance to be struck, one that psychologist Roy Baumeister calls an optimal margin of illusion.[33] Too little reality, and we lay ourselves open to making potentially costly blunders; too much, and the resulting psychache invites mental disease or self-inflicted death. The human mind has to tread a line between the two dangers.

The line may be a broad one: there may be many workable compromises between error-prone delusion and mental disorder. At one extreme, we could view ourselves and our world as it is, warts and all. That ought to help us forecast more accurately, but at the expense of making us susceptible to bouts of CMD — so-called 'depressive realism'.[34] At the other extreme, we could stay cheerfully optimistic, which would give us greater resistance to psychiatric disorders, but at the expense of us making repeated and costly errors.[35] Earlier I drew the analogy of defensive positions on a soccer team, where players can compensate for each other's weaknesses to some extent: the weaker the defenders, the busier the goalkeeper. In such a way, we can expect keepers and fenders to be partially swappable means to the same anti-suicide end. The mind can deal with the danger of psychache at different points on the way to suicide; painful information can be blocked upstream — that is, kept out of awareness by fenders — or the news can be admitted and the resulting psychache neutralised closer to the point of suicide by keepers.

All this suggests that a certain level of self-delusion is a regular human state. It is not a unique mark of the mentally ill, but how the healthy human mind goes about its normal business.[36] In good times, it helps to keep our emotional resting point happier than neutral, buffering us against random adversities. At difficult times, after bereavements and other shocks, our self-deception moves up a gear — 'coping ugly' in George Bonanno's phrase.[37] In old age, as we face the pain of mounting declines and losses, we lean on our self-deceptions all the more: they keep us in good heart. Across the lifespan, some measure of delusion seems to be part and parcel of good mental health. It keeps the downs down.

Keeping ourselves cheerful

What about upping the ups? This is Fender III. Keeping ourselves safely happy involves more than just avoiding pain. We also need a positive source of pleasure. And if our emotional resting point is to stay tilted, being quite happy, pleasure can't be a one-off event — we need a perpetual flow.

I mentioned the basic problem earlier. The intensity of feeling we get from events, good or bad, tends to fade in time, because our senses are set up to discount old news. Like any other animal, our perceptions are usually geared to spot deviations from the average of whatever has gone before, the better to detect any changes. So, light of the same intensity can appear bright or dark, depending on what our eyes have grown accustomed to. The same drink can taste more or less sweet, and the same food more or less salty, depending on what we are used to tasting. As noted before, we stop noticing the touch of clothes against our skin almost as soon as we put them on. Emotional regulation seems to follow a similar dynamic. We may be overjoyed at victory, a gift, a pay raise, or similar triumph, but the elation is only fleeting because the mind automatically restores its composure, as if under thermostatic control. This flattening, dampening effect of homeostasis suggests that, emotionally, we have to run to stand still: we live on what has been described as a hedonic treadmill.[38] To keep on feeling emotionally good, we need to keep on supplying ourselves with exceptional, pleasurable sensations.

But where is this stream of pleasure going to come from? I don't see that it can arise from an animal's regular job of surviving and reproducing, serving the direct needs of fitness. Life was never meant to be pleasurable. I am not saying that animals don't have fun. Female monkeys apparently have orgasms, rats can be heard to chuckle when tickled, and no one can doubt the contentedness of a well-petted pet. But, as we've discussed, animal pleasures are linked to specific fitness-promoting behaviours — inputs matched to outputs. There is fitness value for a mammal in, say, cementing relationships, which is presumably why mammals seem to enjoy mutual grooming, suckling, and perhaps even sometimes (so it is said) recreational sex.[39] There are probably also fitness benefits in animal play, which also seems to appeal to them.[40] But pleasure for a non-human animal is a motivational stimulus, no more. It has no value beyond its fitness-promoting behavioural effect. This is to say, there is nothing intrinsically meaningful or rewarding in an animal's existence, even for those animals that do well. Ecologist Lawrence Slobodkin once wrote that success in the natural world is like winning a game and finding nowhere outside of the game to spend the winnings.[41] Psychologist William James made a similar point: he said that nature cancels herself out — zero equals zero. There is nothing of emotional value left for us humans to feel good about.[42] By any objective assessment, life is not good — it is just life.[43]

If this is true, then the emotional rewards that humans need for our mental health and survival are not going to drop spontaneously out of our regular animal functioning. There won't be a flow of surplus pleasure pouring out of the Darwinian biosphere of its own accord. We'll have to get it from some other source. I suggest we have evolved, by necessity, a novel capacity to manufacture pleasure. We are fun factories. Driven ultimately by the necessity to avoid suicide, so probably uniquely for life on earth, humans create hedonic rewards in a way that has all but detached itself from the normal needs of survival and reproduction.

There is a limit to our fun-seeking because we have other calls on resources. Again, as ever in biology, there are trade-offs to make. But I suggest that, within those constraints, an anti-suicide fender has us spending all the time and energy we can afford thinking and doing things that feel good, just for the sake of it — independently of any direct fitness payoffs. Some feel-good activities are virtually cost free: we can magic satisfaction almost from thin air — the fragrance of a flower, the music of birdsong, the majesty of a sunset. Other pleasures take time and energy. But we can find opportunities for rewards in almost every aspect of life: home, family, friends, work, sport, art, and all the other things we do that make our lives feel worthwhile.[44]

Many, perhaps most, of these pursuits will have echoes of animal motivations, because they derive from what were once fitness-enhancing instincts. They look like the kind of activities that would please other primates: having sex, eating, drinking, grooming, caring, exercising, playing, gaining status, and so on. But it seems likely to me that, at some point in human evolution, the means and the ends switched around. Whereas pleasure was once purely to induce our pre-human ancestors to do fitness-serving actions, now we do the actions to induce fitness-serving pleasure. Perhaps it's like bump-starting a stick-shift car. The spark that ignites the engine was designed to propel the car along the road. But, ingeniously, we can run the whole system the other way. Roll our car along the road, and we make the engine fire.

For sure, some human activities also have some direct fitness value: we may still eat for nutrition, drink for hydration, copulate for conception. But these tasks, once basic biological routines, have been re-purposed. They have been turned primarily to recreational use. We not only have recreational sex; we have recreational eating, drinking, exercising, caring, and all the rest. Human satisfactions link to ancient animal instincts, but the links are indirect. They are evolutionary homologues, not equivalents — in the same way that, say, cats and dolphins both have tails: same origin, different purpose. Or perhaps as a better analogy, it is like the way the Land Rover was devised as a utility vehicle for farmers, but has morphed into a plaything. A modern Land Rover could still be useful on a farm if the need arose, but nowadays it is mainly driven for fun.

So, our reasons for living don't fall out of hifalutin existential philosophy. They are assembled on the ground, from what look to be regular workaday activities. Walk the dog… sort the recycling… go to church… drop by on Granddad…. It feels like just one thing after another. But these kinds of deeds are extraordinary in the context of life on earth because, strictly speaking, they are rarely vital for bodily subsistence. It is not out of direct fitness needs that we, say, prefer our coffee black, choose underwear of a particular style, and listen to Radio WXYZ. From a biological perspective, our lives look irrational. For any other animal, much of what we concern ourselves with would be an unfathomable waste of energy. Normally in nature, the rational thing to do, unless there is a pressing reason to do otherwise, is nothing.[45] Left to its own devices, an animal's default action is *in*action — avoiding unnecessary disturbance. Hence penguins huddle, squirrels hibernate, and well-fed lions lounge. But we humans need purposeful goings-on in our lives — daily projects that feel worthwhile.

Someone or something to love

In particular, it is good for our mental health to have a daily agenda setter, preferably outside of our direct egoistic needs — that is, something or someone to love.[46] It doesn't much matter what that love object is: it could be family, work, sport, travel, or whatever, but we do need something to attend to. And the tougher life gets, the more important a focus for our busy-ness becomes. I suggest this may be why people in potentially suicidogenic pain sometimes flip between debilitating depression and manic activity: keepers have to juggle the need to keep people incapable of suicide with an opposing need for them to have an engaging mission to work on. I don't believe this need is just a matter of mental or physical stimulation, equivalent to the ropes in a chimp enclosure or the wheel in a hamster cage. It's not for exercise, in the sense of preparing us mentally and physically for some future eventuality. Our daily pursuits are the end, the point, both the 'this' and the 'it' in the question that perhaps we all ask ourselves at times — "Is this it?"

The answer is — Yes. This is it. And it needs to be good. Purpose in life is not an optional extra, a psychological cherry to pop on the cake after our more basic requirements have been sorted. It is not, in other words, the last item on a rank order of needs of the sort famously proposed by psychologist Abraham Maslow.[47] Rather, a good enough reason to live has to be in place before we human beings will even take on the task of satisfying our other needs. Without a point to our lives, wherever on a supposed hierarchy we may be, we are exposed to the danger of wilful death; or, if not that, then becoming overwhelmed by keepers, as our emergency defences against self-destruction take over. Late in life, Maslow came to doubt his own theory. It is quite possible, he observed, for people seemingly to want for nothing and still be pathologically purposeless.[48] At the other extreme, Victor Frankl, an Auschwitz survivor, gives first-hand testimony as to how humans can endure unimaginable privation. He explains with one of Nietzsche's aphorisms: "He who has a why to live can bear almost any how."[49]

The psychologist Nicholas Humphrey has, as I have, pondered how and why humans are rarely drawn to suicide. We came to similar conclusions. He suggests that what makes life worth living is some newly evolved appetite for staying alive.[50] I suggest this appetite arose from the evolution of special-purpose appetisers; fenders, a collection of psychological mechanisms that are designed to keep psychache at bay and to equip us with a positive 'why' for living. I think these devices probably account for much of what we think and do in our daily lives. The human mind doesn't micro-manage our survival and reproduction as other animals' minds seem to do with theirs. Instead, we are buffered from misery and encouraged to select reasons to be cheerful. These motivational bodyguards and cheerleaders are not there to serve particular stimulus-response programmes, as is usually nature's wont. Their biological logic, uniquely to our species, is that as long as the human organism is happy to stay alive, then there remains at least the possibility that more ancient urges will incidentally lead us to reproduce.

So, when we support soccer teams, dance at parties, shop for jeans, or whatever else we get up to, we may not be following the same instinctive drives that direct the lives of other animals. We may not be competing for mates, signalling status, arranging alliances, or other chimp-like motives that evolutionists often seem to expect of us. What we do may make no sense by normal biological standards. We might just want to have fun.

No doubt it is possible to find baser instincts at work in human affairs. But to look to these to explain the generality of how we live is to miss what I see as the central feature of the human condition — that we get to choose whether to live at all. Fenders keep us buoyed up with joy, meaning, and hope. In that relatively safe position, we can usually keep our heads emotionally above water, whatever problems would drag us down. So, what may often look to be biologically irrational passions and preoccupations may serve a vital, evolved purpose; to make life worth our while. That brings us to Fender IV, our capacity for love and spiritual belief, which needs a chapter all itself — Chapter 11.

But we first need to take a brief detour.

CHAPTER 9: *Ahead of keepers is a cluster of front-line anti-suicide defences, labelled* fenders, *tasked with avoiding the need for keepers to mobilise. They try to keep us fairly happy most of the time so that we can absorb unpleasant shocks. They manage our exposure to bad news, and provide a flow of pleasant experiences that make us feel good about being alive.*

CHAPTER 10: *Fenders cannot protect us entirely from psychache, which potentially leaves a gap in our anti-suicide defences. Cultural barriers plug this gap. We absorb and transmit rules and beliefs about suicide from the people around us, which protect ourselves and our communities. Contagious waves of self-killings can take hold when these defences break down.*

10

THINKING TWICE

You and I are not alone, however isolated we may feel. We are united by the need to experience our lives as worth living, and by the difficulty of carrying on if this need is not met. We are thus connected with virtually every human that has ever lived, and ever will.

In this and the following chapter, we explore how this point of connection forms the basis of a communal life support system. We'll start by looking at how the culture that surrounds us encourages us to soldier on when we otherwise might not. We need others' help, because the innate defences described so far have a potentially fatal weakness. You will see why if I review the argument so far.

The last chapter proposed that humans are equipped with 'fenders': evolved anti-suicide mechanisms that regulate our experience of pain and pleasure. They manage our happiness homeostatically, like the thermostat on a heater keeps a room comfortably warm despite drafts from the outside. Systems that pull an organism back to a resting point after external shocks are common in nature. But the resting point for an animal's senses is usually neutral — the average of whatever has gone before, the better to notice when anything changes. Human emotions defy this averaging, neutralising effect. Our emotional thermostat is pre-set to warmer than neutral: 'Quite happy' (Fender I). Maintaining that abnormally warm state is hard work; it requires us tactically to blind ourselves to painful realities (Fender II), and to keep ourselves focussed on rewarding, life-affirming activities (Fender III).

The mental machinery that drives these behaviours evolved not because nature cares about our feelings per se. Nature is not interested in making happy animals, only reproductively fit animals. Human happiness was favoured by selection because a serious and specific fitness hazard awaits us, and us alone, in prolonged misery: suicide. Or, if not suicide, then the activating of emergency psychological defences against suicide. I earlier labelled these 'keepers'; they respond to chronic psychache by carefully disabling us with symptoms of depression, addiction, and diverse other forms of common mental disorder.

Keepers and fenders form our species' basic anti-suicide defences. Keepers are costly last-gasp interventions, blocking the path when high risk is detected. Fenders try to keep us clear of the psychache that requires keepers to intervene. Keepers are firefighters, fenders are fire preventors. Together they form a set of powerful adaptations that emerged by selection over perhaps hundreds of thousands of years, deep in pre-human history. It was thanks to their evolution that a population of our hominid forebears, driven by runaway selection towards ever greater intelligence, finally crossed the intellectual threshold for suicide. Ever since then, we have lived with the knowledge of our own mortality, and its implication — that it is possible to end unbearable pain by ending life.

That escape was, and still is, genetically disastrous — a recipe for extinction. This is why I think keepers and fenders, as innate anti-suicide protections, had to evolve before the threshold for suicide could be crossed; they acted as a fortified bridgehead. Selection has probably strengthened the bridgehead over the millennia since. But we can assume that most of the construction work was done by a few pioneers at a time when most of our ancestors still lived safely below the threshold. They were unaware of the possibility of self-killing. Intelligence is probably much like many other biological traits: it varies randomly across populations in a bell-shaped curve. Most individuals are about average, towards the middle of the bell, and declining numbers tail off to the extremes at either side. The bridgehead we are discussing was built in ancestral times by the choices of the smartest, those at the tip of curve's front tail. They were the ones smart enough to be at the cusp of the potential for wilful self-killing.

For those brilliant few, genetically heritable anti-suicide defences made the difference between reproductive success and death. Those who found themselves unprotected died: they and their genes disappeared from the breeding population. But others benefited from genetic mutations that kept them alive long enough to reproduce. Their offspring had the effect of squeezing the entire bell curve a little tighter against the threshold. Generation after generation became smarter and more resistant to suicide. Once effective protections were in place across the population, enough to produce a sustainably low rate of suicide, the threshold disappeared. This breakthrough was a pivotal event in human evolution, perhaps marking the birth of our species. The population raced forward to new heights of intelligence, because now *Homo* could be *sapiens*, and survive.

We shall not what?

Now, before that intellectual Rubicon was crossed, a visionary leader who stood up and cried 'Thou shalt not commit suicide!' would have been shouting into the wind. Without a mass of people who understood the idea of death, who grasped their personal mortality and knew what suicide was, the ban would have fallen on deaf ears — and dumb mouths; news of the ban would have travelled no further, because it lacked a network of understanding people who could pass it on.

That changed once suicide became a population-wide possibility. The act could then be named and shamed, and it probably was. Once the community as a whole crossed the threshold, and personal mortality became thinkable, suicide suddenly became doable, and the opportunity for a new kind of anti-suicide defence opened up: an encultured ban.

A ban would be backed by strong selective pressure because, it seems to me, there's a gap in the defences we have discussed so far, and an anti-suicide tradition may be the only way to plug it. The gap stems from a limitation in fenders' ability to manage pain. As you'll recall, the fenders we discussed in the last chapter seek to shield us from psychache, and they thereby try to make both suicide and keepers unnecessary. They focus on controlling the 'pain' side, the motivational driver, of suicide's pain-and-brain causation. We need to be more precise with the labelling now: let's rename them *pain-type* fenders.

Pain-type fenders are bound sometimes to fail, because they can't completely abolish the root of the problem. Pain is a necessary evil. It is always unpleasant (except, I suppose, in certain carefully controlled conditions — hot curries, adventurous sex, etc.), and it is unpleasant for good reason. As a signal, pain catches our attention — it shouts of danger. And as a motivational spur, it forces us to do something to end it. In this way, pain protects us from fitness hazards in the environment. For humans, the environment is importantly social; thus, social pain is also a necessity, helping us to protect our vital social supports.

So, abolishing pain altogether would be counter-productive. Pain-type fenders have to strike a balance. On the one side, they have to suppress pain enough to avoid both suicide and the need to ignite keepers. On the other side, we need to feel enough pain to find our way safely around our world. Therein lies the snag. Pain-type fenders can keep most people happy most of the time, in a place where painful events can usually be ignored or accommodated without too much disruption. But they can't keep everyone pain-free forever. Exposure to adversity is part of life; it is inevitable. Most of us go through at least one seriously traumatic experience at some point in our lives, such as the sudden death of a loved one, an assault, or a violent accident.[1] Pain-type fenders can only offer a compromise solution, which implies a dangerous weakness in the anti-suicide barrier: the leftover pain.

The barrier holds nonetheless. Many of us, perhaps a fifth at any time, find ourselves having to endure spells of unhappiness, feeling dissatisfied with our lives.[2] But few us, it seems, either attempt suicide or become overpowered by keepers — symptoms of mental disorder. What holds us safe at these hard times is, I suggest, a separate set of fenders that tackle the 'brain' side of suicide's causation. Our ancestors' newly acquired comprehension of the suicide idea opened up the opportunity for new communal defences. These alone could make a surgical strike on the suicide idea — shoving that idea, and that idea alone, beyond mental reach. We could call these new defences *brain-type* fenders, to distinguish them from their more ancient pain-type counterparts.

Brain-type fenders throw a cultural blockade around the thought of self-killing. Indeed, I see three separate blockades, nested inside each other like the concentric walls of a castle. If an attacking force manages to break through one, it still has to contend with the next. The first barrier is a taboo, which makes the suicide idea awkward even to bring to mind — it's literally unthinkable. The second is a belief in an unattractive hereafter: even if one can think about suicide, there is no guarantee that death will bring an end to pain, because there could be even worse suffering to come in an afterlife. The third is the stigma: even if suicide were thinkable, and even if one believed it would end pain, there is still the problem that the act feels self-evidently wrong.

Let's look at these three walls more closely.

The outer wall: Unthinkability

Suicide is taboo. There is something repellent about the whole topic. It's ugly, but it is hard to say why.[3] The ugliness is not intrinsic to the act; it is a perception that springs from our own minds. Like beauty, it's in the eye of the beholder. This negative perspective probably has evolutionary origins, but what has evolved is not an opinion specifically about suicide. As we discussed in earlier chapters, there is probably no distinguishing feature in the suicide idea that our central nervous system can react to. The brain is designed to make emotional, biochemical connections: its instinctive routines can't tell what you are thinking, only how you feel when you think it. What has evolved, rather, is the general-purpose machinery that sets up those emotional connections.

The psychological routine that makes suicide ugly probably came about for other reasons. Originally it kept our hominid ancestors away from the sights and smells that foreshadowed infection — cues that have to be learned from the visible revulsion displayed by other people. So, for example, babies are not born with any particular opinion about faeces. To them, it is merely brown goo, and they can happily get into what their parents see as a disgusting mess if given a chance to play with it. But that special reaction of adults quickly teaches children in turn to be disgusted. It's a visceral response that can last a lifetime. By much the same mechanism, a disgust of suicide is not innate: it is a gut feeling that we acquire and internalise because that is the prevailing attitude of the people around us. Most cultures hold that suicide is disgusting — too revolting to look at, talk about, or even think about.

The suicide taboo holds almost universally across human cultures. It can be found in some form the world over, in almost every place and every kind of society, from pre-literate tribes to Western scientists. As I mentioned in the introduction, one reason the word 'suicide' doesn't feature on this book's cover is that the word alone can put people off.[4] The disgust shows up even in the academic community. Suicide seems to be widely viewed as an inappropriate subject for study, even among psychologists, and few like to get too close.[5] General psychology textbooks give the topic only the most cursory attention, usually then only as part of the symptomology of depression. Science's financial supporters are affected too: suicidology attracts only a fraction of the funding that goes into more palatable areas of health psychology.[6] And among the general public, people are so reluctant to raise the subject that it is side-stepped even in private one-to-ones with psychiatrists and other therapists — that is, in settings where you would think a frank discussion would be in people's own best interest.[7]

The whole topic feels out of bounds — and I suggest the human psyche does its best to keep it that way. People who have not seriously thought about taking their own lives can find the concept outlandish — too strange to get their minds around. And even once we have got our minds around it, it easily becomes strange again. First-hand experience of suicidality can apparently be wiped from memory. In one study, a third of students who admitted they had seriously considered suicide denied it when asked again a few years later.[8] Even actual attempts can be put beyond recall: a third of teenagers who admitted they had tried to take their own lives apparently forgot about it when asked again in their early 20s.[9] This pattern of not remembering may go a long way to explain a paradox in the age statistics for suicidality, that adolescents report having made more suicide attempts over their lifetimes than adults do.[10] What's striking is not so much that the forgetting is so common; it is the enormity of what is being forgotten. This is no minor detail slipping the mind: the memory of a lengthy personal experience, an event of literal life-or-death significance, has to be repressed wholesale. It looks to me that, as the outer cultural wall against suicide, our minds are schooled simply not to go there.

The next wall: Futility

For those whose minds can go there, the next cultural obstacle proclaims that suicide would anyway be pointless: it won't work as a way to escape from pain. It is futile to try to end our suffering by killing ourselves, because there'd only be even worse to come in the next world. To non-believers, this line of thought may sound irrational. But as a brain-type fender, it exploits a level-headed weighing up of pros and cons. Suicide makes sense only if the overall pain to be expected from dying is less than the overall pain of continuing to live. In that calculation, pain to come in the hereafter, as well as the pain of carrying out the act, enter into the equation. If the downsides outweigh the ups, then there is no point in doing it.[11]

This is a complicated matter. What people think will happen to them after death can affect their wish to live or die in different ways. For some, the promise of a happy afterlife gives them resilience; suffering in this life is easier to bear if we know it is not forever.[12] On the other hand, for a few, the thought that death will take them to a better place could make self-killing an appealing option — it might even, in part, motivate acts of suicide terrorism.[13]

But on balance, the popular view of the afterlife looks more likely to put people off suicide than encourage it, for at least two reasons. One is that, however we get there, the hereafter is rarely said to be a pleasant place. Most cultures view it as more a dark underworld than heaven above.[14] Abrahamic teachings of a Godly paradise may be an exception, but even in Judeo-Christian settings, there's a prevailing and deep-seated worry: we aren't sure what awaits us, but it's well worth not finding out. It is telling that one of the best-known passages in Western literature, the "To be, or not to be…" speech in Shakespeare's *Hamlet*, acknowledges precisely this communal, life-preserving dread:

> Who would fardels bear,
> To grunt and sweat under a weary life,
> But that the dread of something after death,
> The undiscovered country, from whose bourn
> No traveller returns, puzzles the will,
> And makes us rather bear those ills we have,
> Than fly to others that we know not of?
> Thus conscience does make cowards of us all

In other words, whatever the Bible would have us believe, we are alive only because we are too scared of the alternative. Note this isn't just Hamlet's opinion; he speaks for "us all". Theatre being commercial pop culture of his time, Shakespeare gave voice to a sentiment that he expected to strike a chord with the crowd.

The sentiment still chimes with us today, so-called passive suicidality cropping up here and there in modern pop lyrics. The rousing climax of *Ol' Man River* — hit song of the often-revived Broadway musical *Show Boat*, a 20th-century ikon of Judeo-Christian pop culture — has us singing along: "I'm tired of living, and scared of dying…"

Word on the street, then, is that being dead is not a nice place. It's like finding a string of 'AVOID!' reviews on TripAdvisor. But it is an especially bad idea to deliberately set out for this destination because, according to widespread reports, suicides get picked out for terrible treatment on arrival. In Eastern traditions, they can expect a poorer quality of re-incarnation. In Abrahamic codes, there are hellish sanctions. Islam, for example, teaches that a suicide will re-experience, over and over, the pain of the lethal act.[15] As if death wasn't scary enough, death by one's own hand is altogether scarier.

The final wall: Stigma

The third, innermost, cultural wall is a moral disapproval. Even for people who can turn their minds to the topic, and even if they thought the act would end their suffering, there is still the problem that suicide feels just plain wrong.

The wrongness often expresses itself in religious beliefs. All major traditions ban some form of self-killing, particularly if the act is motivated by a hankering to end personal troubles[16] — motivated, that is, exactly in the way the pain-and-brain model predicts. It won't be by chance that the focus of this religious proscription tallies with the reason suicide is a biological problem. There is no point in banning something that people aren't minded to do. The religious tenet looks to be purposeful and protective.

But there is no need for religion here. A popular 'Thou shalt not commit suicide' would be expected to spread under its own power, with or without the backing of priests. It has done just that. Until recently, most countries around the world, religious or secular, had legal prohibitions. At the time of writing, more than thirty still do. People don't have to be religious to absorb and transmit a belief that life should be cherished and suicide isn't right.[17] It is trial by public opinion, not by religion, that stigmatises the act: it is the spontaneous court of common prejudice that condemns the actors — as crazy, evil, stupid, selfish, weak, attention-seeking, cowardly, or the like.[18]

Having passed sentence, it is the neighbourhood mob that levies the punishment. Communities the world over come down hard not only on surviving attempters but, where attempts are lethal — as if to compound their grief— bereaved families.[19] We touched on this in an earlier chapter. Among the Baganda in Uganda, close kin of suicides face the burning of their homes, disinheritance, and banishment.[20] Even in the modern West, people losing loved ones in this way find themselves socially distanced, treated as if they are contaminated by association. The rejection can leave scars.[21] This public vengeance is barefaced, legitimised, victimisation.

Punishing the bereaved is obviously unjust. Suicide cannot be predicted by anyone, close relations included. If it cannot be foreseen, it cannot be forestalled. The folk myth, accepted more or less uncritically by science, that suicide is foreseeable has the effect of dumping blame on blameless people. I'll return to this point in the concluding chapter. The curiosity is why so many of us, supposedly fair-minded neighbours, should be so ready to mistreat people in this way — so ready to kick those who are down.

We may not be aware of these punishments' purposeful origin, but I suggest they originally arose for the greater good. It may be by necessity that the community amplifies the grief of the bereaved: the point is to make an example of them. It's meant as a warning, a public deterrent — to make anyone else who might be thinking of suicide to think again. The effect overall does seem to be shielding. An encultured disapproval, backed up by unpleasant outcomes for loved ones, does seem to affect peoples' decision-making. The most powerful moral objection to suicide is that, for those left behind, it is simply cruel.[22]

How might this social disapproval be set up and enforced? There might be a few ways. To rule one out, and as I have said already, I doubt that any particular feeling towards suicide will be innate, in the sense of being pre-programmed at birth. The idea is probably too nebulous for the brain to handle in that way. It is surprisingly hard to nail down — even suicidologists find it hard to agree on a precise definition. And as we discussed in Chapter 5, the idea is made up of an assembly of abstractions, including a notion of death, which only intellectually mature humans are capable of conceiving.

Possibly, perhaps, there could be an innate element of what psychologists call preparedness for learning: we are born with a readiness to learn about certain features in the environment that mattered to our ancestors' survival. So, for example, we may be especially prone to pick up phobias of spiders and snakes, these being types of animals that were a recurring threat in our evolutionary past. What we're born with is not the phobia, but a hair-trigger readiness to become scared of certain classes of objects, together with a template of certain general features to watch out for — spider-like and snake-like things. The system builds in flexibility, because the details of exactly which animals to avoid will vary from place to place, and are best learned on the job, in practical lessons learned in childhood.[23] Attitudes about risk-taking might be absorbed in the same way; children born into warlike, competitive, or other do-or-die conditions might be at an advantage if they learned fast about local rules of survival — including perhaps a bent for impulsive action. Those born into safer worlds might do better by not taking risks.[24] This kind of psychological preparedness could, I suppose, have been co-opted for use in preventing suicide, provided there was something distinctive about the suicide idea that could be built into a pre-programmed routine — which, as I say, I doubt is the case.

More likely, it seems to me, cultural barriers to suicide have to rely on people simply accepting whatever goes around and passing it on. It won't be a wholly reliable mechanism, but it seems to work well enough most of time. The power comes ultimately from an inbuilt advantage that the 'suicide-is-bad' idea has over its 'suicide-is-good' opponent. In a head-to-head contest, given time, 'suicide-is-bad' is bound to win. It is the kind of idea that psychologist Daniel Gilbert calls a 'super-replicator' — it spreads because the opposite idea destroys its own transmission network.[25] To illustrate, take the belief that having children is a recipe for happiness. According to some surveys, people are actually happiest in the years when they are not raising children. But a romantic notion of blissful parenthood travels down the generations nonetheless, pretty well unchallenged. Well, it would do — in much the same way that history gets written by the victors. A vision of happy parenting will perpetuate itself because the attitudes that get transmitted, regardless of their truth, are those of society's stakeholders. If people act according to what they believe, then a belief that child-raising is a miserable ordeal would soon deplete itself of descendants who could pass the idea on. Incest gets a similarly biased treatment, and probably through a similar dynamic: because inbreeding tends to increase the risk of genetic disabilities, a dim view about incest is likely to spread of its own accord, because people with that view will tend to be more successful breeders.[26] Following the same process, the 'suicide-is-good' position contains the seed of its own destruction: it would eventually starve itself of transmitters and be outbred by proponents of 'suicide-is-bad'.

The protective power of stigma

So, while suicide is rare in all human cultures (and I have argued that we can thank keepers and pain-type fenders for that) exactly *how* rare may depend, at least in part, on the intensity of local disapproval. Suicide rates vary from country to country in patterns that endure for generations, roughly in line with the strength of the act's unacceptability.[27] The impact of cultural deterrents can be seen in the way rates gradually realign when migrants move from one culture to another: the rate starts out as whatever they brought with them from the culture of origin. Then, as the migrants assimilate, it shifts towards the rate typical of the host community.[28]

Where the disapproval has loosened, there is often a sharply higher incidence of self-killings. One such hotspot mentioned earlier, in Greenland, suffers a suicide rate many times higher than the global average. Others can be found on certain Micronesian islands, in parts of the Kulbi-Kenipaqan river basin in the Philippines, among the Aguaruna tribe in Peru, in the Kandrian district in New Guinea, and elsewhere around the world.[29] Researchers investigating these communities consistently report what is, to them, a shocking openness in the way the locals talk about suicide, especially among youth. In some places it has become a normal topic of conversation and a regular, almost expected, way for people to deal with difficulties in their lives.

The contagion of suicides that swept across Germany at the close of the war in 1945 offers a catastrophic example of what can happen when the reticence breaks down. Tens of thousands of ordinary Germans took their own lives in conditions where, for a few desperate months, a once strong anti-suicide ethos not only collapsed, but went into reverse. The title of Florian Huber's book about this period illustrates the mood, quoting a father's plea to his son — *Promise Me You'll Shoot Yourself.*[30] The contagious potential of suicide has been known for centuries. Indeed, it is often called the 'Werther effect' after Goethe's 18th-century romantic novel, *The Sorrows of Young Werther*. Goethe's fictional protagonist took his own life, and moved so many young readers to do the same that the novel was banned in some countries. In modern times, many studies confirm that the effect is real — that exposure to suicide sets a precedent for others to follow.[31]

Incidentally, I suspect that much of suicide's heritability — the way risk can run in families — will be down to the transmission of the idea rather than via a genetic predisposition. Suicidal hearsay is an environmental factor that will be very hard for researchers to control for in family studies, because such news is probably going to pass between kin relations sooner or later, even if they are raised and live apart. Awareness alone can be enough to make the otherwise unthinkable thinkable.[32]

Clearly, cultural protections against suicide — brain-type fenders — are not failsafe. They sometimes break down and with lethal consequences. That an anti-suicide tradition is not absolutely universal should not be taken to show that it serves no purpose. It shows, rather, as anthropologist Clyde Kluckhohn argues, that societies as well as individuals can fall sick.[33]

When our cultural shields against suicide fail, the people who bear the brunt seem to be young adults. We can speculate as to why. Adolescence is a time when lessons from the community, including those about suicide, are most readily absorbed.[34] It is an especially vulnerable stage of life because, if the theory of this book is right, there is probably only a fleeting opportunity for the vital anti-suicide learning to take place. If the ability to conceive of the act presupposes the crossing of a threshold of intelligence, then so does the capacity to conceive of the act's immorality. So, both the intellectual possibility of suicide, and the ability to be swayed by cultural decrees against it, arrive at about the same time. Both the hazard and the defence against the hazard show up side by side, at or soon after puberty. It is as if fresh-faced conscripts for a bloody battle got their first combat training only as they are being marched up to the front line. A newly self-conscious teenager may be in special danger if the safety message is late, garbled, or overwhelmed by word on the street that suicide is okay.

This puts policy makers in a bind. On the one hand, lifting negative attitudes might save lives. It could encourage people beset by suicidal thoughts to come forward and seek help. It could especially lessen the stress on survivors of suicide and lower the risk of further deaths among them. With such best intentions, the World Health Organisation and other bodies have led a long campaign to make people feel readier to discuss the topic.[35] It is true that the most helpful way to talk to suicidal people is to listen empathically, without judgement.[36]

On the other hand, and although the word 'stigma' carries negative connotations, it can be used to positive effect. Stigma is useful weapon in public health initiatives elsewhere — to discourage, for example, drunk driving and smoking. So, while some leaders work to weaken the suicide stigma, others have sought to strengthen it.

In 1980s Micronesia, suffering some of the world's highest rates, the diocese's Roman Catholic bishop at the time proposed a shockingly tough, seemingly backwards-looking, measure. Acceding to a desperate grass-roots appeal, the bishop suggested restoring the practice of a bygone era — of denying burial honours for suicides, refusing their families church rites or public prayers. Importantly, the motive had nothing to do with religious doctrine. The proposal was a matter of practical psychology.

It was meant to counteract some of the romantic appeal that suicide had acquired among the young. The effect on suicidality is not known, but even as a suggestion, the bishop's intervention carried weight: it signalled a communal censure, that suicide is not okay. I understand that the proposal was carried out in places for several years. But, as the original officials rotated out of office and the reasoning behind the initiative disappeared in the mist of time, it eventually lapsed.[37]

I take this story as evidence that our urge to punish survivors, unjust though it is, probably arose for positive protective reasons, even if those reasons are long forgotten. The stigmatising of surviving attempters and bereaved kin has logic: it hurts of course, but for the wider community's safety, necessarily so. The message it sends to those thinking about taking their own lives is to think twice. Brain-type fenders press the brake on a suicidal impulse.

I am not saying that stigmatising bereaved people is morally right. I am observing and interpreting the facts as they appear to me, but I see no personal justification for joining in the mistreatment of survivors. Quite the opposite; it becomes easier to empathise when we know something of what people are going through. If we can, let's reach out.[38]

A two-by-two matrix

With brain-type fenders at work alongside their pain-type counterparts, we can see evolved protections against suicide falling into a two-by-two matrix: two types of fenders and two types of keepers, as shown opposite.

I'm sure the reality won't be as neat as these boxes suggest. Some types of defences may blur into each other, some may spread across more than one box, and I may have missed out others altogether. But the chart does, I think, help explain why we react to adversity in different ways at different times of our lives: when we are at greater risk of suicide (keepers, the right-hand column), and when we are at lesser risk (fenders, to the left).

For example, brain-type keepers (bottom right), disable our ability to plan and complete tasks, suicidal or not. Keepers are extreme measures for extreme danger. It is because they interfere with our day-to-day business — stopping us organising anything much — that brain-type keepers are biologically costly and worthwhile only as an emergency solution. By contrast, brain-type fenders (bottom left) are less costly. They target just the idea of suicide, causing the least possible damage to other mental

	FENDERS Front-line, pro-active, psychological defences	**KEEPERS** Last-line, reactive, psychological defences
***PAIN*-TYPE** defences aim to make suicide unnecessary, lessening the motivation to escape emotional pain.	***PAIN*-TYPE FENDERS** • Homeostasis of affect at an above-neutral resting point • Self-serving self-deception • Pleasurable pursuits • Benign worldviews	***PAIN*-TYPE KEEPERS** • Numbing of emotions • Compulsive self-medication • Pain offset relief • Distraction • Select reasons for pain • Detach from reality • General loss of motivation
***BRAIN*-TYPE** defences aim to make suicide difficult, restricting mental access to the means of lethal self-injury.	***BRAIN*-TYPE FENDERS** Encultured blocks against suicide make the act... • unthinkable (taboo) • pointless (painful afterlife) • wrong (stigma)	***BRAIN*-TYPE KEEPERS** • Degraded ability to plan and organise complex tasks • Difficulties with memory, logical thinking, and making decisions

faculties. Being cheap to deploy, they needn't wait for a suicidal crisis to arise before weighing in: they are permanently active, blocking off the suicide idea, just in case anyone finds themselves in enough pain for the idea potentially to become interesting.

Do brain-type fenders, the communal pressure to stay clear of the suicide idea, make life worth living? In one sense, no. Their effect is to trap us into staying alive, even when we would rather not. Life can be reduced to a joyless forced march, people soldiering on only for want of an alternative. Some would like to end it, but they can't. With that escape route culturally blocked off, they find themselves 'condemned to live'.

But in another sense, brain-type fenders do help to make life worth living, in two ways. One is that, without getting too philosophical, they at least grant us the freedom to choose life. Unlike keepers, where choice in the matter is taken away (no one elects to be depressed, addicted, psychotic, or the like), cultural blocks against suicide offer the possibility of being wilfully overridden. This suggests that, for people who comply with anti-suicide rules, however grudgingly, staying alive is a positive decision. It feels more worthwhile than the alternative, even if it is only the better of two evils.

The other reason to think that cultural barriers have a positive effect on our appetite for life is that, while not being positively life-affirming themselves, they keep us alive long enough to rediscover the positives. They're like protective fencing along the side of a high bridge: they don't improve the view, but at least they safely channel our path so we can live to enjoy the view elsewhere. Being hard-wired for joy, the human mind is designed to restore itself to a happier-than-neutral resting point. Sometimes we need only buy a little time to let human nature take its healing course.

That brings us to Fender IV, which was skipped over in Chapter 7 — a benign outlook on the world. I think it can be summed in one word...

CHAPTER 10: *Brain-type fenders form a series of encultured barriers against the suicide idea: taboo, belief in a grim afterlife, and stigma. Their survival value can be inferred from the surge of suicide that can occur when they break down. They don't add to the joy of living, but they can at least hold us safe until we rediscover more positive reasons to live.*

CHAPTER 11: *Human mental health depends on our maintaining an unrealistically hopeful outlook. We must believe that our futures are specially protected from pain, that there is more to life than mere algorithms of physics and biology. Fender IV, introduced in Chapter 7, lets us defend our super-natural paradigms from factual attack, and keep faith.*

11

LOVE

It is a beautiful lie that can makes itself true. In an important sense, love is a self-deception, as we're going to discuss. But if this book is on the right track, human beings' success, indeed our survival, depends on self-deception. We have evolved this way because we live with the option of not living. The biological bottom line is that it is more important to stay alive than get real; so, as and when required, our brains tell us white lies. At times of suffering, our minds may distract us, make up backstories to explain away our pain, and invent alibis by which to endure it. Even in normal times, our minds knowingly withhold facts from us when facts might be too painful to bear. We fill our days with pleasures large and small, activities that feel self-evidently worthwhile to us, but for any other life-form would be a damaging waste of time and energy.

In this chapter, I will argue that the extent of human self-deception brings its own problem. The trouble with fibbing is that it is easy to trip up on our own contradictions. How can we make our life-sustaining misbeliefs hold together as a coherent, believable 'reality'?

We don't get the whole truth

It should be no surprise that we humans are not told the whole truth. Biologically, the whole truth is impossible. Animals only ever get a partial view of the world, because only certain aspects of it are relevant to their biological needs. The perception of reality is a means to an end, a fitness-serving tool; so, every animal's brain creates a customised reality of its own. Bees see colours we can't, the better to home in on flowers. A dog smells in stereo, an olfactory landscape we can hardly imagine. Philosopher Thomas Nagel famously asked, 'What is it like to be a bat?' It's an unanswerable question because it misconceives what is being asked about (in that respect, then, rather like the question 'Why do people kill themselves?'). A bat's reality can't be 'like' anything, because it can only exist in the mind of a bat.[1]

Human reality is as purpose-built as any other animal's. It feels like the real thing, but that perception is an illusion.[2] We can sometimes see glimpses of the fabrication. When, for example, we look in the mirror, we can't see a reflection of our eyes moving. The brain switches vision off when we shift our gaze from one point to another, momentarily blinding us, presumably so that we're not distracted by scenes swimming into each other. We know nothing of these frequent gaps — the brain gives us to believe, rather, that we're seeing the world in continuous video. The milliseconds lost in those gaps are also hidden: in other words, our brains continually lie to us about the passage of time too. We are unaware, by the way, that the image reaching the back of our eyes is in fact upside down, as with a pinhole camera: without telling us, our brain flips everything vertically and serves us with a doctored picture. Other illusions have cropped up already in this book, such as the way we are usually not aware of the contact of our clothes against the skin. In other words, we get only an edited account even of that tiny fragment of the universe that we are physically touching.

So, our perception of reality is all in the mind, and necessarily so. What is odd is not the partial nature of our reality, not that we don't get the whole truth. The oddity is that the picture that humans are presented with is aesthetically enhanced — Photoshopped, smartened up. What we take to be fact is in good part a work of creative fiction. As we saw in Chapter 7, we operate something like an internal news service. It has some connection with reality; its output is real enough at least for us to believe it, and, operating in the real world as we must, real enough not to land us in too much trouble. But nonetheless, it is not wholly truthful. We usually err on the side of being overly optimistic. So, for example, most motorists believe they are better than the average driver, most university professors view themselves to be outstandingly good, and terminally ill patients are often convinced they can recover.[3]

By normal animal standards, misinforming ourselves like this is a strange thing to do, for at least two reasons. We discussed one of them earlier. Information is power. It is in an animal's interest to appraise its reality as accurately and as quickly as possible because it needs to make good decisions. Wrong information leads to mistakes, and measured by biological fitness, mistakes are expensive. A migrating bird cannot afford to be over-optimistic about the fuel it needs for its journey — get that wrong and it won't be coming back. A monkey cannot delude itself about its branch-swinging ability, or it will land in the real world with a bump. Because the human brain feeds us fake news, or at least heavily-spun news, it sets us up to make repeated, stupid, and costly errors. As the computing adage says, garbage in, garbage out. That, for humans, it is worth the cost of being tactically ignorant points to a greater danger of being more fully informed — potentially, I suggest, the suicidal disaster of knowing too much.

Keeping ourselves deceived

The other reason to wonder at our powers of self-deception is the focus of this chapter. It is that keeping ourselves misinformed is a major feat of information management. A lie needs careful protection if it is to survive a prolonged encounter with reality.

Take, for example, the commonplace delusion that we are better-than-average drivers. It's impossible, of course; we can't all be better than average. But it is also hard work. For me to maintain that delusion about myself requires me, day in, day out, to overlook my peccadillos behind the wheel — when sometimes I speed, brake a little late, park sloppily, and the rest. Meanwhile, I need to be super alert to others' mistakes — all the discourtesies and dangerous errors that they don't even seem to notice. I tut-tut, shake my head, and wonder why they are allowed on the road. A speeding ticket for them is justice. When I get one, just bad luck. My insurance premium seems high, but it won't be because of my risk or history; I must be subsidising the bad drivers or getting ripped off by my insurer. My occasional bumps and scratches are not my fault, or they're one-offs so don't count. I am oddly sensitive when other drivers honk at me — How dare they! Who do they think they are? Thus, while the idea that I am a superior driver is a personal myth, it is one that can persist throughout a motoring lifetime in the face of continual daily disproof. The evidence is probably there in plain view that I am just a run-of-the-mill motorist, about as prone to making mistakes as anyone else, but my mind bats the evidence away. (By the way, prodded by this research, I put myself on an advanced driving course; surprise surprise, I found plenty of scope for improvement.)

This ongoing blindness to the facts is extraordinary. It runs counter to the way animals normally operate. When they get new information, they put it good use to update themselves. They are programmed to learn. If a rat fails in a task a few times, it will give up and try something else. Humans seem wired not to do this. We can carry on holding the same misbeliefs and making the same self-defeating mistakes indefinitely. This is one of the curiosities of addictive behaviours: we keep buying lottery tickets that are virtually assured not to be worth the investment, we nurse ancient grudges in the hope one day of getting even, and we can get stuck in failed relationships, recycling the same old disputes. All part, I suggest, of a powerful human tendency (and often-quoted definition of insanity) to repeat the same behaviour while expecting a different result.

The persistence of self-delusion needs explaining. It suggests to me that humans have an ability to build mental models of the world that resist being updated, holding firm despite continually rubbing up against factual disproof. At root, I suggest, we do this for the sake of suicide avoidance. I think it is likely an evolved aspect of human psychology, because it shows evidence of special design and it is hard otherwise to account for.

Our loyalty to old mental frameworks looks much like the way scientists tend to glue themselves to fundamental theories, what philosopher Thomas Kuhn called *paradigms* — mental frameworks that researchers use to make sense of the world and to guide their work.

The term has cropped up before in this book. As you'll recall from Chapter 2, an example of a scientific paradigm is the 18th-century idea of phlogiston, a fiery gas that, for more than a hundred years, was thought to be given off when substances burn. Phlogiston is the opposite of a modern understanding of combustion. We now know that burning involves a gas being captured, not emitted, and the phlogiston idea became obsolete after the discovery of oxygen.

As Kuhn points out, what is perhaps most puzzling about the phlogiston idea is that persisted for as long as it did, in plain sight of evidence that it was flawed. For example, chemists knew that burning happens only in the presence of air, which is hard to explain if the process involves a gas being given off. Phlogiston enthusiasts bent the theory to fit; air was needed, they argued, to absorb the phlogiston. Then it was found that substances get heavier, not lighter, when they burn. Again, the old idea was adjusted to accommodate the new finding: phlogiston must have negative weight, somehow. Some determined scientists simply ignored the anomalies. After oxygen was discovered, a few phlogiston die-hards sought to shoe-horn even that into the old theory. Phlogiston endured even though there was a plausible, but incompatible, alternative idea on the table.

I predict that one day students will look back with equal bemusement at several of the scientific paradigms that currently dominate human psychology and mental health; especially the one I have called 'suigiston' — the notion that suicide's causes are awaiting discovery, and that suicide is thus, in principle, open to prediction. As phlogiston did before it, the suigiston notion has endured for more than hundred years in outright defiance of the facts.

This odd propensity for scientists to stick to their guns, keeping faith with their paradigms in the teeth of counter-evidence, looks to me to be a universal human trait. Psychologist Leon Festinger and his team famously logged the same dynamic underway within an apocalyptic cult, whose members prepared themselves for the end of the world, which they prophesised would happen on 21 December 1954. When the big day came and went, determined believers refused to let go of the basic theory. Instead, it was stretched to fit — the world had been spared, they said, and it was all because of the cult's good preparations.[4]

It appears that scientists (even scientists!) defend their pet theories with this style of dogged post-rationalisation. I suggest we all do this, for the reason that human survival and mental health depend on our ability to keep our paradigms intact. It is not merely that we seek to avoid what Festinger called 'cognitive dissonance' — or what Freud called 'unpleasure' or any of the other names we give to psychological pain, many listed in Chapter 9. Psychache is not of itself a biological threat. The unique danger for humans is that we have a cure-all solution to psychache; wilful self-killing. Ultimately, this is the biological threat that our elaborate self-trickery seeks to manage.

It seems to me that our evolved anti-suicide defences, relying as they do on benign self-deception, presuppose that we can defend those self-deceptions from factual attack. The device that defends misbelief is likely a pain-type fender — Fender IV, to continue the thread from Chapter 9. I offer this as an over-arching evolved psychological mechanism that enables human beings to survive with the intellectual capacity for suicide.

A 'benign world' paradigm

Fender IV's task is to allow each of us to nurture a life-affirming personal paradigm. Specifically, we must believe that we are protected from pain and promised pleasure; that is, that we have futures good enough to be worth hanging in there for. That means, it seems to me, that we need to believe that the universe is not indifferent to our wellbeing, and that we can rely on it to take care of us. Our paradigms hold that the laws of nature and physics are moderated in our favour, enough to shield us from the pain that would ordinarily come our way if those laws had a free rein. This warm view of self-in-the-world has to endure despite the resulting failures of prediction — repeated and, in fitness terms, costly, mistakes. That is to say, Fender IV must defend us from factual updates. It has to manage the continual disappointment of encountering reality.

This task presents a major cognitive challenge. As animals, we have to live in the real world to survive, as must any organism. But at the same time, as human animals, we must keep ourselves tactically insulated from the real world, enough to control our exposure to psychache.

By way of a design solution for Fender IV, let me outline a proposal as to how it might work — how we could stay in this semi-detached state. I suggest each of us holds in the mind a private 'benign world' paradigm — an encouraging legend that explains why we are here and how it is that we are specially protected. It unifies our past and present, and, critically, our optimistic futures. And each of us uses this private myth as a mental template against which incoming facts are compared for their goodness of fit. The previewing of facts happens unconsciously, recalling Chapter 9. We are usually not aware that an internal editor/censor even exists, let alone that it is co-authoring our reality. If an incoming news bulletin fits the story, then it will be approved and released into consciousness. If it doesn't quite fit, it will be edited and presented in an acceptably distorted format. Facts that would cause too much trouble are secretly dropped, or archived beyond conscious access. So, each of us perceives our reality in a sanitised form, our hopeful paradigm acting as a special rose-tinted lens through which we perceive the world.

I suggest three things matter about this paradigm, this personal legend. First, it must be *benign*: it must hold out the promise of a protected future, so that each of us feels that life is worth the trouble. It must lead us to expect emotional rewards beyond what an objective assessment of the real physical and biological world would justify. It must be better than natural, normal, terrestrial reality. In that sense, it must be literally super-natural, para-normal, extra-terrestrial. Second, it needs to be *credible*: it must hold together as a coherent, internally consistent story, at least to our own satisfaction. We must be able to believe that it can actually deliver the good results that it promises. And third, a closely linked need, it must be *defensible*. It must be robust enough to withstand inevitable attack from the stream of facts that would prove it wrong. Now, as long as these three criteria are met, we can look forward to living safely and sanely within our semi-illusory bubble. There we can stay largely free from psychache, and protected, therefore, from both suicide and keepers, the symptoms of mental disorder that block suicide. We live in an enhanced reality — in a world enriched and ordered by our private supernatural ideals. It is heaven on earth.

Most of this proposal is not new. Several other researchers, at least since the work of John Bowlby in the 1960s, have come to the view that people wed themselves to basic, and self-servingly inaccurate, assumptive frameworks about their place in the world.[5] We use private mental models to find meaning in otherwise meaningless events. These models are often, objectively, fantastic. But although illusory, they give us something vital to lean on at times of loss, trauma, and other shocks. Indeed, the work of grieving can be understood as finding a way to reconcile the hopefulness of our worldviews with the painfulness of reality. What is new is my suggestion that these paradigms have adaptive, anti-suicide origins — that they are the purposeful output of a pain-type fender. It is hard to see how our benign self-deceptions could otherwise hold together. I propose that the fitness threat of suicide drove the evolution of our species' over-optimistic belief systems.

Perhaps paradoxically, hopeful worldviews can be cruel. We touched on this earlier. A belief that I am, say, damned by angry gods assumes at least there are gods — at least there is some intelligent power in charge, it is not indifferent to my wellbeing, and it could in principle be appeased. A feeling that I'm hard done by, unjustly persecuted, assumes that at least there is natural justice and eventually that it may be served (to my benefit, of course). It is easier to believe that the world has, for the time being, taken against me, rather than to admit that horrible things just randomly happen. Similarly, many people feel personally, unreasonably, to blame for bereavements and other losses; this paradigm imagines us to be god-like beings, super-humanly powerful. It looks punitive, but it does at least allow us to hold on to the idea that our futures are predictable and, in theory, under control. There is no perfect solution in this domain. Disappointment is going to come with the territory of any benign paradigm, because its very purpose is to raise expectations beyond what could realistically be delivered. The challenge of Fender IV is to manage the disappointments, so that the life-sustaining paradigm lives on.

Choosing our benign world

Within the three criteria I mentioned — that it be benign, believable, and defensible — there could be any number of alternative, but mutually exclusive, paradigms to choose from. The details of the storyline won't much matter. Our supernaturally happy future could be assured by something within ourselves (my special immunity, luck, skill, intelligence, determination, etc.) or outside of ourselves (my tribe, fate, karma, human nature, cosmic consciousness, god/gods, destiny, etc.). Most probably, hedging our bets, I expect we would normally go with some combination of the two. But, in the end, if it fits the general requirements, any dream will do.

Perhaps there are as many personal paradigms as there are human beings. I imagine each of us has a unique angle — much of our myth may be common to other people's, but we add personal touches. I suppose it might be possible for a radical free thinker to devise a worldview from scratch, rather like designing and building one's own home. But there would be a serious risk with going solo. The problem is not so much in building the house but in maintaining it, especially when the storm comes. An isolated paradigm may be difficult to defend single-handedly at times of hardship. The stakes are high, remember; in the presence of the almost ever-present possibility of self-killing, successful defence of an optimistic worldview is a matter literally of life or death. A single item of disproof could be enough to bring the whole life-sustaining edifice crashing. The killer item of counterevidence need not be spectacular, but a last straw, one final adversity that dissolves our faith in God, human nature, our guardian angel, or whatever else we thought had our back. A final blast of cold reality could snuff out the hope of salvation on which our mental health, if not survival, depends. It might be understandable, as the neurology suggests, that the brain registers attacks to deeply held beliefs using similar neural circuits with which it responds to physical threats.[6] For sure, loss of hope is potentially as lethal as any physical attack. We are more likely to die by our own hand than by anyone else's.

In view of the catastrophic consequences of our private paradigms failing, it seems to me that there is little to lose, but much to gain, from not going it alone, even though we could. Spiritual home-making is better done in a team. As part of a group of like-minded believers, individual self-deceptions can be pooled — the task of denying, accommodating, editing, or otherwise dealing with incongruent news can be shared. We can lean on each other's sense of conviction, help each other to keep our faith alive at times of stress, and together find ways to explain away factual anomalies as they crop up. The communal approach should work, provided we do not all find ourselves hopeless at the same time. Then again, if so great a disaster befell the community as to make us all hopeless at the same time, we'd probably be a lost cause anyway.

As the narrative detail of our paradigm doesn't much matter compared to the overriding need for defensibility, the local community's favourite myth is probably as good as any; and it offers the benefit of numbers. The popularity of the local version could, indeed, be taken as a sign of its strength as a sturdy foundation for a life worth living. My membership of the belief group gives me the protection of the group's belief — if it works for them, and if I am one of them, then I can bank on it working for me too. Perhaps going it alone is a privilege of a visionary few, or people living privileged lives. But for most of us, exposed to the usual hardships, it is probably safer to go along with the paradigm of one's nearest and dearest. Why shop elsewhere?

If this proposal is right, then we should expect adaptive defences against suicide to produce benign worldviews that are not only personal but communal. Collective belief systems — supernatural, optimistic, but arbitrary in their details — will spread and be strongly defended. Critically, for their life-affirming illusion to work, they can't be seen as illusory. A paradigmatic worldview needs to be accepted by its adherents not as just another myth among myths, but as an absolute and universal truth.

The joy of this arrangement is its virtual cycle, because belief in a benign world is a self-fulfilling prophesy to an important extent. The white lie creates its own truth. People sharing such beliefs should enjoy better mental health because, protected from psychache, there would be less suicidality and less need for keepers to activate. Believers will tend to feel better, look better, and do better than non-believers. Groups of people so advantaged would, presumably, do better than other groups. There would be a selective advantage in sharing a benign paradigm.

The evolution of religion

This line of argument seems to offer much-needed clues about the evolutionary origins of religion. Religiosity is found virtually everywhere, a universality that points to ancestral roots — it has probably always been a feature of human societies. Why it should be so has been a matter of hot debate among psychologists and evolutionists.

The irrationality of religions is in plain view. Their narratives are evidently the stuff of fantastic imagination: the world's creation stories, for example, a treasury of myth and legend. Religions are clearly costly in the time and resources they consume. They are, therefore, an easy target for avowedly rational, scientific, minds to pick apart.[7] The interesting question is why billions of human beings, many scientists included, nonetheless choose to believe.

Why do so many people find religion appealing? Presumably, there is a commensurately major upside that makes religions' factual distortions and other costs sustainable. This upside is not so easy to see, although various theories have been floated.

Let me run through the top five, as shortlisted by biologist David Sloan Wilson.[8] First, religion may result from an unfortunate flaw in the way humans think. We presume things happen on purpose, for intentional reasons. This stance is generally useful but it has a costly side-effect — we can't help imagining that divine agents are at work. Second, religions might spread because they bring social advantages — groups that are religious may have a competitive edge over other groups because their members are better at working together. Third, religions may be tools of oppression; they are one of the ways by which society's winners — high priests and divinely ordained leaders — keep the losers under control. Fourth, they could be a costly, non-adaptive, side-effect of some adaptation that is as yet unknown. Finally, perhaps religions are living fossils — remnants of an adaptation that used to bring us benefits in the ancient past, but not now.

All these ideas have arguable pros, but considerable cons. Among researchers, the hypothesis that seems to win most votes at the moment seems to be the first. Religion serves no adaptive purpose, so the theory goes; it feeds on us like a parasite, having found a weakness in the human mind. We are said to be so finely attuned to spot the handiwork of active agents in the world, so alert to intentional outcomes, that we can't help but imagine strings are being pulled by a hidden puppeteer. Thus, we are vulnerable to being hoodwinked and exploited by non-existent divine powers.[9]

It is an interesting idea. No doubt we do expect things to happen for a reason. That gut feeling, I suggested earlier, leads us to ask the unanswerable question, "*Why* do people kill themselves?" But the 'divine parasite' hypothesis doesn't comfortably explain religion to my mind, mainly because, over an evolutionary timescale, host organisms do not meekly put up with being parasitised. Selection tends to favour hosts that take measures to protect themselves. Parasites, in turn, cling on only by evolving countermeasures. The result is that parasites and hosts get locked in a running battle, both sides continually morphing in an effort to gain the upper hand.[10] But the imaginary godly parasites that supposedly blight us are static targets, not biological opponents — they have no way to evolve countermeasures. Our evolving resistance ought to be driving them out. But there is no sign of the kind of dynamic fightback that usually characterises host/parasite relationships. The great majority of the world's population, some 84%, continue to identify with a religious denomination, and the percentage is steadily growing.[11] I am suggesting the reverse is true: not that gods exploit humans, but humans exploit gods. It is not that we can't help but see a super-natural purpose — it's that we *need* to believe it. Human thriving, sanity, indeed our survival, depend on our conviction that some benign order holds sway over our lives.

Wilson himself prefers the second explanation — that religion pulls communities together. Religious cohesion, he suggests, may give a group such an advantage in its rivalries with other groups that, eventually, all groups end up having religions. But there are multiple problems with this account too, as Wilson acknowledges. Among the objections is the problem of pinning down a need, there being plenty of other ways to get people to cooperate. And religions are, in any event, much more than social vehicles. The main difficulty for me is that the hypothesis fails to address the felt spiritual experience of religion — the sense of a personal encounter with the divine. Religious belief comes with a distinct feeling that, as Wilson puts it, there is something not only *out* there, but *up* there. That sensation, or rather knowledge, can be so intense and compelling that can call people to defy, not comply, with social norms.[12] The most devout people are often not the most popular or co-operative.

Love and the God archetype

I am offering an alternative explanation, one that looks to me to be the most plausible. I suggest that religion is the purposeful, adaptive outcome of an evolved anti-suicide device, a pain-type fender. Religion is a communal resource that helps to buffer people from psychache. It offers a hopeful, defensible paradigm that gives coherence to people's optimistic self-deceptions, and helps them to maintain a positive reason for living. Religiousness shows remarkable, and for me compelling, evidence of special design in this respect, in four respects.

First, religious belief has a protective effect. Believers tend to be less suicidal, feel happier, and enjoy better mental health.[13] Rituals and ceremonies may be useful social binders, but the positive effect on well-being does not seem to arise from just going through the motions.[14] It is, rather, faith — belief in a benign higher order — that brings a mental health advantage.[15] The picture tells me that the purpose of religion is not primarily to promote social cohesion but, via its positive beliefs, to sustain a personally healthy state of mind.

Second, there is a strong community dynamic in religious belief. For this kind of product, we usually shop locally. There are countless equivalently meaningful religions to select from — that is to say, many equally plausible, but mutually exclusive, paradigms. But religious conversions almost always go along with the local favourite.[16] Arguably this neighbourliness could be taken to support Wilson's view of religion as social glue. But I suggest we should expect this pattern because, as I have argued, the plot detail of our personal worldview is less important than its defensibility. The most reliable belief system is probably the community's, because keeping one's hopeful beliefs upright in rough weather may be easier to do within a group of fellow believers. Despite the passion of our beliefs, our choice of religion is more down to expediency than principle.

Third, the reason expedience matters more than principle is that all successful religions make essentially the same promise: salvation.[17] This universal offer points to outwardly diverse belief systems meeting the same basic need. It is like money — the name of the preferred currency changes from place to place, but all currencies are equivalent in sense that they do the same job, performing the same communal function. Religions everywhere offer a shared code of ritual and liturgy with which members can assure themselves of a bright future, and protect themselves from misfortune. It seems to me that religions support precisely the benign, believable, defensible worldview that would be expected of Fender IV.

A bright future awaits because God(s), karma, the Great Spirit, or what you will, is good. Maybe not completely good, but at least steered by a moral compass. In this light, we can see the divine agents of religions not as parasites or cognitive errors, but as personifications of a benevolent order. In biblical terms, God is love — not merely loving, but love itself. In a godly world, driven by such values as compassion, justice, forgiveness, and charity, we can see our futures to be worth holding out for, in spite of today's suffering. God's authority, a universal moral law, trumps the laws of physics and biology. There is, in other words, more to life than Darwin has to offer. We are not here just to maximise our reproductive output, and we have more to look forward to than a dog-eat-dog existence. We need to believe, to *know*, that William James was wrong about nature cancelling herself out, zero equalling zero. There *is* something left over that we humans can feel warm and hopeful about. Religions differ inasmuch as they offer alternative visions of the same thing: a sense that life is worth the trouble.[18]

I further suggest that our readiness to believe in a divine promise of security, protection from future pain, likely exists as an innate structure. As ancient as humankind, it forms part of the standard human psyche. It links to the machinery of prepared learning that we discussed in Chapter 10 — the kind of inbuilt behavioural programme that makes us predisposed to deal with snakes, spiders, and other recurring encounters that mattered to our ancestors' success in the evolutionary past.

That religion springs from a preparedness for learning is not my idea: Carl Jung, psychiatrist and Sigmund Freud's onetime disciple, made a similar proposal a century ago. Anticipating a tenet of modern evolutionary psychology, Jung held that the mind is not born a blank slate. It comes pre-formatted with certain inherited archetypal ideas, instinctive blueprints that had value in our ancestral past. These archetypes may be realised in diverse ways in peoples' individual life experiences, but their parameters are common to us all.

Archetypes are powerful guiding forces for our thoughts and behaviours, even though we may not be aware of them.[19] It is much like the way babies come into the world pre-equipped with face-recognition software.

They are born already knowing the essentials of what a human face looks like — they don't have to be taught. Hence, even new-borns are drawn to look at faces, and not only real faces, but anything that looks vaguely like a face.[20] Being able to spot faces mattered for survival across human history, to the extent that a 'Face' archetype arose and spread by selection.

Jung's theory also connects to a tenet of animal psychology, imprinting, as explored by zoologist Konrad Lorenz in his work with birds. Lorenz found that goslings hatch apparently already knowing how to identify their mother (a certain size; moving; present at the nest) and what to do on recognising her (Follow her!). Crouched over their nest as he was, and meeting the archetypal criteria well enough, Lorenz's hatchlings took Lorenz to be their mother. They duly followed him anywhere — provided he stayed crouched.[21]

One of the archetypes humans are born with, according to Jung, could be labelled 'God'. In Jung's words, "the idea of the moral order and of God belong to the ineradicable substrate of the human soul."[22] It finds a match in a diversity of spiritual outlooks; the details don't matter, any more than the differences between a crouching Konrad Lorenz and a mother goose mattered to newly hatched goslings. Any God-like notion fits the bill provided it meets the archetype's minimal criteria: specifically, it seems to me, those three points I raised earlier — it must be caring, credible, and defensible.

From this perspective, God and Darwin may not be mutually exclusive. In a real sense, humankind owes its creation to God; and God would not have come about without the evolution of human believers. Around this dialectic, perhaps creationists and evolutionists could join hands.

The God idea can be vitally important for mental health, to the extent that it forms a central therapeutic plank in the modern treatment of addiction. Jung didn't know it at the time, but he pioneered this field via the extraordinary recovery of one of his patients, a businessman and chronic alcoholic by the name of Roland Hazard III. Hazard was so far gone in his addiction that Jung refused him further psychiatric treatment, judging it to be a waste of time. Hazard's only hope, according to Jung, was to throw himself into a religious order of his choice — it didn't matter which — and seek a spiritual experience. Desperate, Hazard followed the advice; and, to his own surprise, made a prompt, full, and lasting recovery. By a chain reaction, so did hundreds of similarly 'hopeless' cases. They went on to form what came to be called Alcoholics Anonymous, today non-denominational (long shorn of its original religious connection) and with a membership of millions.[23]

Echoing Jung's advice to Hazard, AA calls for the suffering individual to pick something — anything — that can serve as a basis for a spiritual outlook, and thereby restore the sufferer's sanity. Jung's theory of archetypes can be seen embedded in AA's main text:

> Deep down in every man, woman, and child, is the fundamental idea of God. It may be obscured by calamity, by pomp, by worship of other things, but in some form or other it is there. For faith in a Power greater than ourselves, and miraculous demonstrations of that power in human lives, are facts as old as man himself. We finally saw that faith in some kind of God was a part of our make-up, just as much as the feeling we have for a friend. Sometimes we had to search fearlessly, but He was there. He was as much a fact as we were. We found the Great Reality deep down within us. In the last analysis it is only there that He may be found. It was so with us.[24]

Interestingly, a higher power of the 'Sky Daddy' variety is not required. Perhaps it's for mental convenience that people like to personalise God in this way; it may be easier to anthropomorphise universal love as a Heavenly Father or Lord Above than to deal with a conceptual abstraction.[25] Atheists can and do get results in AA, by applying the same Jungian principle as do theists. For many, a loving group of AA members can meet the needs of the archetype; 'God' can be taken as an acronym — a 'Group of Drunks' following 'Good Orderly Direction'. Indeed, identification with a caring group seems necessary for success, and that alone can be enough. A group effect seems to arise on the same basis we discussed earlier in the context of religious conversions: "Whatever works for them, if I am one of them, will work for me too."

It sounds religious, but it isn't. To dismiss AA as a cult, as some critics do, is to overlook its roots in evolutionary psychiatry. AA's success indicates, I suggest, that a human capacity for faith may be, as Jung proposed, an ancestral psychological device. It can be seen operating both in formal religions and in secular self-help groups.

AA is not the only therapeutic approach to have stumbled upon the healing power of shared faith. I suspect it is the active ingredient of virtually every brand of psychotherapy. Any therapy boils down to group, if only a group of two, sharing a belief in a paradigm that can be relied upon to deliver a rewarding future. Provided it ticks the boxes of being benign, credible and defensible, the details of a paradigm don't seem to matter: hypnotherapy, CBT, psychoanalysis, homeopathy, antidepressants, take your pick. If the participants genuinely believe it will work, then it probably will.[26] As we will discuss in the final chapter, psychotherapy may necessarily succeed by placebo.

Putting faith into action

What we believe matters, but it also matters what we do. Faith without works is dead, they say. Dead indeed; we are discussing the basis for an appetite for life, and the avoidance of suicide. I suggest that belief in a benign paradigm is not enough. It must be put personally into action, because that action is personal evidence that the paradigm is valid.

Each of us is our own private test case. If I am to believe that the universe and its people care about my wellbeing, and if I feel I am part of that loving universe and one of its people, then I must look to my own caring behaviour towards others as proof that what I believe is true. If I go around exploiting people, then I can fairly assume that others, being like me, are also exploitative. If I care about the people I come across in my daily life, then I can harbour a hope, at least for the time being, that they care as I do. My benign paradigm begins with me. So, I suggest that our sense of wellbeing, our mental health, depends not just on wishing people well but on our willingness to act accordingly — on our readiness to give to others the same selfless love, charity, and forgiveness that we hope to receive for ourselves.

By this mechanism, I suggest we have a biological impetus to do good. We try to do good not because of profitable paybacks from others, but because our own good deeds are intrinsically faith-affirming. Indeed, the most emotionally rewarding opportunities for giving will be where there is no possibility of a payback by any route — where it is done, say, anonymously or as a parting gift.

I suspect that it's for this reason that many of us, perhaps all of us, sprinkle our lives with acts of pure charity. Many people are ready to give change to beggars, tip service staff, volunteer their time, give directions to travellers, help the blind and elderly across roads, hand over lost property, protect wildlife, care for pets, and so on. The same selflessness scaled up, people make large anonymous donations, leave bequests to charities, champion distant political causes, care for the aged and terminally ill, and adopt children.

I don't want to overstate the case. Not all giving is selfless; but enough giving is selfless to suggest that simple charity is an important facet of human nature. A study of $44 million of donations to an online crowd funding platform found that one dollar in every five was given anonymously. For part of that anonymous giving, the researchers could find no trace of an egoistic agenda: the sole motive for giving was that the recipient needed help.[27] So, it seems, an urge for unalloyed altruism plays out in human lives — kindness for its own sake.

Selflessness surfaces in peoples' working hours as well as in their spare time. My impression is that many workers routinely do more than is necessary, and they do it for its own reward, not for any economic or other extrinsic payoff. I can offer only anecdotes and hearsay to support the point, but I take it to be commonplace experience. A teacher nearing retirement — so, for no career advantage — spends more than her contracted time to help a struggling student. A security guard goes beyond the call of duty to help a tourist in difficulty. A priest says a prayer for a dying parishioner and the soon-to-be bereaved. Such workaday gifts are not only materially unrewarded but often unrewardable in a transactional sense. There may be money changing hands — people get paid. And unpaid overtime may get noticed — people get promoted. But this is not about money or status.

Money and status are not particularly strong motivators, at least not in day-to-day human affairs. This is an accepted fact of life in business management. Material rewards and other extrinsic, superficial payoffs were importantly classed as 'hygiene factors' by industrial psychologist Frederick Herzberg. They need to be dealt with at a minimal level, but they're not the main reason why we feel happy in our work or spurred to go the extra mile. The rewards that motivate us are more to do with the intrinsic satisfaction of what we do — such as a sense of achievement, personal growth, and the work feeling worthwhile. In other words, argued Herzberg, human beings are not driven by the same primary instincts that motivate other animals.[28] From the evolutionary stance of this book, we can see why this would be so. Humans have otherworldly needs: we are not designed to live by bread alone.

I am suggesting that selfless giving is something we like to do, and for no other reason than for the emotional uplift to be had from doing it.[29] We give, often anonymously and unseen, because we sense ourselves to be participants in a caring universal order. We act as if that order, a higher power, is watching. As a Jungian archetype, it is indeed watching — from within. So, the urge to nurture our own faith by doing good, by honouring our benign paradigm, is built into our genome. To this extent, we are all saints.

The origins of unconditional giving

If this is true, there may be an important evolutionary dimension to human altruism that goes beyond the transactional rules of normal fitness economics. Evolutionists have long puzzled over our capacity to be generous in situations where, in a cold biological calculation, giving looks pointless, indeed self-harming.[30] Organisms do not normally give away resources, or do anything else for that matter, unless there is a biological reward. Without an obvious selective advantage, pure selflessness doesn't look evolvable.

Many ideas have been put forward to explain the anomaly. Perhaps true altruism is a mistake, a misfiring of our proper evolved programmes; if so, it strikes me as an oddly expensive and prevalent mistake, and one that could have been straightforwardly corrected. Most theories, rather, look to explain acts of apparent altruism as the work of the invisible hand of the market. Our supposedly free gifts aren't as free as they look, so it is said. They may not be direct transactions, but they're transactions nonetheless, done for the sake of egoistic paybacks. We touched on one of these ideas earlier in this book, based on the principle of inclusive fitness. Kin relations have copies of our genes, so there may be a genetic gain to be had from helping kin to raise their offspring — such behaviours may look altruistic, but they are genetically self-serving. Another idea is that what looks like generosity is actually one side of a deal, so-called reciprocal altruism: it's really mutual backscratching, or mutual exploitation, but with a time lag in between the investment and the payoff. Yet another argues that returns on investment come via third parties; supposed charity may really be like depositing savings in a mutual society, to be repaid with interest by other members. Yet others suggest that altruism is virtue signalling — it's really an outlay in advertising, for the purpose of communicating one's attractiveness as a trading partner for future transactions. Evolutionary psychologists Leda Cosmides and John Tooby suggest generosity is a way to buy friends as an insurance against hard times: manipulating a useful person into owing you a favour is a way around the 'banker's paradox' — that when the time comes that you need a loan, your credit may be too poor to get one.[31]

Now, I am not arguing that these economic views of human generosity are wrong. There is, as ever, a fitness balance to be struck. There has to be a limit to our selfless giving because we have other calls on our resources, and we have only so much to give. Humans have to survive in the real biological world as much as any other life-form.

What I am arguing is that, ultimately because of our capacity for suicide, regular biological economics does not have a free hand in human affairs. We won't be able to make sense of human kindness using the same kind of social programmes that play out among, say, chimps or rats. Cosmides and Tooby's banking metaphor won't guide us far into the realm of altruism, because, I suggest, unconditional gifting is not an answer to the banker's paradox; it's a recipe, rather, for the banker's bankruptcy. There is no economic logic in setting up a joint venture with a partner who cannot contribute — or, worse, can be relied upon to give the business's assets away.

Indeed, the mere fact that evolutionists find the economics of human kindness curious — worthy of interest at all — tells me that economics is not the right conceptual tool for the job. The point of transactions and signals in a marketplace is to be clear about what buyers and sellers are agreeing to. If market principles applied, we should be in no doubt about what is going on. I scratch your back, and you'll scratch mine — deal done. It is, after all, our own market. We shouldn't need psychologists to unravel the commercial mystery of human generosity for the same reason that we don't need psychologists to divine the price of a bun; we can ask the baker.

If we find the fitness payoff of charity puzzling by economic standards, it may be because we are using the wrong standards, the wrong paradigm. A better paradigm, I suggest, is a benign world as shaped by Fender IV. It operates outside of rational economics. It is a goodly universe where we can hope for more pleasure and less pain than the unchecked laws of biology and physics could reasonably provide. It is a place where we can all be better-than-average drivers, where tasks take less time than experience says is likely, and where the terminally ill can expect to get well. It is where human beings want to live.

The Golden Rule

The personal necessity to put faith into action shines out of another feature that I offer as a fourth and final reason to think religion may be a display of Fender IV. It is the Golden Rule: do unto others as you would have them do unto you. The rule appears in some version in virtually every religious tradition, and it is golden because it sums a universal formula for human happiness.[32] Love thy neighbour as thyself: the benchmark of how we are to behave towards others is how we would want the universe to behave towards us. Love of others is how we put our faith into action.

The Golden Rule may sound like a reciprocal transaction, but it isn't. No exchange is involved. The Rule explains why human giving is often anonymous, unrewarded, and unrewardable. The Rule is unenforceable; obeying it is a matter of voluntary choice, not social expectation. Its writ applies regardless of whether we trust the 'others', or like them, or even know them. The Rule does not concern itself with what others do to us. How they respond — if they respond at all — is irrelevant. It is not required that others feel obligated because of what we do. They don't have to value it, understand it, or even like it. It is not necessary for them to notice, remember, or even know about our acts of love. The task of adhering to the Golden Rule is ours alone.[33]

The relationship between love received and love given is not transactional. It looks to me to be, rather, a relationship between the leader and the led. You can see the dynamic at work in the biblical axiom, "Freely have you received, freely give." In the middle, between receiving and giving, there is no economic connector, only a comma. The 'freely' cuts both ways. Love received isn't accepted as a contractual liability; it's an example to follow, a baton to relay, something to pay forward. It is the kind of credible, first-hand encouragement that only someone who has been there can offer, along the lines of "Come on in, the water's lovely!" The Golden Rule reassures us that we needn't be scared to give unconditionally.

If there is reciprocity going on here, it is on a conceptual rather than an economic plane. Love received and love given need each other as counterparties. One is religion's universal promise of salvation — what the world is to give to us. The other is the Golden Rule as a universal morality — what we are to give to the world. Each calls for the other. In one direction, if I genuinely believe the promise, that the world and its people care about my wellbeing, then I must behave as if I believe it. I need to act as if I am a participant in that world, and an agent of its care, by following the Golden Rule. In the other direction, I can give to the world unconditionally only if I'm sure the benign world has my back, that I won't just be emptied out. I need to believe that as I give to the world, so the world will give to me. The Golden Rule presupposes a promise of salvation.

One could mistake the Golden Rule as a tool of regular inclusive fitness because we get to draw our own lines around who we see as 'others' — the targets of our unconditional love. The boundary will vary from person to person, and tradition to tradition. The core of family and friends will usually be on the inside, so you could jump to the conclusion that the lines of charity are drawn on nepotistic or tribal criteria. But the Rule can stretch beyond that. Faith in human nature spans the species. Many people accept a responsibility of care towards other animals, or all life, or the global environment. The boundary of 'others' means only that there's some exclusivity built into the Rule. But within our 'others' frontier, inside the limits of our benign world, we can believe that the power of natural selection does not go unchecked. Our happiness requires us to behave as if we are not just out for ourselves, that we exist not just to be breeding machines, and that nature is not entirely red in tooth and claw.

Other people's take on the Golden Rule can be, and often is, different from ours. There is no reason why it should be the same. If we expect it to be the same, then the Rule's non-reciprocal nature can come as a shock. It can be traumatising to find that other peoples' compassion has different boundaries to ours, and that we are on the outside. Illustrating the point, Auschwitz survivor Jean Améry (an Austrian, born Hanns Mayer, he changed his name after the war to disassociate himself from all things German), writes of the psychological scar left by the torture he received at the hands of his SS interrogators. They were fellow German speakers. But to them, Améry was not one of their 'others' — he was a race apart. The emotional effect of the betrayal outlived Améry's physical wounds; it destroyed his faith. Abuse at the hands of people who we expect to care can do that. It feels like reneging on a deal. It left Améry thirsting for revenge.[34]

Resentment, they say, is like drinking poison and expecting someone else to die. Forgiving others' trespasses against us is not easy, but we do it for our benefit, not theirs. The task of maintaining our own benign paradigm — to keep on loving, following the Golden Rule — doesn't go away in the face of hate. It is for our own mental stability that we preserve our caring inner sanctuary, regardless of what others do. Améry, by the way, eventually took his own life.

Love evolved

This chapter has tried to explain what I think may be the biological foundations of love: the unconditional giving of ourselves for others' benefit. In a sense, love is a lie. It is a self-deception, born of an imagined, supernaturally hopeful universe, a place where it is possible to keep on giving and receiving something for nothing. In a normal fitness calculation, truly no-strings altruism makes no sense. But for humans, paradoxically, the lie creates its own truth; love is a signal of faith in a benign paradigm, and it thereby projects that paradigm into real human affairs. We have the evidence of our own eyes that our paradigm is real in the selfless good we see others do, as well as in our own choices. The experience of others' love can restore our faith: it can thereby heal all manner of psychological ailments, as the final chapter will discuss. The act of loving — what M. Scott Peck calls the *work* of love— reveals and reaffirms a guiding code that we can live by.[35] The presence or absence of love often marks the difference between lives that are, and are not, felt to be worthwhile.[36]

Hence, I suggest, people who find life worth living have love in their lives. They put faith into action. They usually have a focus for giving selflessly of themselves, to something or someone, out of genuine concern for those others. Lasting happiness lies in the good we try to do to others, independently of what they do to us, because the surest love is given rather than received. In this way, ascending from our evolved anti-suicide machinery, human love has special, adaptive roots. As Desmond Tutu puts it, we are hardwired for goodness.[37]

CHAPTER 11: *To keep psychache at bay, Fender IV causes us to perceive reality through the rosy lens of a supernaturally hopeful view of ourselves in the world. Religiosity helps us defend this benign personal paradigm from factual attack. The God archetype, true altruism, and the Golden Rule — the morality of love — connect as parts of our evolved faith-affirming machinery.*

CHAPTER 12: *The need for life to be worth living separates humans from other animals. We are well equipped, as products of selection, to cope with the capacity for suicide and to handle adversities in life. These evolved safeguards offer a novel scientific paradigm in mental health, integrating suicide prevention, psychiatry and psychotherapy.*

12

MORE THAN
LUMBERING ROBOTS

This book began with an observation so commonplace that it looks trivial. Most of us, most of the time, want to live and enjoy living. But in the story of life on earth, this is not a trivial state of affairs. It is a big deal, in two senses.

First, that any organism should take pleasure in being alive is a momentous event. It may be an evolutionary novelty, and it is almost certainly a uniquely human privilege. The reason we can be almost sure no other animals likes living is because no other animal needs to. As far as can be known, up to the arrival of our species, life on earth had no choice in the matter. It was under totalitarian genetic control. It is probably fair to think of other animals as, to borrow Richard Dawkins' metaphor, lumbering robots — non-conscious automatons, dumbly serving the interests of their genes.[1]

We are more than that, because, second, a big deal was struck during our species' evolution. With the emergence of modern humans, genes found themselves served not by an unthinkingly compliant slave but by an intelligent and powerful negotiating partner. In our singular case, the robot became human — a person with a mind of her own and interests of her own that demanded to be respected.

In Chapter 4 we imagined a drama playing out between two biological characters that live together in every life-form. One is the organism's phenotype, the physical living being. The other is its genotype, the being's genetic code — an inherited store of information about reproductive threats and opportunities that faced the phenotype's ancestors, and about how those ancestors responded. Phenotype and genotype are partnered up because they need each other. Neither can survive without the other. The phenotype owes its birth and success in life to the genotype's information store. The genotype has only one objective, to reproduce its genes into future generations: for that task, it needs the phenotype to reproduce — and usually, to have any chance of reproducing, it needs the phenotype to stay alive. With the exception of modern humans, the lot of the phenotype is to perform unquestioningly that procreational role. If the phenotype's life is full of pain and suffering, well, tough.

The human phenotype took a different direction when it evolved such intelligence that it became conscious of its own mortality. It came to realise that suffering was optional. It could relieve pain by switching itself off. Remember that pain is a motivator. It is designed precisely to force the phenotype to do something to end the aversive experience. For humans, that something can be self-killing. Hence, for humans, suicide is an ever-present, all-purpose answer to pain. But although self-killing presents a neat solution for the phenotype, it is a disaster for the genotype. The phenotype's death ends any possibility of future reproduction.

So, now there's a stand-off within the human organism. To dramatise the dispute, let's call the characters by name again, Genotype and Phenotype, as they confront each other. Genotype needs Phenotype to survive and reproduce; but Phenotype has other ideas, because its first priority is to stop hurting. "Hold up!" says Phenotype to Genotype, "Not so fast! You want to use my reproduction services? Then make it worth my while. Ease my pain. Give me a reason to stay alive. Then I might — only might — do you the favour of procreating."

The ensuing haggle between Phenotype and Genotype ran on across thousands of generations, Phenotype negotiated from a position of strength because it held, and still holds, the ace in its hand — the ultimate sanction, the extinction of both parties. Phenotype can decide, as many have, "If this life, then I don't want it." Faced with this threat, Genotype has been forced to make extraordinary concessions. It went as far as to create a new experiential reality for Phenotype to enjoy living in.

Thus, our appetite for life is no mere blessing or happy accident. It was paid for by past generations. We are the beneficiaries of decisions made by people who were *not* our ancestors — countless men and women who rejected what they found on offer, removed themselves from the Darwinian struggle, and took their genes with them. Our life worth living was won by their voluntary deaths. The result is the human condition as we know it — that is, natural biology enriched with love, hope, faith, compassion, charity, joy, beauty, and any other super-natural values we may choose to live by. Much of the way humans think and behave looks peculiar by normal biological standards, and it *is* peculiar, precisely because it serves no purpose other than to meet one peculiarly human need — for a life that feels liveable. We are this way only because of the capacity for suicide. Suicide and love of life are sides of the same coin. Without one, we would not have the other.

I have argued that many curious, apparently irrational, aspects of human thought and behaviour stem from this single origin — the evolution of suicide and its corollary, the evolution of life worth living. The curiosities include: the way we respond to emotional pain with depression, addiction, and many other forms of mental ill-health; our denial of painful realities; our over-optimistic view of ourselves and our worlds; our tendency to be quite happy much of the time; the time and energy we devote to pleasurable activities that have little or no direct fitness value; religious and spiritual belief; our capacity for charity, unconditional generosity, love, and forgiveness; and the Golden Rule — that it feels right to treat others as we would like to be treated, to an important extent independently of how others behave towards us. All these strands tie together to form an integrated biological safety net. What they have in common is irrationality. They make little sense in a normal equation of pros and cons of reproductive fitness. But human irrationality is based, paradoxically, on fitness logic; it keeps most us, most of the time, safe from self-destruction.

The pain-and-brain theory

Let's look back at the trail of the previous chapters. We traced the origins of human irrationality to an ancestral chase for intelligence. If you are a social hominid, it pays you to be smart. Being brainy gives you an advantage in your battles, in which you are pitched not so much against the elements, but against your fellows. In that competition, because you are smart, you have the advantage of being able to second guess what others are thinking. You can predict what they'll do next, and you can deceive them about your own intentions. Thanks to your brains, success and riches are yours for the thinking. For this reason, your intelligence is sought after in the dating market. Would-be mates compete for your attention. The brainiest suitors tend to win that battle too, and you will probably choose a clever partner. Between you, if cleverness is in your genes, your children may get a double dose, perhaps being even smarter than you. They will be ahead of their peers, able to pick the brightest mates for themselves, and in turn raise smarter and more successful families. Each generation of your descendants, the brainiest selecting the brainiest, may look forward to ever better reproductive results. Unless, of course, the day comes when they meet their match, outsmarted by the offspring of rivals even smarter than you. The way to beat big brains is with even bigger brains. A cognitive arms race thus rampaged through human evolution; a war of intelligence fought with intelligence. Across thousands of generations, our ancestors' brains expanded, selected in the relentless pursuit of computing power. Until...here we are: *Homo sapiens*, with intelligence, or sapience, as the defining feature of our species.

A price has to be paid, because intelligence was never free. There are many major biological downsides to being smart — physical and psychological. Among the anatomical challenges we discussed, mothers have to give birth to big-brained babies. To accommodate the enlarged infant skull, the female pelvis has widened, probably as far as it practically can. The human brain carries on building itself long after birth, so human immaturity is a drawn-out affair by primate standards. To support this long dependency, human parents tend to form lasting pair bonds, which calls for yet more adjustments — bodily, mental, and social. Such secondary adaptations, forced on us by our intelligence, touch almost every aspect of our lives.

As for the psychological cost of human intelligence, the fallout of one catastrophic downside has been the focus of this book; the option it creates for humans to escape pain by killing themselves. When precursors of modern humans became smart enough to conceive of their own mortality, they stepped over a line. At that threshold, the opportunity to end pain by suicide emerged. This intellectual Rubicon can be seen crossed today in the age pattern of suicide: virtually non-existent before puberty, and suddenly appearing in the teen years. Almost all of us acquire the mental potential for suicide sometime in adolescence, as part of the normal development of the human brain.

Before the evolutionary threshold was crossed, the intellect of the average adult would have been held safely below that of a modern-day pubescent child. But runaway pressure of selection kept shoving average intelligence closer to the suicidal cliff edge. For a long while, it could go no further, because individuals growing up on the wrong side of the line culled themselves, their genes dying out with them. Our ancestors were stuck behind the cusp of suicidality, perhaps for hundreds of thousands of years, while solutions to the problem evolved. Selection favoured genetic mutations that had some anti-suicide effect, even if it was just enough to keep a super-intelligent individual willing to live for now, die another day. Eventually, when these adaptations became effective enough, a population of our ancestors crossed the frontier. Their bloodline shifted rapidly to a level of intelligence beyond what was previously survivable. This is us — behaviourally modern humans.

I have proposed that two matching pairs of anti-suicide adaptations evolved. One pair are emergency measures, labelled *keepers*. These activate among adolescents and adults who are suffering intense and chronic emotional pain, or psychache. One of these forms, *pain-type keepers*, dulls the motivation for self-killing, numbing psychache, or otherwise making it provisionally bearable. The other one, *brain-type keepers*, denies us intellectual access to the means for suicide; they make it hard for us to organise complex projects, suicide included. This internal suicide-prevention team shows up in mental ill-health, in diverse syndromes that psychiatry takes to be mental disorders — depressions, addictions, generalised anxiety, psychoses, obsessive-compulsive disorders, and others.

The job of the other pair of anti-suicide adaptations, which I called *fenders*, is to stop us having to rely on keepers' extreme and costly interventions. *Pain-type fenders* try to keep us clear of psychache in the first place. They block us from experiencing certain painful realities, while creating a pleasurable buffer zone, a happy state in which we can usually cope with painful shocks. These are what make life positively worth living. *Brain-type fenders* are cultural defences — a learned stigma and taboo, and beliefs about a painful afterlife. These mechanisms give us a sense that, even if living hurts, it's still better than the alternative.

Does all this matter? I think very much so. Our species' suicidal niche, and the way we have adapted to it, shines a light on the experience of being human, and it offers a new approach to understanding human psychology. It offers a unifying alternative to several disconnected paradigms that currently dominate Western psychological sciences, and which I suggest are long overdue for review. To conclude the story, let me draw your attention to three examples — ways of thinking that I think could be changed for the better.

A new framework for suicide research

The first of these concerns the main conceptual foundation on which science has sought to understand and prevent suicide over the last hundred years — and failed. I raised the point in Chapter 2. There is a pervasive assumption that suicides must happen for an identifiable reason. Some special process of cause-and-effect must be going on, the thinking goes; so, if we identified the cause, we could stop the effect. I have called this assumed cause 'suigiston'. The approach looks reasonable from a common-sense standpoint. Gut feeling says the suigiston idea ought to fly, but it has not got off the ground.

Three major flaws in the idea tell me that it may never get off the ground. One is a continuing void in theory. Despite more than a century of concerted thinking, no one has come up with a coherent reason as to why suicide, as opposed to some other course of action, would logically follow from any particular set of conditions.

The second flaw is the idea's one-hundred-percent practical failure. Despite decades of research, science has made zero progress in finding any factor or method that comes even close to predicting suicide. There are thousands of known risk factors (age, sex, personality type, access to firearms, and so on) and dozens of allegedly predictive tools (questionnaires, statistical tests, interview techniques) — many ways, then, for health workers to try to divine whether a patient is at risk of taking their own life. But none of them work. No criterion or technique has been found that usefully distinguishes would-be suicides from non-suicides. No test performs much better than chance.[2] The great majority of people classed 'high risk' do not try to kill themselves, while most suicides happen among people who would supposedly be 'low risk'.

The third problem is that, as we have seen in this book, the suigiston paradigm conflicts with our knowledge of the way biological traits evolve — by selection. Suicide is an evolved phenomenon, as are the adaptations that stop us doing it. We should expect selection to have shaped the human brain to react to every scrap of information that usefully predicts self-killing. All the suicides that *can* be foreseen already *are* foreseen by the human organism, and duly blocked from happening. The few remaining suicides that do happen — incidents that find a way through our natural defences — are those that were not seen coming. They *could not* have been seen coming. In statistics, they would be called residuals. They are intrinsically not open to prediction at the level of the individual, or at least not by any means currently imaginable. If the model set out in this book is right, then the quest for suicide's mythical predictors is doomed to carry on failing. There is no reason to think that another century of suigiston-hunting will be any less futile than the last.

The problem with the suigiston paradigm is not just that it's empty: it is actively harmful. Let me run through some of the harms. First, it sets up the bereaved to feel an irrational and unfair sense of guilt. It is traumatising enough to lose a loved one, or indeed a patient, to suicide. For science to imply, on the basis of no evidence, that suicides can somehow be foreseen, and presumably therefore be forestalled, is to add a gratuitously cruel burden to the trauma.

Second, an entire medical profession is caught up in an elaborate charade of risk assessment. Mission impossible, second-guessing suicide, is all in a day's work for psychiatrists; it is a 'core competency requirement'. They find themselves having to keep up to date with, and implement, the latest risk assessment techniques, all equally unproven, for fear of laying themselves open to malpractice suits if they don't. At the same time, in the event of such a suit, they are briefed on how to explain to a tribunal that suicide is, in fact, not foreseeable.[3] While none of this legalistic dance serves the interests of patients, there is an opportunity cost in the time wasted: there are better things health professionals could do with the hours taken up by time-consuming, but uselessly inaccurate, suicide risk assessments.

Third, the labelling of people as 'high risk' or 'low risk' can cause them psychological damage. People classed as 'high risk' are pointlessly stigmatised and made to worry, while the real needs of others routinely go unseen and unaddressed.[4]

Fourth, most perniciously to my mind, the myth that suicide is foreseeable gives a false sense of legitimacy to the prescribing of mindaltering drugs, with significant side-effects, as a supposedly 'evidenced' prevention strategy.[5] Psychopharmacy is evidently not particularly effective at relieving suicidality, and it is no more effective than non-drug therapies.[6] But even in principle, there being no effective way to assess individual risk, drugging cannot work unless whole populations are caught willy-nilly in a prescribing dragnet. A policy of mass medication may be in the commercial interests of the pharmaceutical industry, but it is questionably useful for the great majority of drugged individuals, people who never were going to take their own lives. Even on a mass scale, there is little evidence that drugging works: in the United States, throughout years of prolific antidepressant use, the suicide rate continued to rise.[7] Perhaps mass treatment would be ethical if the side-effects were negligible. It would be akin to putting fluoride in the public water supply to combat tooth decay. It is a fair thought: researchers have actually proposed putting lithium in the water as a suicide prevention measure.[8] I don't know if it would work, but it would at least be honest — free of the pretence that there is some kind of clinical targeting going on.

Any suicide prevention policy is fundamentally flawed if it depends on accurately assessing risk at the level of the individual: it cannot be done. Researchers and clinicians alike tend to fudge this awkward reality. Some cling to the old truism that that absence of evidence is not the same as evidence of absence.[9] But this is a vacuous argument, the 'yeti' position — we haven't found evidence *yet*. If scope for a usefully predictive method existed, we can expect more than a hundred years of psychiatry to have found a trace of it by now. For determined believers, the facts may never persuade them otherwise, but by any reasonable assessment, there comes a point where the evidential silence needs to be heard.

To call off the hunt for suigiston, to accept that suicide's causes are unknown and probably unknowable, is not a counsel of despair. It is an honest facing of facts — a getting real that could bring practical benefits in reducing misery and saving lives. It would help to ease the blameless guilt of survivors and invite a long-overdue review of the drug-led approach of Western suicide prevention. Most importantly, it could redirect attention and resources into developing other strategies that offer better prospects for success. I suggest that the pain-and-brain model of suicide points to ways in which we could co-operate, rather than blindly tamper, with the human organism's own 'pain' and 'brain' anti-suicide machinery.

For example, on the 'brain' side, suicides can be prevented by practical measures that add to the difficulty of organising a self-killing — so-called means restriction.[10] This strategy probably aligns with the way the human mind is built. We are not designed to live in environments where opportunities for lethal self-injury are easily to hand. I have argued that our evolved defences were naturally selected on the basis that ancestral humans did not find suicide practically easy to do. Keepers exploit the lag between thought and action: they dull the motivation for escape and make it difficult for people in suicidal crises to organise complex tasks. Such crises usually ease spontaneously in a matter of hours, even minutes, as the mind's emotional balance restores itself to its usual, slightly warm, position.[11] So, any obstacle, anything that buys a little time, will probably have a shielding effect — or, rather, it will help the human organism to shield itself. Obstructions that make a suicidal project just slightly more complicated or time-consuming — such as barriers at commonly used jump sites, small retail packs of drugs often used for overdosing, or storing one's gun at a depot — would be expected to get results.

Proponents of this kind of prevention method often face public hostility — efforts to veto the installing of anti-jump nets, for example.[12] The objections arise from a misunderstanding. It's mistakenly assumed that suicidal individuals will be in a normal frame of mind, normal enough to swap to using some other means, thus making the means restriction pointless. If one bridge is netted off, they'd just go to another, right? But there is little evidence that this kind of switching happens in practice, and we can see why. It might help if policy makers better understood the protective confusion that is likely to be in play at these critical times. The theory could help with overcoming misinformed objections.

On the 'pain' side, other interventions could usefully tackle the psychache that is responsible for suicidal thoughts. The pain is usually social.[13] Anything that shows people that the world cares about their well-being can be expected to help — a support line to call, a self-help group to team up with, or just a reassuring postcard or a phone call.[14] Sometimes we just need to see a sign that our benign worldview, our faith in human nature, is no mere fantasy. Small gestures can make a big difference, restoring our belief that we have a future worth soldiering on for. We all need hope.

Taking this point further, perhaps the greatest benefit of discarding the suigiston idea is that it could change for the better the therapeutic relationship between mental health workers and their patients. Every wise medic understands that it is the organism that does the healing, not the medic's intervention. The best treatments leverage the organism's own capacity to restore itself. So, when patients present with strains, colds, and other common physiological ailments, a doctor can often make helpful interventions while giving genuine reassurance. A doctor can say something along the lines of "Yes, I see the problem. That looks nasty and I can see it hurts. But don't worry! It happens to many people, virtually all of them recover just fine, and I am confident you will too. The body is very good at healing itself. It usually just needs time and a little T.L.C. — tender loving care. Now, you are going to be sore for a while, but the soreness is there for your own protection. It's telling you to look after yourself. Let's have another look at this in a few weeks, shall we?"

I imagine a day when mental health professionals can have similar conversations over psychological ailments, thereby joining their counterparts elsewhere in medicine. Someone troubled by thoughts of suicide could be offered equally genuine reassurance. The doctor could say something very similar, such as: "Yes, I see the problem. That must be very upsetting. But don't worry. Many people have thoughts like that at difficult stages in their lives, and virtually all of them feel better in time, and I am confident that you will too. The human mind is very good at healing itself. It usually just needs time and a little T.L.C. — tender loving care. You may feel poorly for a while, but that feeling is there for your own protection. It's telling you to look after yourself. Why don't we try to get to the bottom of why you are hurting? The sooner you can deal with that, the sooner you can get back to enjoying life. What kind of support do you feel you need?" In other words, instead of arbitrarily labelling people as 'high risk' and drugging them to correct an imagined mental deficiency, doctors could empathically impart a sense of hope, competence, and empowerment.[15]

If there is a targeted solution to suicidality, then it is going to involve, as the therapist Marsha Linehan points out, building a life worth living. The therapeutic scheme she devised, Dialectical Behavioural Therapy (DBT), focuses on helping people find ways to sort out their painful life situations, with the support of a like-minded group.[16] Dealing with the root cause of psychological pain boils down to changing something or, if it can't be changed, accepting it. It is a two-way action plan that Linehan sums in the word 'dialectical'. DBT won't be unique in this wisdom; it's a staple of AA and other mutual aid groups, for example. But there is no logic in restricting DBT, or any other intervention, to people who have been labelled, almost always wrongly, as 'high risk'. On humanitarian grounds, anyone who is in enough emotional pain to have thoughts of killing themselves deserves help, whatever the risk assessment says.[17] For that matter, equally worthy of help is anyone who is suffering enough psychache to induce mental disorder, with or without suicidal thoughts. Social pain, a biological signal, points to a need almost by definition. Suicidal thoughts and mental disorder are but symptoms of pain's one malady — they are regular human responses to chronic psychache.

So, the key question is this: how do we combat psychache? There's much that can be done at the individual level, as we will discuss. But ultimately this is also a matter for governments and their voters. It has been well said that suicide prevention starts with housing, not hotlines. There is overwhelming evidence that social injustice — especially the experience of disadvantage, exposure to violence and conflict, and displacements for whatever cause — contribute to mental ill-health in all its diverse forms.[18] This is the central point; diverse mental troubles have a common origin in the experience of emotional pain. It brings us to the second paradigm that I suggest is overdue for ditching.

An end to DSM-ism

I raised the problem in Chapter 8: psychiatry's preoccupation with diagnostic labels. Let's give the paradigm a name. I suggest *DSM-ism*, in honour of psychiatry's main catalogue of disorders, the Diagnostic and Statistical Manual, published by the American Psychiatric Association.[19] The DSM dates from the 1950s and is updated now and then according to changing moods of the time. It gives labels for dozens of classifications, such as 'obsessive-compulsive' disorders (OCD), 'schizophrenia', 'post-traumatic stress disorder' (PTSD), and so on. The problem is that there is no evidence that the great majority of these labels refer to real things in the real world. To be fair to DSM's authors, it was never claimed that the labels are real. The DSM scheme was put forward just as a stop-gap, awaiting the day when the causes of 'functional' mental disorders are understood. Until that day comes, disorders have to be decided arbitrarily, by committee, if only to bring consistency to clinical practice and the collection of statistics. Diagnostic labels were never intended to signal the existence of distinct natural phenomena, and there is no reason to think they do.

Here is one piece of evidence that diagnostic labels are *not*, in fact, separate diseases: different diagnoses can be relieved by the same therapy. For example, DBT, mentioned above, was devised to help with a particular disorder; borderline personality disorder. And so it does, with evident success. But it also turns out to alleviate depression, anxiety, and eating disorders.[20] AA's Twelve Step programme was formulated to deal with alcoholism, but with only slight tweaks, it also turns its hand to many other addictions, compulsive behaviours, and other mental health problems.[21] This non-specificity is found across the board for so-called talking therapies: if it works for one psychiatric malady, then it probably also works for others.[22] The same is true of drug therapies. For example, one class of drug, reuptake inhibitors, was originally pitched as an anti-depressant. But it has become a general-purpose go-to drug, commonly used also to treat anxiety, PTSD, OCD, and anorexia nervosa. Another drug, ketamine (which began life as an anaesthetic), is a treatment for both depression and PTSD, and so on.

This pattern of cure-alls gives the lie to the idea that psychiatric labels are equivalent to bodily disorders, such as acne, malaria, or gallstones — each with its own cause, a particular course, and calling for a custom-ised treatment. In physical diseases, a panacea-like effect would be aston-ishing. You are very unlikely to find a cream for acne that turns out, by serendipity, also to relieve malaria and gallstones, because each of these conditions is known to stem from a different biological process. The fact that diverse mental disorders do respond to common treatments suggests that they flow, instead, from a common biological source.

Many other lines of evidence point in the same direction, to an underlying one-ness in psychiatric labels. I discussed some of these in Chapter 8. There are dozens of cross-diagnostic features. They throw a mesh of connections around sundry shades of 'functional' common mental disorder, which I argue is best understood as one thing: CMD. The connections include the following:

- Heightened suicidality: More specifically, CMD associates strongly with suicidal ideas, but only weakly with the progression of those ideas into suicidal actions.[23]

- Common pattern of cause: CMD is usually triggered by emotion-ally painful events.[24]

- Non-specificity of cause: To a large extent, any kind of severe life adversity can trigger any form of CMD.[25]

- Common pattern of recovery: Given favourable conditions, CMD usually lifts in time — with or without medical intervention.[26]

- Extreme comorbidity: People diagnosed with one form of CMD often also meet the criteria for one or more others, concurrently or at different times.[27]

- Lack of 'zones of rarity' — Like colours of the rainbow, there are no natural boundaries between different CMD diagnoses.[28]

- Common cognitive impairments: CMD interferes with memory and logical thinking, making it hard to organize complex tasks.[29]

- Hallucination. Not unique to schizophrenia as is often imagined, the phenomenon also occurs with other forms of CMD.[30]

- Common age of first onset: Although there are distinct disorders in early childhood, CMD usually starts to appear from adolescence onwards, rarely earlier.[31]

- Species-specificity: Despite an intensive search, no animal equivalent has yet been found for CMD syndromes.[32]

- Lack of a biological marker: No biomedical test exists for any individual CMD diagnosis.[33]

- Common risk factor: People tend to be vulnerable or resistant not to particular forms of CMD but to CMD generally.[34]

...and so on.

These cross-overs are rarely discussed. Few researchers are even looking for them. We can guess that if the lens of the research effort was adjusted to see them, more clues as to CMD's one-ness would appear. But, for now, DSM-ism keeps our attention focussed on made-up divisions.

The artificial dividing lines begin in the doctor's consulting room. Patients arrive with often ambiguous blends of symptoms, but clinicians are almost obliged to pigeon-hole them into one or other DSM-style category.[35] From that point on, although they are manufactured, the labels take on a life of their own, like so many Frankenstein's monsters. Each collects its own statistics, recruits its own community of researchers, and builds its own silo of theory and literature. So, there is a branch of medical science focussed on depression and other affective disorders, another specialises in addiction, and so on. The approach could almost be geared to prevent a holistic view. It blocks researchers and clinicians from seeing, let alone understanding, the possibility of a systemic unity.

Psychiatry's confusion reminds me of the old parable of the blind-folded men and the elephant, but here there's just one man. Knowing nothing of elephants, he unwittingly encounters one. The first thing he touches feels like a length of rope (it's the elephant's tail). The next thing could be a wall (that's the elephant's side). Then he finds what might be a tree (that's a leg), a fan (an ear), a spear (a tusk), and a large snake (the trunk). Because each contact feels different, the man thinks he's found a collection of random objects. Psychiatry similarly perceives what it takes to be stand-alone things — classic syndromes of depression, generalised anxiety, psychosis, and so on. But the field blinds itself to the fact that these conditions connect. The continuity of disorders is, you might say, the elephant in the room.

Seeing the connections, taking off the blindfold, may not be easy because DSM-ism has cemented itself into position. Outside of psychiatry, it has hardened into commercial interests, in medical insurance and the pharmaceutical industry. Within psychiatry, it sets the agenda for almost every aspect of research, including most of the evolutionary theorizing that goes on the field. So, there are stand-alone theories to account for the ultimate origin of depression. Other theories deal independently with addiction, schizophrenia, and so on.[36] Each theory assumes that the diagnostic label it tries to explain needs a distinct explanation. It is as if some scientists decided to slice the rainbow into colours and label the arcs — 'blue', 'red', 'yellow', and so on. Other scientists then went off in search of unconnected reasons as to why each arc appears in the sky; one for the blue, another for the red...

Not surprisingly, there is little progress to show for the effort. Psychiatry is obliged to admit, despite decades of theorizing, that the origin of CMD's various hues remains a mystery.[37] I suggest things might be different if the agenda were to not to explain the colours of the rainbow one by one, but instead to understand why, as a single phenomenon, there is a rainbow. The primary need is not to explain why particular forms of CMD occur but why CMD occurs at all.[38]

I predict that, when the blindfold of DSM-ism finally falls away, researchers will find the commonalities of CMD staring them in the face. With the benefit of hindsight psychiatry will say that, at some level, it knew it all along. The disorders we are discussing are already, after all, lumped together. They're classed as 'functional' — or at least they were until the word fell out of vogue. In other words, these are disorders of no known biological cause.[39] At the end of Chapter 8, I described functional mental disorders as a sump of ignorance: the bucket of conditions left after everything with an identifiable biological basis (so-called 'organic' conditions) has been classified elsewhere. So, the mental disorders in question are already acknowledged as being connected, if only in a negative way — by their shared lack of a known origin. That suggests there is at least the potential for understanding. To turn the negative into a positive just calls for the missing origin to be identified.

This book has proposed a plausible, unifying origin. It offers a paradigm for understanding CMD that moves away from the current preoccupation with categorising and labelling. In much of its rich variety, CMD makes sense as the experience of chronic emotional pain alongside diverse combinations of keepers, the organism's protective, anti-suicide responses to that pain. Any condition that approximates to the criteria for keepers set out in Chapter 7 could fairly be interpreted in this way, including, it seems to me, most common psychiatric diagnoses. As I outlined at the end of Chapter 8, on offer is a scientifically coherent stance that sees psychopathology not as a negative — as a deviance, a deficiency, or disorder — but as a positive. CMD is the healthy human mind doing what it is designed to do; to keep itself safe at times of intolerable stress. Armed with this understanding, medical science would be in a position to help people in an informed and constructive way. Clinicians could find ways to work with the organism's own powers of recovery.

Therapy is spiritual

That brings us to the third paradigm change, perhaps the most important. It would have us accept that there is a spiritual basis to human mental health. We could embrace the idea that happiness calls for a certain measure of irrationality.

At first glance, this proposal looks like it swims against the tide — ever-sharper realism and scientific rigour being the flow of our times. For example, one of the most popular genres of therapy is cognitive behavioural therapy — CBT. It's a brainchild of hard psychological science, devised in the 1960s to counter the seeming untestable art of old-school Freudian psychoanalysis. CBT sets out to help people find and correct unhelpfully irrational ways in which they misperceive the world. In many and varied formats (including the DBT, mentioned above), CBT evidently gets results. It can help to ease depression, anxiety, phobias, and many other psychiatric troubles.[40] Drug treatments — antidepressants and the like — also find ready acceptance as rational cures. They also have an aura of a scientific intervention, restoring biochemical imbalances it is said, to the extent that drug therapy increasingly calls the shots in psychiatry.[41]

I am not disputing or belittling these successes. I am saying that they probably happen for one reason, and it is not as rational as it first appears. Most likely, they are spiritual therapies dressed as science. To understand how this could be so, we need to see the bigger picture, which the therapist and statistician Bruce Wampold calls, as the title of his book, *The Great Psychotherapy Debate*.[42]

The most remarkable feature of CBT's success, to my mind, is that it isn't specific to CBT. Other brands of therapy turn out to perform about as well. CBT certainly has the benefit of a larger mass of evidence to show its success, but this is mainly because the evidence is relatively easy to collect. CBT is a short, fixed-term method, and it is easily standardised, which makes it amenable to experimental set-ups. With effort, it can be shown that other, less easily measurable, methods get similar results — even, mark this, traditional Freudian-style psychoanalysis. To find that psychoanalysis and CBT are equally effective is, on the face of it, weird. They were conceived as polar opposites. They reflect fundamentally different opinions about the cause of mental disorders and how the mind works. There is every reason to expect one model to work markedly better than the other, but there is no evidence that it does.

More bizarrely, there is little evidence that, between CBT and psychoanalysis, one therapy is markedly better than the other for any particular type of mental ailment. They turn out to be about equally good at tackling depression, anxiety, phobias, and other problems. They work about equally well for different types of patients too. In short, anyone could potentially get relief from any mental disorder from either therapy. Still more bizarrely, looking beyond the rivalry between CBT and psychoanalysis, there are dozens of other schools of therapy. Each one is founded on its own special perspective of human psychology, and each is viewed by its followers as self-evidently better. But it seems that almost any brand of therapy is about as effective as any other. Although different approaches look different, and surely claim to be different, the element that has the primary therapeutic effect is probably common to them all.

It is not that the differences between rival therapies don't matter. Your success in therapy requires you to believe in its benign paradigm — that you find good enough reason to trust it.[43] The same point arose in Chapter 11, then in the context of the therapeutic power of religious belief — it is fundamentally the same phenomenon, I suggest. In the same way that scientists need paradigms as a framework to guide their thinking, people in therapy need a paradigm as something to work with. It doesn't much matter which one, and there are many equally plausible paradigms to select from. Many are mutually exclusive; that is to say, often you can't sit on the fence — you need to come down in favour of one denomination or another. What matters is that you and your therapist buy into it. The participants need to believe that its theoretical foundations stack up, and there's a good expectation of success. That expectation can be self-fulfilling.

So, the differences between therapies (and religions) are important, but not in the way we might imagine. They are like the different colourings, flavourings, and other inert ingredients of medications. Think of paracetamol, for example. You can take a standard dose in many different forms. The non-paracetamol factors are important. If it weren't for the brand name and packaging, you might not have bought it. If it weren't for the corn starch that physically binds a pill together, you wouldn't be able to pick it up and swallow it. These inactive ingredients can vary greatly — so, you can take paracetamol in the form of a tablet, capsule, soluble powder, or syrup, according to your personal taste. But despite the superficial variety, the primary invisible constituent doesn't change — it's all paracetamol. Similarly, despite the apparent diversity of rival brands of psychotherapy (and religions), they're best understood as alternative vehicles for delivering the same active ingredient.

The active ingredient in therapy (and religion) is a faith relationship. For good results, the helper and the helpee must share a conviction of hope. They need to believe that their shared benign paradigm can be relied upon to provide them with a bright future; it's a promise of salvation. Reinforcing and evidencing their faith, the belief has to be backed up with rituals — actions that translate faith into works. In the case of CBT, there is homework to do. Psychoanalysis has its own routines: adherence to fixed session times and other careful boundaries. I suggest the equivalent ritual for pharmacological therapy includes the taking of a prescribed pill: if the pill produces a mind-altering side-effect, then so much the better — that's evidence that the paradigm is working.[44] It is probably on account of their marked side-effects that antidepressants perform better than inert pills in supposedly 'blind' clinical trials. Before we give credence to the idea that antidepressants and suchlike drug therapies are any more scientific than psychoanalysis — or, for that matter, reiki, homeopathy, or dangling crystals — let's remember that science does not know why depression occurs. Depression remains a 'functional' disorder, with no known biological origin and no biochemical marker to distinguish it from any other form of CMD. With no identifiable target that it is supposed to be 'anti-', an antidepressant is, almost by definition, a shot in the dark. The idea that antidepressants offer some kind of targeted biochemical re-balancing is as rational as a belief in the healing power of Our Lady, chakras, or cosmic energy.

In other words, the active ingredient in all these interventions, psychopharmacology likely included, is a communal placebo — shared, purposeful, wishful thinking.[45] This is paradoxical, because the placebo element in medicine is usually dismissed as a nuisance, an unwelcome sideshow, a confounding factor that is only incidental to the real business of biological repair. But in mental health, placebo appears to be the prime actor. What we believe can fundamentally alter our state of mind. If we genuinely believe a therapy will work, that it will give us a future to look forward to, then it probably will. The parallels between religious and therapeutic belief are too close to be mere co-incidence, it seems to me. Therapy is modern-day faith healing.

Love heals

I will go further and name the faith relationship of therapy (and religion) as the experience of love.[46] Therapists usually refer to it in terms that sound less wishy-washy — quasi-technical labels such as 'presence', 'empathy', 'congruence', and 'unconditional positive regard', but these refer essentially to the same thing. Effective therapy is a demonstration that someone who knows what they are doing can be relied upon to give of themselves for another's benefit. Somebody competent is invested in our wellbeing. That somebody may be therapist in a sweater, or a doctor in a white coat, but it is nonetheless a spiritual meeting. A supernaturally caring, credible, and defensible paradigm holds sway.

Love is at work whether or not money changes hands. Much good work is done by volunteers — trained counsellors and helpers who offer support via telephone helplines, self-help groups, and other mental health charities. Others commit themselves professionally, knowing they may never recoup the cost of their training. Where there is payment, it is often part of the therapeutic ritual for what it symbolises.[47] There are no fees for using AA or similar groups; members donate, always anonymously and voluntarily, as a way of practicing unconditional giving. Therapy fees can be a gesture of commitment, a mark of deference, and a way to absolve people of feeling personally beholden. Money and spirituality can mix.

The active ingredient of therapy is, in any event, beyond economics. A good therapist offers something that money cannot buy. So does a good psychiatrist, priest, friend, spouse, passing traveller, or any other human being with this gift to give. It is intentional selflessness, the Golden Rule in action, a benign worldview on display. It offers a taste of hope. The encounter shouts of the solution; it says, "Don't worry, all will be well." It offers a glimpse of a different way of being, a touch of how it feels to live in a caring universe. It can induce the kind of spiritual awakening we discussed in Chapter 11 — a faith-building, life-affirming experience. It's proof before our own eyes, felt in our own hearts, that we can get, and safely give, something for nothing in this world. It reminds us that we are not slaves to our animal instincts. We're not mere Darwin machines lumbering about in an indifferent cosmos, and we have more to look forward to than pointless suffering. We are spiritual beings.

The free-floating success of psychotherapy — that almost any brand of therapy can relieve almost any mental ailment — is not easy otherwise to explain. It makes sense in the light of the evolutionary analysis I have set out in this book. I have argued that outwardly diverse symptoms of common mental disorder serve a single function. They are signs of activated keepers — adaptations that protect the human organism at times of chronic psychache, when we might otherwise be motivated to seek a permanent escape. The common solution to mental disorder is, therefore, to ease the misery that made that disorder a survival necessity. Once the source of suffering is dealt with, in time, mental illness of almost any kind will usually go away.

The universal solution to emotional pain, and the unifying offer of all therapeutic paradigms, and all religions, is hope. Therapies and religions harness the protective and healing power of other adaptations, fenders, which seek to keep human beings safely happy and able to cope with adversity. If we believe we have a rewarding future, then today's pain becomes bearable. What we believe, then, is of itself curative, regardless of the extrinsic truth of those beliefs. It is healthy to hold an irrational faith in the power of love. Our wellbeing requires us to expect that the universe cares about us, and that it can be relied upon to protect us from pain beyond what an objective analysis would say is likely. Blind faith creates its own reality, one we can feel glad to live in.

We have reached the end of the story. I hope you have found it helpful, personally and professionally, and that it at least sparks a useful debate, especially in the field of mental health. My particular hope is that science could be persuaded to take a fresh and positive look at human irrationality. We could try to adopt an attitude of humility, respect, and awe towards the human mind's ability to manage its own reality. We are all in good part irrational, and necessarily so: our survival depends on it. I take it that there's no difference in principle between the hallucinations of a psychotic patient, the certainty with which some of us deny Darwin's teachings, and the worldviews that enrich our days with acts which look biologically empty, but which often overflow with selflessness. The reality that makes life worthwhile for me may not be right for you, although we can share a belief that our future is surely one to look forward to.

As members of the human species, it is our privilege to have evolved this way. Each of us has the task of nurturing our own faith in the goodness of the world and its people — and living up to that belief. It is not always easy, but as creations of selection, you and I are outstandingly well equipped for the task. Everything we need is within reach. We can be happy. It is what we are designed for.

cas

> *Listen to me ... let me teach you to love life. Whenever you are tempted to quit it, say to yourself, "May I do one more good deed before I die." Then go look for someone needy to help, an unfortunate to console, someone oppressed to defend ... If this consideration holds you back today, it will hold you back tomorrow, and the day after tomorrow, all your life.*

— Jean-Jacques Rousseau

GLOSSARY

Adaptation — A biological trait that evolved by selection to solve a fitness problem in a species' evolutionary past.

CMD — 'Functional' common mental disorder, such as depression, alcoholism, and schizophrenia.

Fenders — Front-line, pro-active, evolved psychological defences against suicide.

Fitness — The success of a biological trait in transferring genes into future generations.

Functional — (In respect of mental disorders) of unknown cause.

Keepers — Last-line, reactive, evolved psychological defences against suicide.

Love — To give of oneself with the intention of benefiting others.

Psychache — Potentially suicidogenic emotional pain.

Suicide — The act of intentionally, deliberately, killing oneself.

Suicidogenic — Leading to suicide.

Psychiatrist — A medical doctor specialising in mental health.

Psychologist — A specialist in the study of the mind.

NOTES

1. The Evolution of Life Worth Living
1   Panksepp (2011)
2   W.H.O. (2014)
3   The main source is Soper (2018).
     General background can also be found
     in Gunn, Malo, and Soper (2020);
     Soper (2019a, 2019b)

2. Why do people kill themselves?
1   Naghavi (2019); Sinyor, Tse, and
     Pirkis (2017); W.H.O. (2019)
2   Astraud, Bridge, and Jollant (2020)
3   Lester (2019); Gunn et al. (2020);
     Soper (2019b)
4   Franklin et al. (2017); Turecki et al.
     (2019)
5   Satcher (1999)
6   Shneidman (1998), p. 245
7   U.S. Department of Health and
     Human Services (HHS), Office of the
     Surgeon General and National Action
     Alliance for Suicide Prevention (2012)
8   Franklin et al. (2017). See also Carter
     et al. (2017); M. M. Large (2017);
     M. M. Large et al. (2016); Mulder,
     Newton-Howes, and Coid (2016)
9   Franklin et al. (2017)
10   Statistical issues are addressed by M.
     M. Large and Ryan (2014) and Soper
     (2019b).

11   For a critique of the misuse of flow
     diagrams and other non-theories
     in psychology, see Tryon (2016).
     Prominent suicide theories are
     reviewed by Gunn and Lester (2014);
     Selby, Joiner, and Ribeiro (2014);
     Paniagua, Black, Gallaway, and
     Coombs (2010)
12   Durkheim (1897/1952)
13   Paniagua et al. (2010) provide a good
     review and critique.
14   Owens, Horrocks, and House (2002)
     find that 7 in 10 surviving suicide
     attempters never try again, and most
     of those survive. Brezo, Paris, Barker,
     et al. (2007) found that a third of their
     cohort of 32 young suicide attempters
     appeared to have a forgotten about
     their attempts by the time they were
     followed up a few years later.
15   Atkinson (1978); Soper (2019b)
16   Nock, Ramirez, and Rankin (2019)
17   Naghavi (2019); Mew et al, (2017)
18   Naghavi (2019)
19   Fox, Huang, Guzmán et al. (2020).
20   Among these outspoken voices: D.
     Murray and Devitt (2017); Carter et al.
     (2017); Hjelmeland and Knizek (2019).
21   Turecki and Brent (2016)
22   Sommers-Flanagan et al. (2017);
     Regehr et al. (2015); Paterson et al.
     (2008).

23 M. Large, Sharma, Cannon, Ryan, and Nielssen (2011)

24 https://www.scientificamerican.com/article/suicide-prediction-remains-difficult-despite-decades-of-research/

25 Nock, Ramirez, et al. (2019), p. 11

26 For example, Turecki and Brent (2016); Sinyor et al (2017)

27 Carter et al. (2017)

28 McHugh and Large (2020)

29 Kuhn (1996)

30 Bering (2018); deCatanzaro (1981); M. B. Miller (2009); Soper (2018); Tolaas (2005).

31 Darwin (1859, p. 201)

32 For a review of the scientific evidence, see Preti (2007). For discussion, see Bering (2018)

33 Schaeffer (1967)

34 Silverman (2013)

35 Woodford (2003); Chitty (1996)

36 Soper (2018)

37 O'Connell and Dunbar (2003)

38 Bering (2018); Fedden (1938); Zilboorg (1936)

39 Durkheim (1897/1952)

40 (Hawkes, O'Connell, et al.,1998).

41 Lankford (2015) discusses suicide and mammalian reproduction. For eusociality; Alexander (1974); Alexander, Noonan, and Crespi (1991). For the lengths humans and other animals go to preserve reproductive potential, see Hausfater and Hrdy (1984); O'Connor (1978). On the genetic downsides of death; Duntley and Buss (2004).

42 Gunn et al. (2019). The Baganda are reported by Mugisha, Hjelmeland, Kinyanda, and Knizek (2011). Fedden (1938) is the seminal source on suicide's 'primitive punishments'.

43 Stanley, Hom, Boffa, Stage, and Joiner (2019).

44 Misjudged motives of attempters are discussed by Bancroft et al. (1979); Hawton, Cole, O'Grady, and Osborn (1982); Valach, Young, and Michel (2011). For stigmatising social reactions, see Knizek, Kinyanda, Akotia, and Hjelmeland (2013); Frey, Hans, and Cerel (2015); Mayer et al. (2020).

45 Lester (1993); Lester and Walker (2006).

3. 'Just so': How the human got his suicidality

1 deCatanzaro (1980)

2 Falger and Falger (2003)

3 Soper (2018)

4 Lester (2014); Soper (2018).

5 See Soper (2018) for sources. The logic of infanticide is discussed by Hausfater and Hrdy (1984) and M. Harris (1974).

6 deCatanzaro (1981), p. 143

7 Kerr and Shakespeare (2002)

8 Tooby and Cosmides (1997)

9 Williams (1966, 1996)

10 Shanahan (2008) offers heartbeat as an example of an evolutionary by-product.

11 Prey animals with machine guns suggested by Fitel and Sober (1998), cited by Shanahan (2008).

12 Syme, Garfield, and Hagen (2016); Syme and Hagen (2018); Wiley (2020)

13 Jordan and McIntosh (2011)

14 M Pompili et al. (2016)

15 Czeisler et al. (2020)

16 Brezo, Paris, Barker, et al. (2007); Walker, Moreau, and Weissman (1990)

17 Bancroft et al. (1979); Oexle et al. (2019); Saunders, Hawton, Fortune, and Farrell (2012)

18 Lester and Walker (2006)

19   Corrigan, Sheehan, Al-Khouja, and
      Team (2017); Oexle et al. (2019)
20   Bancroft et al. (1979); Mayer et al.
21   For a review, see Soper (2019b)
22   See Atkinson (1978); Douglas (1967);
      Soper (2019b)
23   Aubin, Berlin, and Kornreich (2013);
      Gallup and Weedon (2013); Orbell
      and Morikawa (2011); Riordan (2019);
      Tanaka and Kinney (2011)
24   Aubin et al. (2013); deCatanzaro (1980)

4. Pain: The motivation
1   Tolaas (2005) discusses Darwin's
      reticence.
2   Darwin (1897), p. 137
3   Kerr and Shakespeare (2002); R.
      Hofstadter (1955)
4   Freud (1920/1991)
5   For discussion of Freud as an evolu-
      tionist, see Gilbert (1989)
6   H. A. Murray and Kluckhohn (1948),
      p. 15. Original italics.
7   Lengvenyte, Strumila, Courtet, Kim,
      and Olié (2020); Humphrey (2018)
8   Paniagua et al. (2010)
9   Shneidman (1985), p. 124
10   Shneidman (1993), p. 145 (original
      italics)
11   Gunn and Lester (2014); Selby et al.
      (2014)
12   C. Klein (2007)
13   McFarland and Sibly (1975)
14   Biro (2010)
15   Hooley, Franklin, and Nock (2014)
16   Eisenberger (2011); Lieberman (2013)
17   Gunn (2017)
18   Bowlby (1969/1997)
19   Eisenberger (2012)
20   Bering (2012)
21   Brand and Yancey (1993)

5. Brain: The means
1   For an example of the myth still dong
      the rounds, see Peña-Guzmán (2017).
      For why it is a myth, see Andreotti
      and Sabatier (2013); Legros, Martin-
      Eauclaire, and Cattaert (1998).
2   Graphed U.S. data is from https://
      webappa.cdc.gov/sasweb/ncipc/
      mortrate.html. See Nock et al. (2013)
      for global patterns
3   Kessler et al. (2012)
4   Nock et al. (2013)
5   Czeisler et al. (2020)
6   Brezo, Paris, Barker, et al. (2007)
7   Nock et al. (2013)
8   https://www.dailysun.co.za/
      News/National/child-6-kills-him-
      self-20170912 and https://www.
      dailymail.co.uk/news/article-1264617/
      Girl-6-sent-room-punishment-
      youngest-people-committed-
      suicide-US.html
9   Maurizio Pompili, Vichi, De Leo,
      Pfeffer, and Girardi (2012)
10   See Pfeffer (1986) for a review.
11   Shaffer (1974); Shaffer and Fisher
      (1981)
12   Hurley (2002); Lunsky, Raina, and
      Burge (2012); Merrick, Merrick,
      Lunsky, and Kandel (2005)
13   Merrick et al. (2005); Merrick,
      Merrick, Lunsky, and Kandel (2006)
14   Baechler (1975/1979)
15   Deisenhammer et al. (2009)
16   Lansdown and Benjamin (1985);
      Speece and Brent (1984); Cuddy-
      Casey and Orvaschel (1997).
17   Anil, Preston, McKinstry, Rodwayl,
      and Brown (1996); Bracke (1992)
18   Cheney and Seyfarth (1990)
19   King (2013)

20 Elkind (1967); Kastenbaum and Costa (1977). For the 'tattered cloak of immortality', see Gordon (1986).

21 D. R. Hofstadter (1981a)

22 Borges et al. (2012)

23 Barresi and Moore (1996).

24 Dunbar (2004, 2007a)

25 S. Solomon, Greenberg, and Pyszczynski (2004); Varki and Brower (2013)

26 https://deathcafe.com/

27 Baumeister (1990)

28 For discussion of 'Therefore I must kill myself', see Shneidman (1982).

29 Reader, Hager, and Laland (2011)

30 Barrett, Cosmides, and Tooby (2007); Isler and Van Schaik (2012); Pinker (2010)

31 For the 'Machiavellian Intelligence' Hypothesis, see Humphrey (1976, 1980); Jolly (1966); Chance and Mead (1953); Dunbar (2007b).

32 Flinn and Alexander (2007)

33 Roth and Dicke (2012)

6. The problem of being human

1 Shneidman (1977)

2 Alvarez (1971), p. 67. Alvarez goes on to quote Robert Lowell's remark which might be the corollary: 'If there were some little switch in the arm which one could press in order to die immediately and without pain, then everyone would sooner or later commit suicide' (p. 117)

3 Allen (2011)

4 Caspari and Lee (2004); Hill, Hurtado, and Walker (2007)

5 Lewontin (1972)

6 Tooby and Cosmides (1992)

7 Zilboorg (1936)

8 Aiello and Wheeler (1995); Campbell (2010); Cunnane, Harbige, and Crawford (1993)

9 G. F. Miller and Penke (2007)

10 H. Kaplan, Hill, Lancaster, and Hurtado (2000); Silk (1978)

11 Gopnik (2010)

12 Flinn, Quinlan, Ward, and Coe (2007); H. S. Kaplan and Lancaster (2003)

13 Falk (1990); G. F. Miller (2007)

14 Rosenberg and Trevathan (2002)

15 Wells (1975)

16 Vercken, Wellenreuther, Svensson, and Mauroy (2012)

17 Isler and Van Schaik (2012)

18 Shettleworth (2010)

19 O'Connell and Dunbar (2003)

20 Varki and Brower (2013) reach similar conclusions but for different reasons.

21 G. F. Miller and Penke (2007)

22 R. G. Klein and Edgar (2002)

23 Potts (1998)

24 Shneidman (2001)

7. Why *don't* people kill themselves?

1 For recent examples of an appeal to a supposed 'survival instinct', see Joiner (2005); Nock, Boccagno, Kleiman, Ramirez, and Wang (2019).

2 Gunn et al. (2020); Soper (2019b)

3 Tooby and Cosmides (1992); Elowitz and Lim (2010); Janssen and Waarlo (2010)

4 Tooby and Cosmides (2008)

5 LeDoux (1996); MacLean (1993); Panksepp (1998)

6 'the most sophisticated computer in the known universe' is from Lieberman (2013), p. 200

7 Melzack and Wall (1967)

8 Beecher (1946, 1955)

9   For placebo effects in psychotherapy, see Fish (1973); Wampold and Imel (2015). For discussion of mental pain, see Tossani (2013)

10 Cabanac (2013); McNamara and Houston (1986); Young (1959)

11 I have changed my mind slightly about this point since my 2018 book was published. At that time I categorised 'Loss of psychomotor energy' as a denial of the means of suicide. It probably is that too, but on further reflection I think it is better explained here, as a suppression of the motivation for suicide.

12 Biro (2010); Franklin, Aaron, Arthur, Shorkey, and Prinstein (2012); Melzack and Wall (1967); Moont, Pud, Sprecher, Sharvit, and Yarnitsky (2010)

13 Engel (2002)

14 Bushnell, Čeko, and Low (2013)

15 Eccleston (2001)

16 Klinger (1977); Linehan, Goodstein, Nielsen, and Chiles (1983); von Andics (1947)

17 McKay and Dennett (2009)

18 Eccleston (2001)

19 Woody and Boyer (2011)

20 Williams (1966)

21 Blanchard, Griebel, Pobbe, and Blanchard (2011)

22 Bateson, Brilot, and Nettle (2011)

23 Woody and Boyer (2011)

24 This summary is slightly different to other versions presented in previous publications. The fundamentals are unchanged.

8. The diseases that keep us alive

1   A.P.A. (2013), p. 20

2   Bell et al. (2020)

3   At the time of writing, non-suicidal self-injury is not as yet confirmed as a diagnostic category. In DSM-V it is classed as a 'condition for further study' (A.P.A., 2013)

4   Baethge et al. (2005)

5   A.P.A. (2013)

6   Angold, Costello, and Erkanli (1999); First and Pincus (2009); Newman, Moffitt, Caspi, and Silva (1998)

7   Davies (2013)

8   Marshall (2020)

9   Allsopp, Read, Corcoran, and Kinderman (2019)

10 Shorter (2013)

11 For example, see Brüne (2016).

12 I am here referring in the singular (common mental disorder) to what Goldberg and Goodyer (2005) discuss in the plural (common mental disorders).

13 Anderzhanova, Kirmeier, and Wotjak (2017); Gould et al. (2017); S. M. Peters, Pothuizen, and Spruijt (2015); Willner and Belzung (2015).

14 McGonigle and Ruggeri (2014)

15 W.H.O. (2010)

16 Plante (2013)

17 Goldberg and Goodyer (2005); T. O. Harris (2000b)

18 Ibid. See also Jenkins, Madigan, and Arseneault (2015)

19 Ibid. See also Kessler et al. (2010).

20 Kessler et al. (2007); Kesler et al (2005)

21 Angold and Rutter (1992); Garber, Gallerani, and Frankel (2009); Goldberg and Goodyer (2005); Weiss and Garber (2003); Weissman, Wolk, et al. (1999)

22 Goldberg and Goodyer (2005); T. O. Harris (2000b)

23 G. W. Brown (2009); T. O. Harris (2000a); Ormel and Neeleman (2000)

24   Menninger (1963), p. 279—280.
25   Fox (2002); Surtees and Wainwright (2000).
26   Jablensky (2009); Reed, Fitzmaurice, and Zanarini (2012)
27   Galanter and Kaskutas (2008)
28   Arsenault-Lapierre, Kim, and Turecki (2004); Bertolote and Fleischmann (2002); Cavanagh, Carson, Sharpe, and Lawrie (2003); Overholser, Braden, and Dieter (2012); Stone et al. (2018)
29   Bruffaerts, Kessler, Demyttenaere, Bonnewyn, and Nock (2015); Dhingra, Boduszek, and O'Connor (2015); Glenn and Nock (2014); Kessler, Borges, and Walters (1999); Klonsky, May, and Saffer (2016); Nock, Alonso, et al. (2012); Nock et al. (2013); Nock, Hwang, Sampson, and Kessler (2010); Nock et al. (2015); Nock et al. (2013)
30   Handley et al. (2016); Weissman, Bland, et al. (1999)
31   Carter et al. (2017); Franklin et al. (2017)
32   W.H.O. (2018b)
33   https://www.npr.org/sections/goatsandsoda/2016/04/21/474847921/the-arctic-suicides-its-not-the-dark-that-kills-you?t=1591032430697
34   M. F. Brown (1986); Hezel (1987); Jollant, Malafosse, Docto, and Macdonald (2014)
35   M. M. Large and Ryan (2014)
36   US-DHHS (2014)
37   Inskip, Harris, and Barraclough (1998)
38   Chung et al. (2019)
39   Wu and Fang (2014)
40   Goldberg and Goodyer (2005)
41   Bateson et al. (2011)
42   P. Gilbert and Allan (1998); Hendin (1975); A. Solomon (2014)
43   Menninger (1938); Seeburger (2013). The '…I got drunk instead' is based on a memoire in 'Bill's Story' (Alcoholics Anonymous, 2001).
44   Franklin et al. (2012); Heilbron, Franklin, Guerry, and Prinstein (2014); Klonsky (2009)
45   Laing (1960)
46   Himmelhoch (1988)
47   Antrobus and Bortolotti (2016); Bolton and Hill (1996); Hundert (1992).
48   Gohier et al. (2009); McDermott and Ebmeier (2009); McGirr et al. (2007)
49   Fairburn, Cooper, and Shafran (2003); Harvey (2004); Hawton, Sutton, Haw, Sinclair, and Deeks (2005); McGirr and Turecki (2011)
50   First and Pincus (2009); McGrath et al. (2020)
51   Newman et al. (1998)
52   Hirschman (1992)
53   A.P.A. (2013)
54   Arsenault-Lapierre et al. (2004); Krueger and Tackett (2006).
55   Menninger (1938) made this point long ago. For a modern version, see Marshall (2020).
56   Hyman (2019)
57   Caspi and Moffitt (2018)
58   LeDoux (1996); Westen, Novotny, and Thompson-Brenner (2004)
59   Oltmanns and Powers (2012)
60   This point, and phrase, is from Storr (1960).
61   A.P.A. (2020)
62   Oexle et al. (2015)

9. Happiness

1   Norris (1992)
2   Boden, Kulkarni, Shurick, Bonn-Miller, and Gross (2014); Bonanno, Westphal, and Mancini (2011)
3   Keller and Miller (2006)

4   Auerbach, Stewart, and Johnson (2017); Klonsky and May (2015)
5   E. C. Harris and Barraclough (1997)
6   Townsend, Hawley, Stephenson, and Williams (2020)
7   Tooby and Cosmides (1992)
8   I meant 'warm' metaphorically here, but the link between emotional warmth and body temperature may be literal. Bargh (2017) suggests that physical warming could be a cheap, effective therapy for depression.
9   Bonanno (2009); Folkman and Moskowitz (2000); Surtees and Wainwright (2000)
10 Proudfit, Dunning, Foti, and Weinberg (2014)
11 Barber and Miller (2014); Drum, Brownson, Denmark, and Smith (2009)
12 Diener and Diener (1996); Heintzelman and King (2014)
13 Helson (1964)
14 Shneidman (1998)
15 Cramer (2000); Freud (1936/1993); Vaillant (1977)
16 Parkes and Prigerson (2010)
17 Malone, Cohen, Liu, Vaillant, and Waldinger (2013)
18 Paulhus and Buckels (2012); Taylor and Brown (1988)
19 Bolton and Hill (1996); Parkes and Prigerson (2010)
20 Erdelyi (1974); Greenwald (1980); Gur and Sackeim (1979); Schwartz and Wiggins (1992)
21 Gazzaniga (2006)
22 Aspinwall, Richter, and Hoffman (2001); Taylor and Brown (1988)
23 Sedikides, Gaertner, and Vevea (2005)
24 Lagisz et al. (2020)
25 Sharot (2011)
26 Trivers (2010)
27 Paulhus (1998)
28 Green and Swets (1966); Haselton, Nettle, and Murray (2016)
29 Haselton and Buss (2000)
30 Neuhoff (2001)
31 Freud (1936/1993)
32 Proulx and Inzlicht (2012), p.322
33 Baumeister (1989)
34 Alloy and Abramson (1979); Kim and Chiu (2011); Moore and Fresco (2012)
35 Hansen and Pronin (2012)
36 E. Peters (2010)
37 Bonanno (2009)
38 Brickman and Campbell (1971)
39 Estupinyà (2016)
40 Panksepp (1998)
41 Slobodkin (1978)
42 James (1902)
43 Benatar (2015)
44 Kuhl, Quirin, and Koole (2015); Pinker (1997)
45 Cosmides and Tooby (1994)
46 Beaver (1972); Linehan et al. (1983); von Andics (1947)
47 Maslow (1943)
48 Thorne (2012)
49 Frankl (1946/2011)
50 Humphrey (2018)

10. Thinking twice

1   Norris (1992)
2   Eurostat (2017)
3   Colt (1991); Fedden (1938)
4   Joiner (2005) reports a similar experience.
5   Rogers (2001)
6   Linehan (2006)
7   Bruffaerts et al. (2012)
8   Goldney, Smith, Winefield, Tiggeman, and Winefield (1991)
9   Brezo, Paris, Tremblay, et al. (2007)
10 Nock, Borges, et al. (2012)
11 This point is made by Klinger (1977).
12 Colucci and Martin (2008)

13 Sela and Shackelford (2014)

14 Kluckhohn (1962)

15 Walsh (2009)

16 Fedden (1938); Koenig, King, and Carson (2012)

17 Hook (1927)

18 M. F. Brown (1986); Colt (1991); Corrigan et al. (2017)

19 Ibid. See also Bohannan (1960); Knizek et al. (2013); Mugisha et al. (2011)

20 Mugisha et al. (2011)

21 Chapple, Ziebland, and Hawton (2015)

22 Colucci and Martin (2008); Hook (1927); Linehan et al. (1983)

23 Seligman (1971)

24 Chisholm and Sieff (2015); Smirnov, Arrow, Kennett, and Orbell (2007)

25 D. Gilbert (2006)

26 Wolf (2014)

27 Hoskin, Friedman, and Cawte (1969); Schmidtke (1997); Schomerus et al. (2015); Stack and Kposowa (2008)

28 Spallek et al. (2015)

29 M. F. Brown (1986); Hezel, Rubinstein, and White (1985); Jollant et al. (2014); Macdonald (2007)

30 Huber (2015/2019).

31 Andriessen, Rahman, Draper, Dudley, and Mitchell (2017)

32 This point is made by Al Alvarez (1971)

33 Kluckhohn (1962)

34 Bogin (2010); Macdonald (2007)

35 Mayer et al. (2020); Tadros and Jolley (2001); W.H.O. (2014)

36 Nicholas et al. (2020)

37 Hezel, (2020), personal communication; Hezel (1989).

38 Useful advice can be found here: https://psychcentral.com/blog/suicide-after-suicide-what-we-must-do-to-break-the-cycle/.

11. Love

1 D. R. Hofstadter (1981b)

2 For a good introduction, see Hood (2012).

3 Goldbeck (1997); Gosselin, Gagnon, Stinchcombe, and Joanisse (2010); Mele (2001)

4 Festinger (1957); Festinger, Riecken, and Schachter (1956)

5 Bowlby (1969/1997); Epstein (1994); Janoff-Bulman (1989); Janoff-Bulman and Yopyk (2004); Parkes and Prigerson (2010)

6 J. T. Kaplan, Gimbel, and Harris (2016)

7 Dawkins (2006)

8 Wilson (2010)

9 Bloom (2009); Boyer and Bergstrom (2008)

10 Dawkins (1976)

11 https://www.pewforum.org/2015/04/02/religious-projections-2010-2050/

12 James (1902)

13 Koenig et al. (2012); Lester (2017); Plöderl, Kunrath, and Fartacek (2019); Rosmarin and Koenig (2020)

14 Lester (2017); Lew et al. (2018); Rieger, Peter, and Roberts (2014)

15 Jongkind, Brink, Schaap-Jonker, Velde, and Braam (2018)

16 Sagan (2006)

17 Riesebrodt (2007/2010)

18 Dennett (1995), p. 519

19 Stevens (2002)

20 Valentin and Abdi (2003)

21 Lorenz (1949/2002). Parallels between Jungian archetypes and imprinting are noted by Stevens (1982); Stevens (2002).

22 *Combined Works*, vol. 8, para. 528, quoted by Stevens (1990), p. 247

23 Bluhm (2006); Galanter and Kaskutas (2008)

24 Alcoholics Anonymous (2001), p. 55
25 Hedges (2018)
26 Fish (1973); Wampold and Imel (2015)
27 Sisco and Weber (2019)
28 Herzberg (1966)
29 Batson, Lishner, and Stocks (2015); Sisco and Weber (2019)
30 Imada (2020)
31 Tooby and Cosmides (1996); Trivers (1971)
32 Küng (1999); Smith (1991); Swidler and Küng (1991)
33 D. Gilbert (2006)
34 Améry (1966/1980)
35 Peck (1978/2003)
36 D. Gilbert (2006); von Andics (1947)
37 Tutu and Tutu (2010)

12. More than lumbering robots

1 Dawkins (1976)
2 Carter et al. (2017); Franklin et al. (2017); M. M. Large (2017); M. M. Large et al. (2016); Mulder et al. (2016)
3 Schultz (2000); Simon (2002)
4 Chung et al. (2019); M. Large et al. (2011)
5 Hjelmeland, Jaworski, Knizek, and Marsh (2019); Zalsman et al. (2017)
6 Fox, Huang, Guzmán et al. (2020).
7 Maris (2015)
8 Memon et al. (2020)
9 See, for example, Franklin et al. (2017)
10 Barber and Miller (2014); Gunnell and Miller (2010)
11 Drum et al. (2009); Millner, Lee, and Nock (2017)
12 D. N. Miller (2013); M. J. Miller, Azrael, and Hemenway (2006)
13 Soper (2018)
14 Hassanian-Moghaddam, Sarjami, Kolahi, and Carter (2011)
15 Bolton and Hill (1996)
16 Linehan (2020)
17 Jobes and Joiner (2019)
18 Patel (2015)
19 A.P.A. (2013)
20 Linehan (2020); Lothes, Mochrie, and St John (2014)
21 Galanter and Kaskutas (2008)
22 Wampold and Imel (2015)
23 Bruffaerts et al. (2015); E. C. Harris and Barraclough (1997)
24 Goldberg and Goodyer (2005); T. O. Harris (2000b)
25 Goldberg and Goodyer (2005); Kessler et al. (2010)
26 G. W. Brown (2009); Goldberg and Goodyer (2005)
27 McGrath et al. (2020)
28 Kendell and Jablensky (2003)
29 Mansell, Harvey, Watkins, and Shafran (2008)
30 Baethge et al. (2005)
31 Kessler et al. (2007)
32 Willner and Belzung (2015)
33 First and Pincus (2009); Marshall (2020)
34 Caspi and Moffitt (2018); Marshall (2020)
35 Carlat (2010); Davies (2013)
36 Brüne (2016)
37 A.P.A. (2013)
38 Marshall (2020)
39 Bell et al. (2020)
40 Thoma, Pilecki, and McKay (2015)
41 Carlat (2010)
42 Wampold and Imel (2015)
43 Fish (1973)
44 Carlat (2010); Davies (2013)
45 Colloca (2018); Fish (1973); Frank (1974); Gaab, Locher, and Blease (2018)
46 Peck (1978/2003); Thorne (2012); Truax and Carkhuff (1967)
47 Gray (2013)

REFERENCES

Aiello, L. C., & Wheeler, P. (1995). The expensive-tissue hypothesis: The brain and the digestive system in human and primate evolution. *Current Anthropology, 36*(2), 199–221.

Alcoholics Anonymous. (2001). *Alcoholics Anonymous: The Story of How Many Thousands of Men and Women Have Recovered from Alcoholism* (4th ed.). New York, NY: Alcoholics Anonymous World Services Inc.

Alexander, R. D. (1974). The evolution of social behavior. *Annual Review of Ecology and Systematics, 5*(1), 325–383.

Alexander, R. D., Noonan, K. M., & Crespi, B. J. (1991). The evolution of eusociality. In P. W. Sherman, J. U. M. Jarvis, & R. D. Alexander (eds.), *The Biology of the Naked Mole-Rat* (pp. 3–44). Princeton, NJ: Princeton University Press.

Allen, J. P. (2011). *The Debate between a Man and His Soul: A Masterpiece of Ancient Egyptian Literature.* Leiden, Netherlands: Brill.

Alloy, L. B., & Abramson, L. Y. (1979). Judgement of contingency in depressed and nondepressed students: Sadder but wiser? *Journal of Experimental Psychology: General, 108*(4), 441.

Allsopp, K., Read, J., Corcoran, R., & Kinderman, P. (2019). Heterogeneity in psychiatric diagnostic classification. *Psychiatry Research, 279*, 15–22.

Alvarez, A. (1971). *The Savage God: A Study of Suicide.* London, UK: Weidenfeld & Nicholson.

Améry, J. (1966/1980). *At the Mind's Limits* (S. Rosenfeld & S. P. Rosenfeld, trans., 2nd ed.). Bloomington, IN: Indiana University Press.

Anderzhanova, E., Kirmeier, T., & Wotjak, C. T. (2017). Animal models in psychiatric research: The RDoC system as a new framework for endophenotype-oriented translational neuroscience. *Neurobiology of Stress, 7*, 47–56.

Andreotti, N., & Sabatier, J.-M. (2013). The deciphered genome of *Mesobuthus martensii* uncovers the resistance mysteries of scorpion to its own venom and toxins at the ion channel level. *Toxins, 5*(11), 2209–2211.

Andriessen, K., Rahman, B., Draper, B., Dudley, M., & Mitchell, P. B. (2017). Prevalence of exposure to suicide: A meta-analysis of population-based studies. *Journal of Psychiatric Research, 88*, 113–120.

Angold, A., Costello, E. J., & Erkanli, A. (1999). Comorbidity. *Journal of Child Psychology and Psychiatry, 40*(1), 57–87.

Angold, A., & Rutter, M. (1992). Effects of age and pubertal status on depression in a large clinical sample. *Development and Psychopathology, 4*(01), 5–28.

Anil, M., Preston, J., McKinstry, J., Rodwayl, R., & Brown, S. (1996). An assessment of stress caused in sheep by watching slaughter of other sheep. *Animal Welfare, 5*(4), 435–441.

Antrobus, M., & Bortolotti, L. (2016). Depressive delusions. *Filosofia Unisinos, 17*(2), 192.

A.P.A. (2013). *Diagnostic and Statistical Manual of Mental Disorders: DSM-5.* New York, NY: American Psychiatric Association.

A.P.A. (2020). What is mental illness? Retrieved from https://www.psychiatry.org/patients-families/what-is-mental-illness.

Arsenault-Lapierre, G., Kim, C., & Turecki, G. (2004). Psychiatric diagnoses in 3275 suicides: A meta-analysis. *BMC Psychiatry, 4*(1), 37.

Aspinwall, L. G., Richter, L., & Hoffman, R. R. (2001). Understanding how optimism works: An examination of optimists' adaptive moderation of belief and behavior. In E. C. Chang (ed.), *Optimism and Pessimism: Implications for Theory, Research, and Practice* (pp. 217–238). Washington, DC: American Psychological Association.

Astraud, L.-P., Bridge, J. A., & Jollant, F. (2020). Thirty years of publications in suicidology: A bibliometric analysis. *Archives of Suicide Research,* 1–14.

Atkinson, J. M. (1978). *Discovering Suicide: Studies in the Social Organization of Sudden Death.* London, UK: McMillan.

Aubin, H.-J., Berlin, I., & Kornreich, C. (2013). The evolutionary puzzle of suicide. *International Journal of Environmental Research & Public Health, 10*(12), 6873–6886.

Auerbach, R. P., Stewart, J. G., & Johnson, S. L. (2017). Impulsivity and suicidality in adolescent inpatients. *Journal of Abnormal Child Psychology, 45*(1), 91–103.

Baechler, J. (1975/1979). *Les Suicides* (B. Cooper, trans.). New York, NY: Basic Books.

Baethge, C., Baldessarini, R. J., Freudenthal, K., Streeruwitz, A., Bauer, M., & Bschor, T. (2005). Hallucinations in bipolar disorder: Characteristics and comparison to unipolar depression and schizophrenia. *Bipolar Disorders, 7*(2), 136–145.

Baldessarini, R. J. (2020). Epidemiology of suicide: Recent developments. *Epidemiology and Psychiatric Sciences, 29.* https://doi.org/10.1017/S2045796019000672.

Bancroft, J., Hawton, K., Simkin, S., Kingston, B., Cumming, C., & Whitwell, D. (1979). The reasons people give for taking overdoses: A further inquiry. *British Journal of Medical Psychology, 52*(4), 353–365.

Barber, C. W., & Miller, M. J. (2014). Reducing a suicidal person's access to lethal means of suicide: A research agenda. *American Journal of Preventive Medicine, 47*(3), S264–S272.

Bargh, J. A. (2017). *Before You Know It: The Unconscious Reasons We Do What We Do.* London, UK: William Heinemann.

Barresi, J., & Moore, C. (1996). Intentional relations and social understanding. *Behavioral and Brain Sciences, 19*(1), 107–122.

Barrett, H. C., Cosmides, L., & Tooby, J. (2007). The hominid entry into the cognitive niche. In S. W. Gangestad & J. A. Simpson (eds.), *The Evolution of Mind: Fundamental Questions and Controversies* (pp. 241–248). New York, NY: Guilford.

Bateson, M., Brilot, B., & Nettle, D. (2011). Anxiety: An evolutionary approach. *Canadian Journal of Psychiatry, 56*(12), 707–714.

Batson, C. D., Lishner, D. A., & Stocks, E. L. (2015). The empathy–altruism hypothesis. In D. A. Schroeder & W. G. Graziano (eds.), *Oxford Handbook of Prosocial Behavior* (pp. 259–268). Oxford, UK: Oxford University Press.

Baumeister, R. F. (1989). The optimal margin of illusion. *Journal of Social and Clinical Psychology, 8*(2), 176–189.

Baumeister, R. F. (1990). Suicide as escape from self. *Psychological Review, 97*(1), 90–113.

Beaver, C. (1972). Hope and suicide in the concentration camp. In E. Shneidman (ed.), *Death and the College Student* (pp. 19–29). New York, NY: Behavioral Publications.

Beecher, H. K. (1946). Pain in men wounded in battle. *Annals of Surgery, 123*(1), 96.

Beecher, H. K. (1955). The powerful placebo. *Journal of the American Medical Association, 159*(17), 1602–1606.

Bell, V., Wilkinson, S., Greco, M., Hendrie, C., Mills, B., & Deeley, Q. (2020). What is the functional/organic distinction actually doing in psychiatry and neurology? *Wellcome Open Research, 5*(138), 138.

Benatar, D. (2015). Life is not good. In T. K. Shackelford & R. D. Hansen (eds.), *The Evolution of Morality* (pp. 137–140). Cham, Switzerland: Springer.

Bering, J. M. (2012). *Why Is the Penis Shaped Like That?* London, UK: Transworld.

Bering, J. M. (2018). *A Very Human Ending: How Suicide Haunts Our Species*. London, UK: Transworld.

Bertolote, J. M., & Fleischmann, A. (2002). A global perspective in the epidemiology of suicide. *Suicidologi, 7*(2).

Biro, D. (2010). Is there such a thing as psychological pain? And why it matters. *Culture, Medicine, and Psychiatry, 34*(4), 658–667.

Blanchard, D. C., Griebel, G., Pobbe, R., & Blanchard, R. J. (2011). Risk assessment as an evolved threat detection and analysis process. *Neuroscience & Biobehavioral Reviews, 35*(4), 991–998.

Bloom, P. (2009). Religious belief as an evolutionary accident. In J. Schloss & M. Murray (eds.), *The Believing Primate: Scientific, Philosophical, and Theological Reflections on the Origin of Religion* (pp. 118–127). Oxford, UK: Oxford University Press.

Bluhm, A. C. (2006). Verification of C. G. Jung's analysis of Rowland Hazard and the history of Alcoholics Anonymous. *History of Psychology, 9*(4), 313.

Boden, M. T., Kulkarni, M., Shurick, A., Bonn-Miller, M. O., & Gross, J. J. (2014). Responding to trauma and loss: An emotion regulation perspective. In M. Kent, M. C. Davis, & J. W. Reich (eds.), *The Resilience Handbook: Approaches to Stress and Trauma* (pp. 86–99). New York, NY: Routledge.

Bogin, B. (2010). Evolution of human growth. In M. P. Muehlenbein (ed.), *Human Evolutionary Biology* (pp. 376–395). Cambridge, UK: Cambridge University Press.

Bohannan, P. (ed.) (1960). *African Homicide and Suicide*. Princeton, NJ: Princeton University Press.

Bolton, D., & Hill, J. (1996). *Mind, Meaning, and Mental Disorder: The Nature of Causal Explanation in Psychology and Psychiatry*. Oxford, UK: Oxford University Press.

Bonanno, G. A. (2009). *The Other Side of Sadness: What the New Science of Bereavement Tells Us about Life after Loss.* New York, NY: Basic Books.

Bonanno, G. A., Westphal, M., & Mancini, A. D. (2011). Resilience to loss and potential trauma. *Annual Review of Clinical Psychology, 7*, 511–535.

Borges, G., Chiu, W. T., Hwang, I., Panchal, B. N., Ono, Y., Sampson, N., . . . Nock, M. K. (2012). Prevalence, onset, and transitions among suicidal behaviors. In M. K. Nock, G. Borges, & Y. Ono (eds.), *Suicide: Global Perspectives from the WHO World Mental Health Surveys* (pp. 65–74). Cambridge, UK: Cambridge University Press.

Bowlby, J. (1969/1997). *Attachment and Loss: Attachment* (2nd ed., vol. 1). London, UK: Pimlico.

Boyer, P., & Bergstrom, B. (2008). Evolutionary perspectives on religion. *Annual Review of Anthropology, 37*, 111–130.

Bracke, M. (1992). *Can animals have a preference not to be killed? Observations on red deer, laying hens and mice which were exposed to conspecifics being killed: A study in cognitive ethology.* Doctoral dissertation, Edinburgh School of Agriculture, Edinburgh, UK.

Brand, P. W., & Yancey, P. (1993). *Pain: The Gift Nobody Wants.* New York, NY: HarperCollins.

Brezo, J., Paris, J., Barker, E. D., Tremblay, R., Vitaro, F., Zoccolillo, M., . . . Turecki, G. (2007). Natural history of suicidal behaviors in a population-based sample of young adults. *Psychological Medicine, 37*(11), 1563–1574.

Brezo, J., Paris, J., Tremblay, R., Vitaro, F., Hébert, M., & Turecki, G. (2007). Identifying correlates of suicide attempts in suicidal ideators: a population-based study. *Psychological Medicine, 37*(11), 1551–1562.

Brickman, P., & Campbell, D. T. (1971). Hedonic relativism and planning the good society. In M. H. Appley (ed.), *Adaptation-Level Theory: A Symposium* (pp. 287–305). New York, NY: Academic.

Brown, G. W. (2009). Medical sociology and issues of aetiology. In M. G. Gelder, N. C. Andreasen, J. J. López-Ibor, & J. R. Geddes (eds.), *New Oxford Textbook of Psychiatry* (pp. 268–275). Oxford, UK: Oxford University Press.

Brown, M. F. (1986). Power, gender, and the social meaning of Aguaruna suicide. *Man, 21*(2), 311–328.

Bruffaerts, R., Demyttenaere, K., Borges, G., Chiu, W. T., Kovess-Masfety, V., Gureje, O., . . . Nock, M. K. (2012). Treatment of suicidal persons around the world. In M. K. Nock, G. Borges, & Y. Ono (eds.), *Suicide: Global Perspectives from the WHO World Mental Health Surveys* (pp. 199–212). Cambridge, UK: Cambridge University Press.

Bruffaerts, R., Kessler, R. C., Demyttenaere, K., Bonnewyn, A., & Nock, M. K. (2015). Examination of the population attributable risk of different risk factor domains for suicidal thoughts and behaviors. *Journal of Affective Disorders, 187*, 66–72.

Brüne, M. (2016). *Textbook of Evolutionary Psychiatry and Psychosomatic Medicine: The Origins of Psychopathology* (2nd ed.). Oxford, UK: Oxford University Press.

Bushnell, M. C., Čeko, M., & Low, L. A. (2013). Cognitive and emotional control of pain and its disruption in chronic pain. *Nature Reviews Neuroscience, 14*(7), 502–511.

Cabanac, M. (2013). Sensory pleasure and homeostasis. In B. L. Ong (ed.), *Beyond Environmental Comfort* (pp. 17–35). Abingdon, UK: Routledge.

Campbell, B. (2010). Human biology, energetics, and the human brain. In M. P. Muehlenbein (ed.), *Human Evolutionary Biology* (pp. 425–438). Cambridge, UK: Cambridge University Press.

Carlat, D. (2010). *Unhinged: The Trouble with Psychiatry*. New York, NY: Free Press.

Carter, G., Milner, A., McGill, K., Pirkis, J., Kapur, N., & Spittal, M. J. (2017). Predicting suicidal behaviours using clinical instruments: systematic review and meta-analysis of positive predictive values for risk scales. *British Journal of Psychiatry, 210*(6), 387–395.

Caspari, R., & Lee, S.-H. (2004). Older age becomes common late in human evolution. *Proceedings of the National Academy of Sciences of the United States of America, 101*(30), 10895-10900.

Caspi, A., & Moffitt, T. E. (2018). All for one and one for all: Mental disorders in one dimension. *American Journal of Psychiatry, 175*(9), 831–844.

Cavanagh, J. T. O., Carson, A. J., Sharpe, M., & Lawrie, S. M. (2003). Psychological autopsy studies of suicide: A systematic review. *Psychological Medicine, 33*(3), 395–405.

Chance, M. R. A., & Mead, A. P. (1953). *Social behaviour and primate evolution*. Paper presented at the Symposia of the Society for Experimental Biology.

Chapple, A., Ziebland, S., & Hawton, K. (2015). Taboo and the different death? Perceptions of those bereaved by suicide or other traumatic death. *Sociology of Health & Illness, 37*(4), 610–625.

Cheney, D. L., & Seyfarth, R. M. (1990). *How Monkeys See the World: Inside the Mind of Another Species*. Chicago, IL: University of Chicago Press.

Chisholm, J. S., & Sieff, D. F. (2015). Live fast, die young: An evolved response to hostile environments? In D. F. Sieff (ed.), *Understanding and Healing Emotional Trauma: Conversations with Pioneering Clinicians and Researchers* (pp. 163–181). London, UK: Routledge.

Chitty, D. (1996). *Do Lemmings Commit Suicide? Beautiful Hypotheses and Ugly Facts*. New York, NY: Oxford University Press.

Chung, D., Hadzi-Pavlovic, D., Wang, M., Swaraj, S., Olfson, M., & Large, M. (2019). Meta-analysis of suicide rates in the first week and the first month after psychiatric hospitalisation. *BMJ Open, 9*(3), e023883.

Colloca, L. (2018). The fascinating mechanisms and implications of the placebo effect. *International Review of Neurobiology, 138*, xv.

Colt, G. H. (1991). *The Enigma of Suicide*. New York, NY: Summit.

Colucci, E., & Martin, G. (2008). Religion and spirituality along the suicidal path. *Suicide and Life-Threatening Behavior, 38*(2), 229–244.

Corrigan, P. W., Sheehan, L., Al-Khouja, M. A., & The Stigma of Suicide Research Team (2017). Making sense of the public stigma of suicide. *Crisis, 38*, 351–359.

Cosmides, L., & Tooby, J. (1994). Better than rational: Evolutionary psychology and the invisible hand. *American Economic Review, 84*(2), 327–332.

Cramer, P. (2000). Defense mechanisms in psychology today: Further processes for adaptation. *American Psychologist, 55*(6), 637–646.

Cuddy-Casey, M., & Orvaschel, H. (1997). Children's understanding of death in relation to child suicidality and homicidality. *Clinical Psychology Review, 17*(1), 33–45.

Cunnane, S. C., Harbige, L. S., & Crawford, M. A. (1993). The importance of energy and nutrient supply in human brain evolution. *Nutrition and Health, 9*(3), 219–235.

Czeisler, M. É., Lane, R. I., Petrosky, E., Wiley, J. F., Christensen, A., Njai, R., . . . Rajaratnam, S. M. W. (2020). *Substance Use, and Suicidal Ideation During the Covid-19 Pandemic*. Washington, DC: US Department of Health and Human Services/Centers for Disease Control and Prevention.

Darwin, C. (1859). *On the Origin of Species by Means of Natural Selection, Or the Preservation of Favoured Races in the Struggle for Life*. London, UK: John Murray.

Darwin, C. (1879/2004). *The Descent of Man* (2nd ed.). London, UK: Penguin.

Davies, J. (2013). *Cracked: Why Psychiatry Is Doing More Harm Than Good*. London, UK: Icon.

Dawkins, R. (1976). *The Selfish Gene* (3rd ed.). Oxford, UK: Oxford University Press.

Dawkins, R. (2006). *The God Delusion*. New York, NY: Houghton Mifflin.

deCatanzaro, D. (1980). Human suicide: A biological perspective. *Behavioral and Brain Sciences, 3*(02), 265–272.

deCatanzaro, D. (1981). *Suicide and Self-Damaging Behavior: A Sociobiological Perspective*. New York, NY: Academic Press.

Deisenhammer, E. A., Ing, C.-M., Strauss, R., Kemmler, G., Hinterhuber, H., & Weiss, E. M. (2009). The duration of the suicidal process: how much time is left for intervention between consideration and accomplishment of a suicide attempt? *Journal of Clinical Psychiatry, 70*(1), 19.

Dennett, D. C. (1995). *Darwin's Dangerous Idea*. London, UK: Penguin.

Dhingra, K., Boduszek, D., & O'Connor, R. C. (2015). Differentiating suicide attempters from suicide ideators using the Integrated Motivational–Volitional model of suicidal behaviour. *Journal of Affective Disorders, 186*, 211–218.

Diener, E., & Diener, C. (1996). Most people are happy. *Psychological Science, 7*(3), 181–185.

Douglas, J. D. (1967). *Social Meanings of Suicide*. Princeton, NJ: Princeton University Press.

Drum, D. J., Brownson, C., Denmark, A. B., & Smith, S. E. (2009). New data on the nature of suicidal crises in college students: Shifting the paradigm. *Professional Psychology: Research and Practice, 40*(3), 213–222.

Dunbar, R. (2004). *The Human Story: A New History of Mankind's Evolution*. London, UK: Faber & Faber.

Dunbar, R. (2007a). Brain and cognition in evolutionary perspective. In S. M. Platek, J. P. Keenan, & T. K. Shackelford (eds.), *Evolutionary Cognitive Neuroscience* (pp. 21–46). Cambridge, MA: MIT Press.

Dunbar, R. (2007b). Evolution of the social brain. In S. W. Gangestad & J. A. Simpson (eds.), *The Evolution of Mind: Fundamental Questions and Controversies* (pp. 280–286). New York, NY: Guilford Press.

Duntley, J. D., & Buss, D. M. (2004). The evolution of evil. In A. G. Miller (ed.), *The Social Psychology of Good and Evil* (pp. 102–124). New York, NY: Guilford Press.

Durkheim, E. (1897/1952). *La Suicide* (J. Spaulding & G. Simpson, trans.). Henley, UK: Routledge.

Eccleston, C. (2001). Role of psychology in pain management. *British Journal of Anaesthesia, 87*(1), 144–152.

Eisenberger, N. I. (2011). The neural basis of social pain: findings and implications. In G. MacDonald & L. A. Jensen-Campbell (eds.), *Social Pain: Neuropsychological and Health Implications of Loss and Exclusion* (pp. 53–78). Washington, DC: American Psychological Association.

Eisenberger, N. I. (2012). The pain of social disconnection: examining the shared neural underpinnings of physical and social pain. *Nature Reviews Neuroscience, 13*(6), 421–434.

Elkind, D. (1967). Egocentrism in adolescence. *Child Development, 38*(4), 1025–1034.

Elowitz, M., & Lim, W. A. (2010). Build life to understand it. *Nature, 468*(7326), 889.

Engel, C. (2002). *Wild Health*. Boston, MA: Houghton Mifflin Harcourt.

Epstein, S. (1994). Integration of the cognitive and the psychodynamic unconscious. *American Psychologist, 49*(8), 709.

Erdelyi, M. H. (1974). A new look at the new look: Perceptual defense and vigilance. *Psychological Review, 81*(1), 1.

Estupinyà, P. (2016). Sex in evolution. In $S= EX^2$ (pp. 155–163). Cham, Switzerland: Springer.

Eurostat. (2017). Percentage of the population rating their satisfaction as high, medium or low by domain, sex, age and educational attainment level. Retrieved from http://appsso.eurostat.ec.europa.eu/nui/submitViewTableAction.do.

Fairburn, C. G., Cooper, Z., & Shafran, R. (2003). Cognitive behaviour therapy for eating disorders: A 'transdiagnostic' theory and treatment. *Behaviour Research and Therapy, 41*(5), 509–528.

Falger, V. S. E., & Falger, E. L. F. (2003). The cultural evolution of dying: Euthanasia in the Netherlands. In A. Somit & S. A. Peterson (eds.), *Human Nature and Public Policy: An Evolutionary Approach* (pp. 77–96). New York, NY: Palgrave Macmillan.

Falk, D. (1990). Brain evolution in Homo: The 'radiator' theory. *Behavioral and Brain Sciences, 13*(02), 333–344.

Fedden, R. (1938). *Suicide: A Social and Historical Study*. London, UK: Peter Davies.

Festinger, L. (1957). *A Theory of Cognitive Dissonance*. Stanford, CA: Stanford University Press.

Festinger, L., Riecken, H., & Schachter, S. (1956). *When Prophecy Fails: A Social and Psychological Study of a Modern Group That Predicted the Destruction of the World*. Minneapolis, MN: University of Minnesota.

First, M. B., & Pincus, H. A. (2009). Diagnosis and classification. In M. G. Gelder, N. C. Andreasen, J. J. López-Ibor, & J. R. Geddes (eds.), *New Oxford Textbook of Psychiatry* (pp. 99–121). Oxford, UK: Oxford University Press.

Fish, J. (1973). *Placebo Therapy*. San Francisco, CA: Jossey-Bass.

Fitelson, B., & Sober, E. (1998). Plantinga's probability arguments against evolutionary naturalism. *Pacific Philosophical Quarterly, 79*(2), 115–129.

Flinn, M. V., & Alexander, R. D. (2007). Runaway social selection in human evolution. In S. W. Gangestad & J. A. Simpson (eds.), *The Evolution of Mind: Fundamental Questions and Controversies* (pp. 249–255). New York, NY: Guilford.

Flinn, M. V., Quinlan, R. J., Ward, C., & Coe, M. (2007). Evolution of the human family: Cooperative males, long social childhoods, smart mothers, and extended kin networks. In C. Salmon & T. K. Shackelford (eds.), *Family Relationships: An Evolutionary Perspective* (pp. 16–38). Oxford, UK: Oxford University Press.

Folkman, S., & Moskowitz, J. T. (2000). Positive affect and the other side of coping. *American Psychologist, 55*(6), 647.

Fox, H. A. (2002). The natural course of depression: Kraepelin and beyond. *Harvard Review of Psychiatry, 10*(4), 249–253.

Fox, K. R., Huang, X., Guzmán, E. M., Funsch, K. M., Cha, C. B., Ribeiro, J. D., & Franklin, J. C. (2020). Interventions for suicide and self-injury: A meta-analysis of randomized controlled trials across nearly 50 years of research. *Psychological Bulletin*, doi:10.1037/bul0000305.

Frank, J. D. (1974). *Persuasion and Healing: A Comparative Study of Psychotherapy* (rev. ed.). New York, NY: Schocken.

Frankl, V. E. (1946/2011). *Man's Search for Meaning* (I. Lasch, trans.). New York, NY: Random House.

Franklin, J. C., Aaron, R. V., Arthur, M. S., Shorkey, S. P., & Prinstein, M. J. (2012). Nonsuicidal self-injury and diminished pain perception: the role of emotion dysregulation. *Comprehensive Psychiatry, 53*(6), 691–700.

Franklin, J. C., Ribeiro, J. D., Fox, K. R., Bentley, K. H., Kleiman, E. M., Huang, X., . . . Nock, M. K. (2017). Risk factors for suicidal thoughts and behaviors: A meta-analysis of 50 years of research. *Psychological Bulletin, 143*(2), 187–232.

Freud, S. (1920/1991). *Beyond the Pleasure Principle* (J. Strachey, trans.). London, UK: Penguin.

Freud, S. (1936/1993). *The Ego and the Mechanisms of Defence* (C. Baines, trans. 2nd ed.). London, UK: Hogarth.

Frey, L. M., Hans, J. D., & Cerel, J. (2015). Perceptions of suicide stigma: How do social networks and treatment providers compare? *Crisis, 37*(2), 95–103.

Gaab, J., Locher, C., & Blease, C. (2018). Placebo and psychotherapy: Differences, similarities, and implications. In *International Review of Neurobiology* (vol. 138, pp. 241–255).

Galanter, M., & Kaskutas, L. A. (eds.). (2008). *Research on Alcoholics Anonymous and Spirituality in Addiction Recovery* (vol. 18). New York, NY: Springer.

Gale, T. M., Hawley, C. J., Butler, J., Morton, A., & Singhal, A. (2016). Perception of suicide risk in mental health professionals. *PloS One, 11*(2), 1–12.

Gallup, G. G., & Weedon, S. L. (2013). Suicide bombers: Does an evolutionary perspective make a difference? *Evolutionary Psychology, 11*(4), 791–794.

Garber, J., Gallerani, C. M., & Frankel, S. A. (2009). Depression in children. In I. H. Gotlib & C. I. Hammen (eds.), *Handbook of Depression* (2nd ed., pp. 405–443). New York, NY: Guilford.

Gazzaniga, M. S. (2006). *The Ethical Brain: The Science of Our Moral Dilemmas.* New York, NY: Harper Perennial.

Gilbert, D. (2006). *Stumbling on Happiness.* London, UK: Harper.

Gilbert, P. (1989). *Human Nature and Suffering.* Hove, UK: Lawrence Earlbaum Associates.

Gilbert, P., & Allan, S. (1998). The role of defeat and entrapment (arrested flight) in depression: An exploration of an evolutionary view. *Psychological Medicine, 28*(3), 585–598.

Glenn, C. R., & Nock, M. K. (2014). Improving the short-term prediction of suicidal behavior. *American Journal of Preventive Medicine, 47*(3), S176–S180.

Gohier, B., Ferracci, L., Surguladze, S. A., Lawrence, E., El Hage, W., Kefi, M. Z., . . . Le Gall, D. (2009). Cognitive inhibition and working memory in unipolar depression. *Journal of Affective Disorders, 116*(1), 100–105.

Goldbeck, R. (1997). Denial in physical illness. *Journal of Psychosomatic Research, 43*(6), 575–593.

Goldberg, D., & Goodyer, I. (2005). *The Origins and Course of Common Mental Disorders.* Hove, UK: Routledge.

Goldney, R. D., Smith, S., Winefield, A., Tiggeman, M., & Winefield, H. (1991). Suicidal ideation: Its enduring nature and associated morbidity. *Acta Psychiatrica Scandinavica, 83*(2), 115–120.

Gopnik, A. (2010). How babies think. *Scientific American, 303*(1), 76–81.

Gordon, A. K. (1986). The tattered cloak of immortality. In C. A. Corr & J. McNeil (eds.), *Adolescence and Death* (pp. 16–31). New York, NY: Springer.

Gosselin, D., Gagnon, S., Stinchcombe, A., & Joanisse, M. (2010). Comparative optimism among drivers: An intergenerational portrait. *Accident Analysis & Prevention, 42*(2), 734–740.

Gould, T., Georgiou, P., Brenner, L., Brundin, L., Can, A., Courtet, P., . . . Gottesman, I. (2017). Animal models to improve our understanding and treatment of suicidal behavior. *Translational Psychiatry, 7*(4), e1092.

Gray, A. (2013). *An Introduction to the Therapeutic Frame.* London, UK: Routledge.

Green, D., & Swets, J. (1966). *Signal Detection Theory and Psychophysics.* New York, NY: Wiley.

Greenwald, A. G. (1980). The totalitarian ego: Fabrication and revision of personal history. *American Psychologist, 35*(7), 603.

Gunn, J. F. (2017). The social pain model. *Crisis, 38*(5), 281–286.

Gunn, J. F., & Lester, D. (2014). *Theories of Suicide: Past, Present and Future.* Springfield, IL: Charles C Thomas.

Gunn, J. F., Malo, P., & Soper, C. A. (2020). Evolutionary psychology and suicidology. In T. K. Shackelford (ed.), *The SAGE Handbook of Evolutionary Psychology* (vol. 3). Thousand Oaks, CA: SAGE.

Gunnell, D., & Miller, M. J. (2010). Strategies to prevent suicide. *BMJ, 341*, c3054.

Gur, R. C., & Sackeim, H. A. (1979). Self-deception: A concept in search of a phenomenon. *Journal of Personality and Social Psychology, 37*(2), 147.

Handley, T. E., Kay-Lambkin, F. J., Baker, A. L., Lewin, T. J., Kelly, B. J., Inder, K. J., . . . Kavanagh, D. J. (2016). Investigation of a suicide ideation risk profile in people with co-occurring depression and substance use disorder. *Journal of Nervous and Mental Disease, 204*(11), 820–826.

Hansen, K. E., & Pronin, E. (2012). Illusions of self-knowledge. In S. Vazire & T. D. Wilson (eds.), *Handbook of Self-Knowledge* (pp. 345–362). New York, NY: Guilford Press.

Harris, E. C., & Barraclough, B. (1997). Suicide as an outcome for mental disorders. A meta-analysis. *British Journal of Psychiatry, 170*(3), 205–228.

Harris, M. (1974). *Cows, Pigs, Wars and Witches: The Riddles of Culture*. New York, NY: Random House.

Harris, T. O. (2000a). Introduction to the work of George Brown. In T. O. Harris (ed.), *Where Inner and Outer Worlds Meet: Psychosocial Research in the Tradition of George W Brown* (pp. 1–52). London, UK: Routledge.

Harris, T. O. (ed.) (2000b). *Where Inner and Outer Worlds Meet: Psychosocial Research in the Tradition of George W Brown*. London, UK: Routledge.

Harvey, A. G. (2004). *Cognitive Behavioural Processes across Psychological Disorders: A Transdiagnostic Approach to Research and Treatment*. Oxford, UK: Oxford University Press.

Haselton, M. G., & Buss, D. M. (2000). Error management theory: A new perspective on biases in cross-sex mind reading. *Journal of Personality and Social Psychology, 78*(1), 81–91.

Haselton, M. G., Nettle, D., & Murray, D. R. (2016). The evolution of cognitive bias. In D. M. Buss (ed.), *The Handbook of Evolutionary Psychology: Vol. 2, Integrations* (2nd ed., pp. 968–987). New York, NY: John Wiley & Sons.

Hassanian-Moghaddam, H., Sarjami, S., Kolahi, A.-A., & Carter, G. L. (2011). Postcards in Persia: Randomised controlled trial to reduce suicidal behaviours 12 months after hospital-treated self-poisoning. *British Journal of Psychiatry, 198*(4), 309–316.

Hausfater, G., & Hrdy, S. B. (1984). *Infanticide: Comparative and Evolutionary Perspectives*. New York, NY: Aldine.

Hawkes, K., O'Connell, J. F., Jones, N. B., Alvarez, H., & Charnov, E. L. (1998). Grandmothering, menopause, and the evolution of human life histories. *Proceedings of the National Academy of Sciences, 95*(3), 1336-1339.

Hawton, K., Cole, D., O'Grady, J., & Osborn, M. (1982). Motivational aspects of deliberate self-poisoning in adolescents. *British Journal of Psychiatry, 141*(3), 286–291.

Hawton, K., Sutton, L., Haw, C., Sinclair, J., & Deeks, J. J. (2005). Schizophrenia and suicide: Systematic review of risk factors. *British Journal of Psychiatry, 187*(1), 9–20.

Hedges, P. (2018). Encounters with Ultimacy? Autobiographical and critical perspectives in the academic study of religion. *Open Theology, 4*(1), 355–372.

Heilbron, N., Franklin, J. C., Guerry, J. D., & Prinstein, M. J. (2014). Social and ecological approaches to understanding suicidal behaviors and nonsuicidal self-injury. In M. K. Nock (ed.), *The Oxford Handbook of Suicide and Self-Injury* (pp. 206–234). Oxford, UK: Oxford University Press.

Heintzelman, S. J., & King, L. A. (2014). Life is pretty meaningful. *American Psychologist, 69*(6), 561–574.

Helson, H. (1964). *Adaptation-Level Theory*. Oxford, UK: Harper & Row.

Hendin, H. (1975). Growing up dead: Student suicide. *American Journal of Psychotherapy, 29*(3), 327–338.

Herzberg, F. I. (1966). *Work and the Nature of Man*. New York, NY: World Publishing Co.

Hezel, F. X. (1987). Truk suicide epidemic and social change. *Human Organization, 46*(4), 283–291.

Hezel, F. X. (1989). What can we do to prevent suicide? *Journal of the Pacific Society*(43), 63–66.

Hezel, F. X., Rubinstein, D. H., & White, G. M. (eds.). (1985). *Culture, Youth and Suicide in the Pacific*. Honolulu, HI: Pacific Island Studies Program.

Hill, K., Hurtado, A. M., & Walker, R. S. (2007). High adult mortality among Hiwi hunter-gatherers: Implications for human evolution. *Journal of Human Evolution, 52*(4), 443-454.

Himmelhoch, J. M. (1988). What destroys our restraints against suicide? *Journal of Clinical Psychiatry, 49*(9, suppl.), 46–52.

Hirschman, E. C. (1992). The consciousness of addiction: Toward a general theory of compulsive consumption. *Journal of Consumer Research, 19*(2), 155–179.

Hjelmeland, H., Jaworski, K., Knizek, B. L., & Marsh, I. (2019). Problematic advice from suicide prevention experts. *Ethical Human Psychology and Psychiatry, 20*(2), 79–85.

Hjelmeland, H., & Knizek, B. L. (2019). The emperor's new clothes? A critical look at the interpersonal theory of suicide. *Death Studies, 44*(4), 168–178.

Hofstadter, D. R. (1981a). Reflection on D. E. Harding 'On Having No Head'. In D. R. Hofstadter & D. C. Dennett (eds.), *The Mind's I: Fantasies and Reflections on Mind and Soul* (pp. 30–33). New York, NY: Basic Books.

Hofstadter, D. R. (1981b). Reflection on Thomas Nagel 'What is it like to be a bat?'. In D. R. Hofstadter & D. C. Dennett (eds.), *The Mind's I: Fantasies and Reflections on Mind and Soul* (pp. 403–414). New York, NY: Basic Books.

Hofstadter, R. (1955). *Social Darwinism in American Thought* (rev. ed.). Boston: Beacon.

Hood, B. (2012). *The Self Illusion*. London, UK: Constable.

Hook, S. (1927). The ethics of suicide. *International Journal of Ethics, 37*(2), 173–188.

Hooley, J. M., Franklin, J. C., & Nock, M. K. (2014). Chronic pain and suicide: Understanding the association. *Current Pain and Headache Report, 18*(8), 435.

Hoskin, J. O., Friedman, M. I., & Cawte, J. E. (1969). A high incidence of suicide in a preliterate primitive society. *Psychiatry, 32*(2), 200–210.

Huber, F. (2015/2019). *Promise Me You'll Shoot Yourself* (I. Taylor, trans.). London, UK: Allen Lane.

Humphrey, N. (1976). The social function of intellect. In P. Bateson & R. A. Hinde (eds.), *Growing points in ethology* (pp. 303–317). Cambridge, UK: Cambridge University Press.

Humphrey, N. (1980). Nature's psychologists. In B. D. Josephson & V. S. Ramachandran (eds.), *Consciousness and the Physical World* (pp. 57–80). London, UK: Pergamon Press.

Humphrey, N. (2018). The lure of death: Suicide and human evolution. *Philosophical Transactions of the Royal Society, B, 373*, 1–8.

Hundert, E. M. (1992). The brain's capacity to form delusions as an evolutionary strategy for survival. In M. Spitzer, F. Uehlein, M. A. Schwartz, & C. Mundt (eds.), *Phenomenology, Language & Schizophrenia* (pp. 346–354). New York, NY: Springer.

Hurley, A. D. (2002). Potentially lethal suicide attempts in persons with developmental disabilities: Review and three new case reports. *Mental Health Aspects of Developmental Disabilities, 5*(3), 90–95.

Hyman, S. E. (2019). New evidence for shared risk architecture of mental disorders. *JAMA Psychiatry, 76*(3), 235–236.

Imada, H. (2020). Preference for anonymous giving. *Letters on Evolutionary Behavioral Science, 11*(1), 22–26.

Inskip, H., Harris, E. C., & Barraclough, B. (1998). Lifetime risk of suicide for affective disorder, alcoholism and schizophrenia. *British Journal of Psychiatry, 172*(1), 35–37.

Isler, K., & Van Schaik, C. P. (2012). How our ancestors broke through the gray ceiling: Comparative evidence for cooperative breeding in early homo. *Current Anthropology, 53*(S6), S453-S465.

Jablensky, A. (2009). Course and outcome of schizophrenia and their prediction. In M. G. Gelder, N. C. Andreasen, J. J. Lopez-Ibor, & J. R. Geddes (eds.), *New Oxford Textbook of Psychiatry, Vol. 1* (2nd ed., pp. 568–578). Oxford, UK: Oxford University Press.

James, W. (1902). *The Varieties of Religious Experience.* New York, NY: Longmans.

Janoff-Bulman, R. (1989). Assumptive worlds and the stress of traumatic events: Applications of the schema construct. *Social Cognition, 7*(2), 113–136.

Janoff-Bulman, R., & Yopyk, D. J. (2004). Random outcomes and valued commitments: Existential dilemmas and the paradox of meaning. In J. Greenberg, S. L. Koole, & T. Pyszczynski (eds.), *Handbook of Experimental Existential Psychology* (pp. 122–138). New York, NY: Guilford.

Janssen, F., & Waarlo, A. J. (2010). Learning biology by designing. *Journal of Biological Education, 44*(2), 88–92.

Jenkins, J., Madigan, S., & Arseneault, L. (2015). Psychosocial adversity. In A. Thapar, D. S. Pine, J. F. Leckman, S. Scott, M. J. Snowling, & E. Taylor (eds.), *Rutter's Child and Adolescent Psychiatry* (6th ed., pp. 330–340). Chichester, UK: John Wiley & Sons.

Jobes, D. A., & Joiner, T. E. (2019). Reflections on suicidal ideation. *Crisis, 40*(4), 227–230.

Joiner, T. E. (2005). *Why People Die by Suicide.* Cambridge, MA: Harvard University Press.

Jollant, F., Malafosse, A., Docto, R., & Macdonald, C. J.-H. (2014). A pocket of very high suicide rates in a non-violent, egalitarian and cooperative population of South-East Asia. *Psychological Medicine, 44*(11), 2323–2329.

Jolly, A. (1966). Lemur social behavior and primate intelligence. *Science, 153*(3735), 501–506.

Jongkind, M., Brink, B., Schaap-Jonker, H., Velde, N., & Braam, A. W. (2018). Dimensions of religion associated with suicide attempt and suicide ideation in depressed, religiously affiliated patients. *Suicide and Life-Threatening Behavior, 49*(2), 505–519.

Jordan, J. R., & McIntosh, J. L. (eds.). (2011). *Grief after Suicide: Understanding the Consequences and Caring for the Survivors*. New York, NY: Routledge.

Kaplan, H., Hill, K., Lancaster, J., & Hurtado, A. M. (2000). A theory of human life history evolution: Diet, intelligence, and longevity. *Evolutionary Anthropology: Issues, News, and Reviews, 9*(4), 156–185.

Kaplan, H. S., & Lancaster, J. B. (2003). An evolutionary and ecological analysis of human fertility, mating patterns, and parental investment. In R. A. Bulatao & K. W. Wachter (eds.), *Offspring: Human Fertility Behavior in Biodemographic Perspective* (pp. 170–223). Washington, DC: National Academies Press.

Kaplan, J. T., Gimbel, S. I., & Harris, S. (2016). Neural correlates of maintaining one's political beliefs in the face of counterevidence. *Scientific Reports, 6*, 39589.

Kastenbaum, R., & Costa, P. T. (1977). Psychological perspectives on death. *Annual Review of Psychology, 28*(1), 225–249.

Keller, M. C., & Miller, G. F. (2006). Resolving the paradox of common, harmful, heritable mental disorders: Which evolutionary genetic models work best? *Behavioral and Brain Sciences, 29*(4), 385–404; discussion 405–352.

Kendell, R., & Jablensky, A. (2003). Distinguishing between the validity and utility of psychiatric diagnoses. *American Journal of Psychiatry, 160*(1), 4–12.

Kerr, A., & Shakespeare, T. (2002). *Genetic Politics: From Eugenics to Genome*. Cheltenham, UK: New Clarion.

Kessler, R. C., Aguilar-Gaxiola, S., Borges, G., Chiu, W. T., Fayyad, J., Browne, M. O., . . . Nock, M. K. (2012). Persistence of suicidal behaviors over time. In M. K. Nock, G. Borges, & Y. Ono (eds.), *Suicide: Global Perspectives from the WHO World Mental Health Surveys* (pp. 75–85). Cambridge, UK: Cambridge University Press.

Kessler, R. C., Amminger, G. P., Aguilar-Gaxiola, S., Alonso, J., Lee, S., & Ustun, T. B. (2007). Age of onset of mental disorders: a review of recent literature. *Current Opinion in Psychiatry, 20*(4), 359.

Kessler, R. C., Berglund, P., Demler, O., Jin, R., Merikangas, K. R., & Walters, E. E. (2005). Lifetime prevalence and age-of-onset distributions of DSM-IV disorders in the National Comorbidity Survey Replication. *Archives of General Psychiatry, 62*(6), 593–602.

Kessler, R. C., Borges, G., & Walters, E. E. (1999). Prevalence of and risk factors for lifetime suicide attempts in the National Comorbidity Survey. *Archives of General Psychiatry, 56*(7), 617–626.

Kessler, R. C., McLaughlin, K. A., Green, J. G., Gruber, M. J., Sampson, N. A., Zaslavsky, A. M., . . . Angermeyer, M. (2010). Childhood adversities and adult psychopathology in the WHO World Mental Health Surveys. *British Journal of Psychiatry, 197*(5), 378–385.

Kim, Y.-H., & Chiu, C.-Y. (2011). Emotional costs of inaccurate self-assessments: Both self-effacement and self-enhancement can lead to dejection. *Emotion, 11*(5), 1096.

King, B. J. (2013). *How Animals Grieve*. Chicago, IL: University of Chicago Press.

Klein, C. (2007). An imperative theory of pain. *Journal of Philosophy, 104*(10), 517–532.

Klein, R. G., & Edgar, B. (2002). *The Dawn of Human Culture*. New York, NY: Wiley.

Klinger, E. (1977). *Meaning and Void: Inner Experience and the Incentives in People's Lives*. Minneapolis, MN: University of Minnesota Press.

Klonsky, E. D. (2009). The functions of self-injury in young adults who cut themselves: Clarifying the evidence for affect-regulation. *Psychiatry Research, 166*(2), 260–268.

Klonsky, E. D., & May, A. M. (2015). Impulsivity and suicide risk: Review and clinical implications. *Psychiatric Times, 32*(8), 13–21.

Klonsky, E. D., May, A. M., & Saffer, B. Y. (2016). Suicide, suicide attempts, and suicidal ideation. *Annual Review of Clinical Psychology, 12*, 307–330.

Kluckhohn, C. (1962). *Culture and Behavior*. New York, NY: The Free Press.

Knizek, B. L., Kinyanda, E., Akotia, C. S., & Hjelmeland, H. (2013). Between Hippocrates and God: Ugandan mental health professional's views on suicide. *Mental Health, Religion & Culture, 16*(8), 767–780.

Koenig, H. G., King, D., & Carson, V. B. (2012). *Handbook of Religion and Health* (2nd ed.). Oxford, UK: Oxford University Press.

Krueger, R. F., & Tackett, J. L. (eds.). (2006). *Personality and Psychopathology*. New York, NY: Guilford Press.

Kuhl, J., Quirin, M., & Koole, S. L. (2015). Being someone: The integrated self as a neuropsychological system. *Social and Personality Psychology Compass, 9*(3), 115–132.

Kuhn, T. S. (1996). *The Structure of Scientific Revolutions* (3rd ed.). Chicago, IL: University of Chicago Press.

Küng, H. (1999). Explanatory remarks concerning a 'declaration of the religions for a global ethic' (L. Swidler, trans.). In L. Swidler (ed.), *For All Life: Toward a Universal Declaration of a Global Ethic; An Interreligious Dialogue* (pp. 22–30). Ashland, OR: White Cloud Press.

Lagisz, M., Zidar, J., Nakagawa, S., Neville, V., Sorato, E., Paul, E. S., . . . Løvlie, H. (2020). Optimism, pessimism and judgement bias in animals: A systematic review and meta-analysis. *Neuroscience & Biobehavioral Reviews, 118*, 3–17.

Laing, R. D. (1960). *The Divided Self: An Existential Study in Sanity and Madness*. London, UK: Tavistock.

Lankford, A. (2015). Is suicide terrorism really the product of an evolved sacrificial tendency? A review of mammalian research and application of evolutionary theory. *Comprehensive Psychology, 4*(21), 12–19.

Lansdown, R., & Benjamin, G. (1985). The development of the concept of death in children aged 5–9 years. *Child: Care, Health and Development, 11*(1), 13–20.

Large, M. M., Sharma, S., Cannon, E., Ryan, C. J., & Nielssen, O. (2011). Risk factors for suicide within a year of discharge from psychiatric hospital: A systematic meta-analysis. *Australian & New Zealand Journal of Psychiatry, 45*(8), 619–628.

Large, M. M. (2017). Emerging consensus on the positive predictive (and clinical) value of suicide risk assessment. *British Journal of Psychiatry, Letter, 21 March*. Retrieved from http://bjp.rcpsych.org/content/emerging-consensus-positive-predictive-and-clinical-value-suicide-risk-assessment.

Large, M. M., Kaneson, M., Myles, N., Myles, H., Gunaratne, P., & Ryan, C. J. (2016). Meta-analysis of longitudinal cohort studies of suicide risk assessment among psychiatric patients: Heterogeneity in results and lack of improvement over time. *PloS One, 11*(6), e0156322.

Large, M. M., & Ryan, C. J. (2014). Suicide risk assessment: Myth and reality. *International Journal of Clinical Practice, 68*(6), 679–681.

LeDoux, J. (1996). *The Emotional Brain: The Mysterious Underpinnings of Emotional Life*. New York, NY: Simon & Schuster.

Legros, C., Martin-Eauclaire, M. F., & Cattaert, D. (1998). The myth of scorpion suicide: Are scorpions insensitive to their own venom? *Journal of Experimental Biology, 201*(18), 2625–2636.

Lengvenyte, A., Strumila, R., Courtet, P., Kim, S. Y., & Olié, E. (2020). 'Nothing hurts less than being dead': Psychological pain in case descriptions of psychiatric euthanasia and assisted suicide from the Netherlands. *Canadian Journal of Psychiatry.*

Lester, D. (1993). The stigma against dying and suicidal patients: A replication of Richard Kalish's study twenty-five years later. *OMEGA Journal of Death and Dying, 26*(1), 71–75.

Lester, D. (2014). Suicide, ethology and sociobiology. In J. F. Gunn & D. Lester (eds.), *Theories of Suicide: Past, Present and Future* (pp. 55–71). Springfield, IL: Charles C Thomas.

Lester, D. (2017). Does religiosity predict suicidal behavior? *Religions, 8*(11), 238.

Lester, D. (2019). *The End of Suicidology: Can We Ever Understand Suicide?* New York, NY: Nova Science Publishers.

Lester, D., & Walker, R. L. (2006). The stigma for attempting suicide and the loss to suicide prevention efforts. *Crisis, 27*(3), 147.

Lew, B., Huen, J., Yuan, L., Stack, S., Maniam, T., Yip, P., . . . Jia, C.-x. (2018). Religious orientation and its relationship to suicidality: A study in one of the least religious countries. *Religions, 9*(1), 15.

Lewontin, R. C. (1972). The apportionment of human diversity. In T. Dobzhansky, M. K. Hecht, & W. C. Steere (eds.), *Evolutionary Biology* (vol. 6, pp. 381–398). New York, NY: Appleton Century Crofts.

Lieberman, M. D. (2013). *Social: Why Our Brains Are Wired to Connect*. Oxford, UK: Oxford University Press.

Linehan, M. M. (2006). Foreword. In T. E. Ellis (ed.), *Cognition and Suicide: Theory, Research, and Therapy* (pp. xxi–xvi). Washington, DC: American Psychological Association.

Linehan, M. M. (2020). *Building a Life Worth Living*. New York, NY: Random House.

Linehan, M. M., Goodstein, J. L., Nielsen, S. L., & Chiles, J. A. (1983). Reasons for staying alive when you are thinking of killing yourself: The reasons for living inventory. *Journal of Consulting and Clinical Psychology, 51*(2), 276–286.

Lorenz, K. (1949/2002). *King Solomon's Ring: New Light on Animal Ways* (M. K. Wilson, trans.). London, UK: Routledge.

Lothes, J. E., Mochrie, K. D., & St John, J. (2014). The effects of a DBT informed partial hospital program on: Depression, anxiety, hopelessness, and degree of suffering. *Journal of Psychology & Psychotherapy, 4*(3), 1.

Lunsky, Y., Raina, P., & Burge, P. (2012). Suicidality among adults with intellectual disability. *Journal of Affective Disorders, 140*(3), 292–295.

Macdonald, C. J.-H. (2007). *Uncultural Behavior: An Anthropological Investigation of Suicide in the Southern Philippines.* Honolulu, HI: University of Hawai'i Press.

MacLean, P. D. (1993). Cerebral evolution of emotion. In M. Lewis & J. M. Haviland-Jones (eds.), *Handbook of Emotions* (2nd ed., pp. 67–83). New York, NY: Guilford.

Malone, J. C., Cohen, S., Liu, S. R., Vaillant, G. E., & Waldinger, R. J. (2013). Adaptive midlife defense mechanisms and late-life health. *Personality and Individual Differences, 55*(2), 85–89.

Mansell, W., Harvey, A. G., Watkins, E. R., & Shafran, R. (2008). Cognitive behavioral processes across psychological disorders: A review of the utility and validity of the transdiagnostic approach. *International Journal of Cognitive Therapy, 1*(3), 181–191.

Maris, R. W. (2015). *Pillaged: Psychiatric Medications and Suicide Risk.* Columbia, SC: University of South Carolina Press.

Marshall, M. (2020). The hidden links between mental disorders. *Nature, 581,* 19–21.

Maslow, A. H. (1943). A theory of human motivation. *Psychological Review, 50*(4), 370.

Mayer, L., Rüsch, N., Frey, L. M., Nadorff, M. R., Drapeau, C. W., Sheehan, L., & Oexle, N. (2020). Anticipated suicide stigma, secrecy, and suicidality among suicide attempt survivors. *Suicide and Life-Threatening Behavior, 50*(3), 706–713.

McDermott, L. M., & Ebmeier, K. P. (2009). A meta-analysis of depression severity and cognitive function. *Journal of Affective Disorders, 119*(1), 1–8.

McFarland, D., & Sibly, R. (1975). The behavioural final common path. *Philosophical Transactions of the Royal Society of London B: Biological Sciences, 270*(907), 265–293.

McGirr, A., Renaud, J., Seguin, M., Alda, M., Benkelfat, C., Lesage, A., & Turecki, G. (2007). An examination of DSM-IV depressive symptoms and risk for suicide completion in major depressive disorder: A psychological autopsy study. *Journal of Affective Disorders, 97,* 203–209.

McGirr, A., & Turecki, G. (2011). Schizophrenia, other psychotic disorders, and suicidal behaviour. In R. C. O'Connor, S. Platt, & J. Gordon (eds.), *International Handbook of Suicide Prevention: Research, Policy and Practice* (pp. 75–92). Chichester, UK: John Wiley and Sons.

McGonigle, P., & Ruggeri, B. (2014). Animal models of human disease: Challenges in enabling translation. *Biochemical Pharmacology, 87*(1), 162–171.

McGrath, J., Lim, C., Plana-Ripoll, O., Holtz, Y., Agerbo, E., Momen, N., . . . Aguilar-Gaxiola, S. (2020). Comorbidity within mental disorders: A comprehensive analysis based on 145,990 survey respondents from 27 countries. *Epidemiology and Psychiatric Sciences, 29.* doi:10.1017/S2045796020000633.

McHugh, C. M., & Large, M. M. (2020). Can machine-learning methods really help predict suicide? *Current Opinion in Psychiatry, 33*(4), 369–374.

McKay, R. T., & Dennett, D. C. (2009). The evolution of misbelief. *Behavioral and Brain Sciences, 32*(06), 493–510.

McNamara, J. M., & Houston, A. I. (1986). The common currency for behavioral decisions. *American Naturalist, 127*(3), 358–378.

Mele, A. R. (2001). *Self-Deception Unmasked.* Princeton, NJ: Princeton University Press.

Melzack, R., & Wall, P. D. (1967). Pain mechanisms: A new theory. *Survey of Anesthesiology, 11*(2), 89–90.

Memon, A., Rogers, I., Fitzsimmons, S. M., Carter, B., Strawbridge, R., Hidalgo-Mazzei, D., & Young, A. H. (2020). Association between naturally occurring lithium in drinking water and suicide rates: Systematic review and meta-analysis of ecological studies. *British Journal of Psychiatry.* doi:10.1192/bjp.2020.128.

Menninger, K. A. (1938). *Man Against Himself.* New York, NY: Harcourt Brace Jovanovich.

Menninger, K. A. (1963). *The Vital Balance: The Life Process in Mental Health and Illness.* New York, NY: Viking.

Merrick, J., Merrick, E., Lunsky, Y., & Kandel, I. (2005). Suicide behavior in persons with intellectual disability. *Scientific World Journal, 5,* 729–735.

Merrick, J., Merrick, E., Lunsky, Y., & Kandel, I. (2006). A review of suicidality in persons with intellectual disability. *Israel Journal of Psychiatry and Related Sciences, 43*(4), 258.

Mew, E. J., Padmanathan, P., Konradsen, F., Eddleston, M., Chang, S.-S., Phillips, M. R., & Gunnell, D. (2017). The global burden of fatal self-poisoning with pesticides 2006–15: Systematic review. *Journal of Affective Disorders, 219,* 93–104.

Miller, D. N. (2013). Lessons in suicide prevention from the Golden Gate Bridge: Means restriction, public health, and the school psychologist. *Contemporary School Psychology, 17*(1), 71–79.

Miller, G. F. (2007). Brain evolution. In S. W. Gangestad & J. A. Simpson (eds.), *The Evolution of Mind: Fundamental Questions and Controversies* (pp. 287–293). New York, NY: Guilford Press.

Miller, G. F., & Penke, L. (2007). The evolution of human intelligence and the coefficient of additive genetic variance in human brain size. *Intelligence, 35*(2), 97–114.

Miller, M. B. (2009). *Suicide and Evolution.* Saarbrücken, Germany: Verlag.

Miller, M. J., Azrael, D., & Hemenway, D. (2006). Belief in the inevitability of suicide: Results from a national survey. *Suicide and Life-Threatening Behavior, 36*(1), 1–11.

Millner, A. J., Lee, M. D., & Nock, M. K. (2017). Describing and measuring the pathway to suicide attempts: A preliminary study. *Suicide and Life-Threatening Behavior, 47*(3), 353–369.

Moont, R., Pud, D., Sprecher, E., Sharvit, G., & Yarnitsky, D. (2010). 'Pain inhibits pain' mechanisms: Is pain modulation simply due to distraction? *Pain, 150*(1), 113–120.

Moore, M. T., & Fresco, D. M. (2012). Depressive realism: A meta-analytic review. *Clinical Psychology Review, 32*(6), 496–509.

Mugisha, J., Hjelmeland, H., Kinyanda, E., & Knizek, B. L. (2011). Distancing: A traditional mechanism of dealing with suicide among the Baganda, Uganda. *Transcultural Psychiatry, 48*(5), 624–642.

Mulder, R., Newton-Howes, G., & Coid, J. W. (2016). The futility of risk prediction in psychiatry. *British Journal of Psychiatry, 209*(4), 271–272.

Murray, D., & Devitt, P. (2017). Suicide risk assessment doesn't work. *Scientific American* (28 March). Retrieved from https://www.scientificamerican.com/article/suicide-risk-assessment-doesnt-work/.

Murray, H. A., & Kluckhohn, C. (1948). Outline of a conception of personality. In C. Kluckhohn & H. A. Murray (eds.), *Personality in Nature, Society, and Culture* (pp. 3–32). Oxford, UK: Knopf.

Naghavi, M. (2019). Global, regional, and national burden of suicide mortality 1990 to 2016: Systematic analysis for the Global Burden of Disease Study 2016. *BMJ, 364*(l94), 1–11.

Neuhoff, J. G. (2001). An adaptive bias in the perception of looming auditory motion. *Ecological Psychology, 13*(2), 87–110.

Newman, D. L., Moffitt, T. E., Caspi, A., & Silva, P. A. (1998). Comorbid mental disorders: Implications for treatment and sample selection. *Journal of Abnormal Psychology, 107*(2), 305–311.

Nicholas, A., Pirkis, J., & Reavley, N. (2020). What responses do people at risk of suicide find most helpful and unhelpful from professionals and non-professionals? *Journal of Mental Health*, 1–10.

Nock, M. K., Alonso, J., Borges, G., Chatterji, S., Deming, C. A., Chiu, W. T., . . . Sampson, N. (2012). Mental disorders, comorbidity, and suicidal behavior. In M. K. Nock, G. Borges, & Y. Ono (eds.), *Suicide: Global Perspectives from the WHO World Mental Health Surveys* (pp. 179–184). Cambridge, UK: Cambridge University Press.

Nock, M. K., Boccagno, C. E., Kleiman, E. M., Ramirez, F., & Wang, S. B. (2019). Suicidal and nonsuicidal self-injury. In M. J. Prinstein, E. A. Youngstrom, E. J. Mash, & R. A. Barkley (eds.), *Treatment of Disorders in Childhood and Adolescence* (4th ed., pp. 258–277). New York, NY: Guilford.

Nock, M. K., Borges, G., Bromet, E. J., Cha, C. B., Kessler, R. C., & Lee, S. (2012). The epidemiology of suicide and suicidal behavior. In M. K. Nock, G. Borges, & Y. Ono (eds.), *Suicide: Global Perspectives from the WHO World Mental Health Surveys* (pp. 5–32). Cambridge, UK: Cambridge University Press.

Nock, M. K., Green, J., Hwang, I., McLaughlin, K. A., Sampson, N. A., Zaslavsky, A. M., & Kessler, R. C. (2013). Prevalence, correlates, and treatment of lifetime suicidal behavior among adolescents: Results from the National Comorbidity Survey Replication Adolescent Supplement. *JAMA Psychiatry, 70*(3), 300–310.

Nock, M. K., Hwang, I., Sampson, N. A., & Kessler, R. C. (2010). Mental disorders, comorbidity and suicidal behavior: Results from the National Comorbidity Survey Replication. *Molecular Psychiatry, 15*(8), 868–876.

Nock, M. K., Ramirez, F., & Rankin, O. (2019). Advancing our understanding of the who, when, and why of suicide risk. *JAMA Psychiatry, 76*(1), 11–12.

Nock, M. K., Ursano, R. J., Heeringa, S. G., Stein, M. B., Jain, S., Raman, R., . . . Fullerton, C. S. (2015). Mental disorders, comorbidity, and pre-enlistment suicidal behavior among new soldiers in the US Army: Results from the Army Study to Assess Risk and Resilience in Servicemembers (Army STARRS). *Suicide and Life-Threatening Behavior, 45*(5), 588–599.

Norris, F. H. (1992). Epidemiology of trauma: Frequency and impact of different potentially traumatic events on different demographic groups. *Journal of Consulting and Clinical Psychology, 60*(3), 409–418.

O'Connell, S., & Dunbar, R. (2003). A test for comprehension of false belief in chimpanzees. *Evolution and Cognition, 9*(2), 131–140.

O'Connor, R. J. (1978). Brood reduction in birds: selection for fratricide, infanticide and suicide? *Animal Behaviour, 26*, 79–96.

Oexle, N., Ajdacic-Gross, V., Kilian, R., Müller, M., Rodgers, S., Xu, Z., . . . Rüsch, N. (2015). Mental illness stigma, secrecy and suicidal ideation. *Epidemiology and Psychiatric Sciences, 26*(1), 53–60.

Oexle, N., Herrmann, K., Staiger, T., Sheehan, L., Rüsch, N., & Krumm, S. (2019). Stigma and suicidality among suicide attempt survivors: A qualitative study. *Death Studies, 43*(6), 381–388.

Oltmanns, T. F., & Powers, A. D. (2012). Knowing our pathology. In S. Vazire & T. D. Wilson (eds.), *Handbook of Self-Knowledge* (pp. 258–273). New York, NY: Guilford Press.

Orbell, J., & Morikawa, T. (2011). An evolutionary account of suicide attacks: The kamikaze case. *Political Psychology, 32*(2), 297–322.

Ormel, J., & Neeleman, J. (2000). Towards a dynamic stress-vulnerability model of depression. In T. O. Harris (ed.), *Where Inner and Outer Worlds Meet: Psychosocial Research in the Tradition of George W. Brown* (pp. 151–170). London, UK: Routledge.

Overholser, J. C., Braden, A., & Dieter, L. (2012). Understanding suicide risk: Identification of high-risk groups during high-risk times. *Journal of Clinical Psychology, 68*(3), 349–361.

Owens, D., Horrocks, J., & House, A. (2002). Fatal and non-fatal repetition of self-harm: A systematic review. *British Journal of Psychiatry, 181*(3), 193–199.

Paniagua, F. A., Black, S. A., Gallaway, M. S., & Coombs, M. A. (2010). *The Interpersonal-Psychological Theory of Attempted and Completed Suicide*. Bloomington, IN: AuthorHouse.

Panksepp, J. (1998). *Affective Neuroscience: The Foundations of Human and Animal Emotions*. New York, NY: Oxford University Press.

Panksepp, J. (2011). The basic emotional circuits of mammalian brains: Do animals have affective lives? *Neuroscience & Biobehavioral Reviews, 35*(9), 1791–1804.

Parkes, C. M., & Prigerson, H. G. (2010). *Bereavement: Studies of Grief in Adult Life*. Hove, UK: Routledge.

Patel, V. (2015). Addressing social injustice: A key public mental health strategy. *World Psychiatry, 14*(1), 43.

Paterson, B., Dowding, D., Harries, C., Cassells, C., Morrison, R., & Niven, C. (2008). Managing the risk of suicide in acute psychiatric inpatients: A clinical judgement analysis of staff predictions of imminent suicide risk. *Journal of Mental Health, 17*(4), 410–423.

Paulhus, D. L. (1998). Interpersonal and intrapsychic adaptiveness of trait self-enhancement: A mixed blessing? *Journal of Personality and Social Psychology, 74*(5), 1197.

Paulhus, D. L., & Buckels, E. (2012). Classic self-deception revisited. In S. Vazire & T. D. Wilson (eds.), *Handbook of Self-Knowledge* (pp. 363–378). New York, NY: Guilford.

Peck, M. S. (1978/2003). *The Road Less Travelled: A New Psychology of Love, Traditional Values, and Spiritual Growth* (25th anniversary ed.). New York, NY: Touchstone.

Peña-Guzmán, D. M. (2017). Can nonhuman animals commit suicide? *Animal Sentience, 2*(20), 1.

Peters, E. (2010). Are delusions on a continuum? The case of religious and delusional beliefs. In I. Clarke (ed.), *Psychosis and Spirituality: Consolidating the New Paradigm* (2nd ed., pp. 191–207). Chichester, UK: Wiley.

Peters, S. M., Pothuizen, H. H., & Spruijt, B. M. (2015). Ethological concepts enhance the translational value of animal models. *European Journal of Pharmacology, 759*, 42–50.

Pfeffer, C. R. (1986). *The Suicidal Child*. London, UK: Guilford Press.

Pinker, S. (1997). *How the Mind Works*. New York, NY: Norton.

Pinker, S. (2010). The cognitive niche: Coevolution of intelligence, sociality, and language. *Proceedings of the National Academy of Sciences, 107*(supp. 2), 8993–8999.

Plante, T. G. (2013). *Abnormal Psychology across the Ages (3 vols.)*. Santa Barbara, CA: ABC-CLIO.

Plöderl, M., Kunrath, S., & Fartacek, C. (2019). God bless you? The association of religion and spirituality with reduction of suicide ideation and length of hospital stay among psychiatric patients at risk for suicide. *Suicide and Life-Threatening Behavior, 50*(1), 95–110.

Pompili, M., Murri, M. B., Patti, S., Innamorati, M., Lester, D., Girardi, P., & Amore, M. (2016). The communication of suicidal intentions: A meta-analysis. *Psychological Medicine*, 1–15.

Pompili, M., Vichi, M., De Leo, D., Pfeffer, C., & Girardi, P. (2012). A longitudinal epidemiological comparison of suicide and other causes of death in Italian children and adolescents. *European Child & Adolescent Psychiatry, 21*(2), 111–121.

Potts, R. (1998). Environmental hypotheses of hominin evolution. *American Journal of Physical Anthropology, 107*(S27), 93–136.

Preti, A. (2007). Suicide among animals: A review of evidence. *Psychological Reports, 101*(3), 831–848.

Proudfit, G. H., Dunning, J. P., Foti, D., & Weinberg, A. (2014). Temporal dynamics of emotion regulation. In J. J. Gross (ed.), *Handbook of Emotion Regulation* (2nd ed., pp. 43–57). New York, NY: Guilford.

Proulx, T., & Inzlicht, M. (2012). The five "A" s of meaning maintenance: Finding meaning in the theories of sense-making. *Psychological Inquiry*, 23(4), 317-335.

Reader, S. M., Hager, Y., & Laland, K. N. (2011). The evolution of primate general and cultural intelligence. *Philosophical Transactions of the Royal Society B: Biological Sciences, 366*(1567), 1017–1027.

Regehr, C., LeBlanc, V. R., Bogo, M., Paterson, J., & Birze, A. (2015). Suicide risk assessments: Examining influences on clinicians' professional judgment. *American Journal of Orthopsychiatry, 85*(4), 295.

Reed, L. I., Fitzmaurice, G., & Zanarini, M. C. (2012). The course of dysphoric affective and cognitive states in borderline personality disorder: A 10-year follow-up study. *Psychiatry Research, 196*, 96–100.

Rieger, S. J., Peter, T., & Roberts, L. W. (2014). 'Give me a reason to live!': Examining reasons for living across levels of suicidality. *Journal of Religion and Health, 54*(6), 2005–2019.

Riesebrodt, M. (2007/2010). *The Promise of Salvation: A Theory of Religion.* (S. Rendall, trans.). Chicago, IL: University of Chicago Press.

Riordan, D. (2019). Suicide and human sacrifice: Sacrificial victim hypothesis on the evolutionary origins of suicide. *Suicidology Online, 10*(2), 1–10.

Rogers, J. R. (2001). Theoretical grounding: The 'missing link' in suicide research. *Journal of Counseling & Development, 79*(1), 16–25.

Rosenberg, K., & Trevathan, W. (2002). Birth, obstetrics and human evolution. *BJOG, 109*(11), 1199–1206.

Rosmarin, D. H., & Koenig, H. G. (eds.). (2020). *Handbook of Spirituality, Religion, and Mental Health.* London, UK: Elsevier Science.

Roth, G., & Dicke, U. (2012). Evolution of the brain and intelligence in primates. In M. A. Hofman & D. Falk (eds.), *Progress in Brain Research* (vol. 195, pp. 413–430). Amsterdam: Elsevier.

Sagan, C. (2006). *The Varieties of Scientific Experience: A Personal View of the Search for God.* New York, NY: Penguin.

Satcher, D. (1999). *The Surgeon General's Call to Action to Prevent Suicide.* Washington, DC: US Public Health Service.

Saunders, K. E., Hawton, K., Fortune, S., & Farrell, S. (2012). Attitudes and knowledge of clinical staff regarding people who self-harm: A systematic review. *Journal of Affective Disorders, 139*(3), 205–216.

Schaeffer, H. (1967). Can a mouse commit suicide? In E. Shneidman (ed.), *Essays in Self Destruction.* Northvale, NJ: Jason Aronson.

Schmidtke, A. (1997). Suicide in Europe. *Suicide and Life-Threatening Behavior, 27*(1), 127–136.

Schomerus, G., Evans-Lacko, S., Rüsch, N., Mojtabai, R., Angermeyer, M., & Thornicroft, G. (2015). Collective levels of stigma and national suicide rates in 25 European countries. *Epidemiology and Psychiatric Sciences, 24*(2), 166–171.

Schultz, D. T. (2000). Defending suicide-related malpractice cases: A lawyer's perspective. *Journal of Psychiatric Practice, 6*(6), 345–348.

Schwartz, M. A., & Wiggins, O. P. (1992). The phenomenology of schizophrenic delusions. In M. Spitzer, F. Uehlein, M. A. Schwartz, & C. Mundt (eds.), *Phenomenology, Language & Schizophrenia* (pp. 305–318). New York, NY: Springer Science & Business Media.

Sedikides, C., Gaertner, L., & Vevea, J. L. (2005). Pancultural self-enhancement reloaded: A meta-analytic reply to Heine (2005). *Journal of Personality and Social Psychology, 89*(4), 539–551.

Seeburger, F. F. (2013). Thinking addiction. In L. C. J. Wong, G. R. Thompson, & P. T. Wong (eds.), *The Positive Psychology of Meaning and Addiction Recovery* (pp. 59–76). Birmingham: Purpose Research.

Sela, Y., & Shackelford, T. K. (2014). The myth of the myth of martyrdom. *Behavioral and Brain Sciences, 37*(04), 376–377.

Selby, E. A., Joiner, T. E., & Ribeiro, J. D. (2014). Comprehensive theories of suicidal behaviors. In M. K. Nock (ed.), *The Oxford Handbook of Suicide and Self-Injury* (pp. 286–307). Oxford, UK: Oxford University Press.

Seligman, M. E. P. (1971). Phobias and preparedness. *Behavior Therapy, 2*(3), 307–320.

Shaffer, D. (1974). Suicide in childhood and early adolescence. *Journal of Child Psychology and Psychiatry, 15*(4), 275–291.

Shaffer, D., & Fisher, P. (1981). The epidemiology of suicide in children and young adolescents. *Journal of the American Academy of Child Psychiatry, 20*(3), 545–565.

Shanahan, T. (2008). Why don't zebras have machine guns? Adaptation, selection, and constraints in evolutionary theory. *Studies in History and Philosophy of Science Part C: Studies in History and Philosophy of Biological and Biomedical Sciences, 39*(1), 135–146.

Sharot, T. (2011). *The Optimism Bias: A Tour of the Irrationally Positive Brain.* New York, NY: Vintage.

Shettleworth, S. J. (2010). Clever animals and killjoy explanations in comparative psychology. *Trends in Cognitive Sciences, 14*(11), 477–481.

Shneidman, E. S. (1977). *Definition of Suicide.* Lanham, MA: Jason Aronson.

Shneidman, E. S. (1982). On 'Therefore I must kill myself'. *Suicide and Life-Threatening Behavior, 12*(1), 52–55.

Shneidman, E. S. (1985). *Definition of Suicide.* New York, NY: John Wiley & Sons.

Shneidman, E. S. (1993). Commentary: Suicide as psychache. *Journal of Nervous and Mental Disease, 181*(3), 145–147.

Shneidman, E. S. (1998). Further reflections on suicide and psychache. *Suicide and Life-Threatening Behavior, 28*(3), 245–250.

Shneidman, E. S. (2001). Anodyne therapy: Relieving the suicidal patient's psychache. In H. G. Rosenthal (ed.), *Favorite Counseling and Therapy Homework Assignments* (1st ed., pp. 180–183). New York, NY: Routledge.

Shorter, E. (2013). The history of DSM. In *Making the DSM-5* (pp. 3–19). New York, NY: Springer.

Silk, J. B. (1978). Patterns of food sharing among mother and infant chimpanzees at Gombe National Park, Tanzania. *Folia Primatologica, 29*(2), 129–141.

Silverman, M. M. (2013). Defining suicide and suicidal behavior. In D. Lester & J. R. Rogers (eds.), *Suicide: A Global Issue* (pp. 1–30). Santa Barbara, CA: Praeger.

Simon, R. I. (2002). Suicide and litigation: Lessons learned in risk management. *Psychiatric Times, 19*(9), 49–49.

Sinyor, M., Tse, R., & Pirkis, J. (2017). Global trends in suicide epidemiology. *Current Opinion in Psychiatry, 30*(1), 1–6.

Sisco, M. R., & Weber, E. U. (2019). Examining charitable giving in real-world online donations. *Nature Communications, 10*(1), 1–8.

Slobodkin, L. B. (1978). Is history a consequence of evolution? In P. Bateson & P. Klopfer (eds.), *Social Behavior* (vol. 3, pp. 233–255). New York, NY: Springer.

Smirnov, O., Arrow, H., Kennett, D., & Orbell, J. (2007). Ancestral war and the evolutionary origins of 'heroism'. *Journal of Politics, 69*(4), 927.

Smith, H. (1991). *The World's Religions: Our Great Wisdom Traditions* (2nd ed.). San Francisco, CA: Harper Collins.

Solomon, A. (2014). *The Noonday Demon: An Atlas of Depression*. New York, NY: Simon and Schuster.

Solomon, S., Greenberg, J., & Pyszczynski, T. (2004). The cultural animal: Twenty years of terror management theory and research. In J. Greenberg, S. L. Koole, & T. Pyszczynski (eds.), *Handbook of Experimental Existential Psychology* (pp. 13–34). New York, NY: Guilford Press.

Sommers-Flanagan, J., & Shaw, S. L. (2017). Suicide risk assessment: What psychologists should know. *Professional Psychology: Research and Practice, 48*(2), 98.

Soper, C. A. (2018). *The Evolution of Suicide*. Cham, Switzerland: Springer.

Soper, C. A. (2019a). Adaptation to the suicidal niche. *Evolutionary Psychological Science, 5*(4), 454–471.

Soper, C. A. (2019b). Beyond the search for *suigiston*: How evolution offers oxygen for suicidology. In V. Zeigler-Hill & T. K. Shackelford (eds.), *Evolutionary Perspectives on Death* (pp. 37–61). Cham, Switzerland: Springer.

Spallek, J., Reeske, A., Norredam, M., Nielsen, S. S., Lehnhardt, J., & Razum, O. (2015). Suicide among immigrants in Europe – A systematic literature review. *European Journal of Public Health, 25*(1), 63–71.

Speece, M. W., & Brent, S. B. (1984). Children's understanding of death: A review of three components of a death concept. *Child Development*, 1671–1686.

Stack, S., & Kposowa, A. J. (2008). The association of suicide rates with individual-level suicide attitudes: A cross-national analysis. *Social Science Quarterly, 89*(1), 39–59.

Stanley, I., Hom, M., Boffa, J., Stage, D. R. L., & Joiner, T. E. (2019). PTSD from a suicide attempt: An empirical investigation among suicide attempt survivors. *Journal of Clinical Psychology, 75*(10), 1879–1895.

Stevens, A. (1982). *Archetype: A Natural History of the Self.* London, UK: Routledge & Kegan Paul.

Stevens, A. (1990). *On Jung.* New York, NY: Routledge.

Stevens, A. (2002). *Archetype Revisited: An Updated Natural History of the Self.* London, UK: Brunner-Routledge.

Stone, D. M., Simon, T. R., Fowler, K. A., Kegler, S. R., Yuan, K., Holland, K. M., . . . Crosby, A. E. (2018). Vital signs: Trends in state suicide rates – United States, 1999–2016 and circumstances contributing to suicide – 27 states, 2015. *Morbidity and Mortality Weekly Report, 67*(22), 617.

Storr, A. (1960). *The Integrity of the Personality.* London, UK: Heinemann.

Surtees, P., & Wainwright, N. (2000). The timing of lives: loss events over the lifecourse and the onset of depression. In T. O. Harris (ed.), *Where Inner and Outer Worlds Meet: Psychosocial Research in the tradition of George W. Brown* (pp. 171–194). London, UK: Routledge.

Swidler, L., & Küng, H. (1991). Toward a universal declaration of a global ethos. *Journal of Ecumenical Studies, 28*(1), 123–125.

Syme, K. L., Garfield, Z. H., & Hagen, E. H. (2016). Testing the bargaining vs. inclusive fitness models of suicidal behavior against the ethnographic record. *Evolution and Human Behavior, 37*(3), 179–192.

Syme, K. L., & Hagen, E. H. (2018). When saying 'sorry' isn't enough: Is some suicidal behavior a costly signal of apology? A cross-cultural test. *Human Nature, 30*(1), 117–141.

Tadros, G., & Jolley, D. (2001). The stigma of suicide. *British Journal of Psychiatry, 179*(2), 178–178.

Tanaka, M., & Kinney, D. K. (2011). An evolutionary hypothesis of suicide: Why it could be biologically adaptive and is so prevalent in certain occupations. *Psychological Reports, 108*(3), 977–992.

Taylor, S. E., & Brown, J. D. (1988). Illusion and well-being: a social psychological perspective on mental health. *Psychol Bull, 103*(2), 193–210.

Thoma, N., Pilecki, B., & McKay, D. (2015). Contemporary cognitive behavior therapy: A review of theory, history, and evidence. *Psychodynamic Psychiatry, 43*(3), 423–461.

Thorne, B. (2012). *Counselling and Spiritual Accompaniment: Bridging Faith and Person-Centred Therapy.* Chichester, UK: John Wiley & Sons.

Tolaas, J. (2005). *Evolution and Suicide.* Salt Lake City, UT: American University & Colleges Press.

Tooby, J., & Cosmides, L. (1992). The psychological foundations of culture. In J. H. Barkow, L. Cosmides, & J. Tooby (eds.), *The Adapted Mind: Evolutionary Psychology and the Generation of Culture* (pp. 19–136). New York, NY: Oxford University Press.

Tooby, J., & Cosmides, L. (1996). Friendship and the banker's paradox: Other pathways to the evolution of adaptations for altruism. *Proceedings of the British Academy, 88*, 119–144.

Tooby, J., & Cosmides, L. (1997). Letter to the editor of the *New York Review of Books* on Stephen Jay Gould's 'Darwinian Fundamentalism' (June 12, 1997) and 'Evolution: The Pleasures of Pluralism' (June 26, 1997). *New York Review of Books.* Retrieved from http://www.sscnet.ucla.edu/comm/steen/cogweb/Debate/CEP_Gould.html.

Tooby, J., & Cosmides, L. (2008). The evolutionary psychology of the emotions and their relationship to internal regulatory variables. In M. Lewis, J. M. Haviland-Jones, & L. F. Barrett (eds.), *Handbook of Emotions* (3rd ed., pp. 114–137). New York, NY: Guilford.

Tossani, E. (2013). The concept of mental pain. *Psychotherapy and Psychosomatics, 82*(2), 67–73.

Townsend, A. K., Hawley, D. M., Stephenson, J. F., & Williams, K. E. (2020). Emerging infectious disease and the challenges of social distancing in human and non-human animals. *Proceedings of the Royal Society B, 287*(1932), 20201039.

Trivers, R. L. (1971). The evolution of reciprocal altruism. *Quarterly Review of Biology, 46*(1), 35–57.

Trivers, R. L. (2010). Deceit and self-deception. In P. M. Kappeler & J. B. Silk (eds.), *Mind the Gap* (pp. 373–393). Heidelberg, Germany: Springer.

Truax, C. B., & Carkhuff, R. R. (1967). *Toward Effective Counseling and Psychotherapy: Training and Practice*. Abingdon, UK: Transaction.

Tryon, W. W. (2016). Transtheoretic transdiagnostic psychotherapy. *Journal of Psychotherapy Integration, 26*(3), 273.

Turecki, G., & Brent, D. A. (2016). Suicide and suicidal behaviour. *The Lancet, 387*(10024), 1227–1239.

Turecki, G., Gunnell, D., O'Connor, R., Oquendo, M., Pirkis, J., & Stanley, B. (2019). Suicide and suicide risk. *Nature Reviews Disease Primers, 5*, 74.

Tutu, D., & Tutu, M. (2010). *Made for Goodness: And Why This Makes All the Difference*. London, UK: Rider.

U.S. Department of Health and Human Services. (2014). Does depression increase the risk for suicide? Retrieved from https://www.hhs.gov/answers/mental-health-and-substance-abuse/does-depression-increase-risk-of-suicide/index.html.

U.S. Department of Health and Human Services (HHS), Office of the Surgeon General, & National Action Alliance for Suicide Prevention. (2012). *2012 National Strategy for Suicide Prevention: Goals and Objectives for Action*. Washington, DC: HHS.

Vaillant, G. E. (1977). *Adaptation to Life*. Boston, MA: Little, Brown & Co.

Valach, L., Young, R. A., & Michel, K. (2011). Understanding suicide as an action. In K. Michel & D. A. Jobes (eds.), *Building a Therapeutic Alliance with the Suicidal Patient*. Washington, DC: American Psychological Association.

Valentin, D., & Abdi, H. (2003). Early face recognition: What can we learn from a myopic baby neural network. In O. Pascalis & A. Slater (eds.), *The Development of Face Processing in Infancy and Early Childhood: Current Perspectives*. New York, NY: Nova Science.

Varki, A., & Brower, D. (2013). *Denial: Self-Deception, False Beliefs, and the Origins of the Human Mind*. New York, NY: Twelve.

Vercken, E., Wellenreuther, M., Svensson, E. I., & Mauroy, B. (2012). Don't fall off the adaptation cliff: When asymmetrical fitness selects for suboptimal traits. *PloS One, 7*(4), e34889.

von Andics, M. (1947). *Suicide and the Meaning of Life*. London, UK: Hodge.

Walker, M., Moreau, D., & Weissman, M. M. (1990). Parents' awareness of children's suicide attempts. *American Journal of Psychiatry, 147*(10), 1364–1366.

Walsh, F. (2009). Spiritual resources in family adaptation to death and loss. In F. Walsh (ed.), *Spiritual Resources in Family Therapy* (2nd ed., pp. 81–102). New York, NY: Guilford Press.

Wampold, B. E., & Imel, Z. E. (2015). *The Great Psychotherapy Debate: The Evidence for What Makes Psychotherapy Work* (2nd ed.). New York, NY: Routledge.

Weiss, B., & Garber, J. (2003). Developmental differences in the phenomenology of depression. *Development and Psychopathology, 15*(02), 403–430.

Weissman, M. M., Bland, R. C., Canino, G. J., Greenwald, S., Hwu, H.-G., Joyce, P. R., . . . Lepine, J.-P. (1999). Prevalence of suicide ideation and suicide attempts in nine countries. *Psychological Medicine, 29*(1), 9–17.

Weissman, M. M., Wolk, S., Wickramaratne, P., Goldstein, R. B., Adams, P., Greenwald, S., . . . Steinberg, D. (1999). Children with prepubertal-onset major depressive disorder and anxiety grown up. *Archives of General Psychiatry, 56*(9), 794–801.

Wells, C. (1975). Ancient obstetric hazards and female mortality. *Bulletin of the New York Academy of Medicine, 51*(11), 1235.

Westen, D., Novotny, C. M., & Thompson-Brenner, H. (2004). The empirical status of empirically supported psychotherapies: Assumptions, findings, and reporting in controlled clinical trials. *Psychological Bulletin, 130*(4), 631–663.

W.H.O. (2010). *The ICD-10 Classification of Mental and Behavioural Disorders: Clinical Descriptions and Diagnostic Guidelines* (2010 ed.). Geneva, Switzerland: World Health Organization.

W.H.O. (2014). *Preventing Suicide: A Global Imperative*. Geneva, Switzerland: World Health Organization.

W.H.O. (2018a). Suicide. Retrieved from https://www.who.int/news-room/fact-sheets/detail/suicide.

W.H.O. (2018b). Suicide rate estimates, age-standardized: Estimates by country. Retrieved from https://apps.who.int/gho/data/node.main.mhsuicideasdr?lang=en.

W.H.O. (2019). *Suicide in the World*. Geneva, Switzerland: World Health Organisation.

Wiley, J. (2020). Psychological aposematism: An evolutionary analysis of suicide. *Biological Theory*. doi:10.1007/s13752-020-00353-8.

Williams, G. C. (1966). *Adaptation and Natural Selection: A Critique of Some Current Evolutionary Thought*. Princeton, NJ: Princeton University Press.

Williams, G. C. (1996). *Plan and Purpose in Nature*. London, UK: Weidenfeld & Nicholson.

Willner, P., & Belzung, C. (2015). Treatment-resistant depression: Are animal models of depression fit for purpose? *Psychopharmacology, 232*(19), 3473–3495.

Wilson, D. S. (2010). *Darwin's Cathedral: Evolution, Religion, and the Nature of Society*. Chicago, IL: University of Chicago Press.

Wolf, A. P. (2014). *Incest Avoidance and the Incest Taboos: Two Aspects of Human Nature*. Stanford, CA: Stanford University Press.

Woodford, R. (2003, September). Lemming suicide myth: Disney film faked bogus behavior. *Alaska Fish & Wildlife News*. Retrieved from http://www.adfg.alaska.gov/index.cfm?adfg=wildlifenews.view_article&articles_id=56.

Woody, E., & Boyer, P. (2011). Threat-detection and precaution: Introduction to the special issue. *Neuroscience & Biobehavioral Reviews, 35*(4), 989–990.

Wu, Z., & Fang, Y. (2014). Comorbidity of depressive and anxiety disorders: Challenges in diagnosis and assessment. *Shanghai Archives of Psychiatry, 26*(4), 227–231.

Young, P. T. (1959). The role of affective processes in learning and motivation. *Psychological Review, 66*(2), 104.

Zalsman, G., Hawton, K., Wasserman, D., van Heeringen, K., Arensman, E., Sarchiapone, M., . . . Zohar, J. (2017). Evidence-based national suicide prevention taskforce in Europe: A consensus position paper. *European Neuropsychopharmacology, 27*(4), 418–421.

Zilboorg, G. (1936). Suicide among civilized and primitive races. *American Journal of Psychiatry, 92*(6), 1347–1369.

INDEX